RR

Hirsch ... was born in ... in 1910. In early schooling ... at the Junior Latin School, after which he went to study the Modern Languages, ... Russian and Spanish, at Boston College. In 19.. he received his Ph.D. in Slavic Languages and Literatures from Harvard University. He is now Associate Professor of Slavic Literatures at Columbia University. Dr. Smith has written extensively on Russian ... Polish literatures for scholarly journals. Both ... this report and should. He is the author of forthcoming studies and translations of the ... nineteenth century Polish dramatist Alexander Fredro, and he is currently writing on a comprehensive study of Russian drama.

HAROLD B. SEGEL was born in Boston in 1930. His early schooling was at the Boston Latin School, after which he went on to major in Modern Languages, concentrating on Russian and Spanish, at Boston College. In 1955 he received his Ph.D. in Slavic Languages and Literatures from Harvard University. He is now Associate Professor of Slavic Literatures at Columbia University. Dr. Segal has written extensively on Russian and Polish literatures for scholarly journals both in this country and abroad. He is the author of forthcoming books on the plays and memoirs of the nineteenth-century Polish dramatist Alexander Fredro, and he is currently working on a comprehensive study of Russian drama.

The Literature of
Eighteenth-Century Russia

The Empress Catherine II. A portrait appearing as the frontispiece to a set of prints based on paintings of the empress in the possession of the Earl of Oxford (George Walpole). London 1788.

THE LITERATURE OF EIGHTEENTH-CENTURY RUSSIA

An Anthology of Russian Literary Materials of the Age of Classicism and the Enlightenment From the Reign of Peter the Great (1689–1725) to the Reign of Alexander I (1801–1825)

Edited and translated, and with an introduction and notes,
by

Harold B. Segel

VOLUME II

 *A Dutton* *Paperback*

New York
E. P. DUTTON & CO., INC.
1967

"THE LITERATURE OF EIGHTEENTH-CENTURY RUSSIA"
First published 1967 by E. P. Dutton & Co., Inc.

All rights reserved. Printed in the U.S.A.

Copyright © 1967 by Harold B. Segel

FIRST EDITION

Published simultaneously in Canada by Clarke, Irwin
& Company Limited, Toronto and Vancouver.

Library of Congress catalog card number: 67–21985

CONTENTS

7

LIST OF ILLUSTRATIONS

Volume II

ACKNOWLEDGMENT

The starred (*) illustrations have been supplied by the British Museum, are used with their permission, and are copyright by them.

PREFACE

The eighteenth century marked a period of decisive transition in the history of Russian literature. The tastes and practices of old Muscovy were discarded and those of Western Europe were transplanted on Russian soil. This process of change was by no means rapid; at times it moved haltingly, uncertain of its next step. But when the process was over, a fertile ground was readied for the rich harvest of the century that followed.

For Russian literature the eighteenth century was a period then of formation, of growth; it was the bridge over which the written word crossed from the medieval into the modern world. Examined closely, the literature of the century falls into three distinct periods. The first, that of Peter the Great, saw the continued use of old forms that had been developed over the second half of the seventeenth century. The transformation Peter sought to achieve in Russian life at first affected only material culture; its impact on literature was felt later. The second period extended from the death of Peter to the elevation to the throne of Catherine II. Belatedly, the changes wrought elsewhere in Russian life by the program of the Petrine reforms were now reflected in literature.

The nearly forty years that separate the greatest Russian rulers of the eighteenth century were a time of active concern with the state of literary culture in Russia. To the antique apparatus of Muscovite literature there were now opposed the conventions and techniques of Western classicism. Because its evolution in Russia was inorganic, classicism could neither develop as much more than a school of style nor long endure without serious modification. This process of modification, which began to take place significantly only in the 1760's and 1770's, led to the dissolution of classicism and prepared the way for literary sentimentalism. In the 1730's and 1740's, however, Russian writers were hastening to exercise their talents in all the new forms brought in from the classicist West and by the adoption of which they sought to accomplish, at last, the modernization of Russian literary culture. For poets in the 1730's, 1740's, and 1750's an abiding concern was the

11

development of an appropriate prosodic system, one natural to the Russian language. The old syllabic system was replaced by the syllabo-tonic, and by the middle of the century one of the major obstacles to the progress of Russian poetic achievement had been overcome.

Writers and literary theoreticians also addressed themselves in this period to the problem of the need for a truly Russian literary language. Although a definitive solution was to remain elusive until the early nineteenth century, until, in fact, the appearance of Pushkin, the problems were recognized and dealt with in a relatively satisfactory manner before Catherine ascended the throne.

This period—from the death of Peter to 1764—was in itself a formative one; it was followed by the third, and last, distinguishable period in the history of Russian literature of the eighteenth century, a period in which conditions were ripe for the elaboration of a modern, secular, European-Russian literary culture on the foundation of the preparatory work of the 1730's, 1740's, and 1750's. This is the period coinciding more or less with the reign of Catherine II, when Russian literary culture began to emerge from its adolescence and show its first signs of maturity and sophistication. It was, understandably, the first period in which Russian literature demonstrated a capacity for greatness, and in which achievements of Russian letters came to the attention of foreign readers.

The first volume of this anthology traced the development of Russian literature from the reign of Peter the Great down to and including the major monuments of non-fictional prose in Catherine's era. The introduction of excerpts from the satirical journals of the 1760's and 1770's and the travel writings of the 1770's–1790's in Volume I was done to achieve a meaningful balance between the two parts of the work. In the realm of prose, fiction lagged behind non-fiction until the last decade of the century and the appearance of the stories and tales of Karamzin. Beside their intrinsic interest from the point of view of the evolution of Russian prose style, the satirical journals and the travel writings shed considerable light on several of the most vital aspects of Russian culture and thought in Catherine's time: the profound problem of Russia's indebtedness to Western culture and the evolution of a national consciousness, the breakdown of Catherine's fragile liberalism under the weight of the Pugachëv Uprising and the French Revolution, and the gradual entry of Russian literary art into the arena of social awareness and social action. There is perhaps no better introduction to the literature and culture of Catherine's period than the outstanding non-fiction of that age; it justifiably demands a prior consideration over the fiction of the second half of the eighteenth century and was thus included in the first volume.

The second volume contains selections from the imaginative literature of the reigns of Catherine and Paul I. Narrative prose is represented by the work of Fëdor Ėmin, Mikhail Chulkov, and especially Nikolai Karamzin. The poetry of the age is best found in the epics of Mikhail Kheraskov, the fables of Ivan Khemnitser, the mock-epic or heroic-comic poems of Vasilii Maikov and Ippolit Bogdanovich, and most especially in the odes and lyrics of Gavrila Derzhavin, the first outstanding Russian poet and the best poet of the language before Pushkin. In the realm of dramatic literature, which developed relatively late in Russia, classicist tragedy had one major representative in eighteenth-century Russia—Aleksandr Sumarokov. His *Dimitrii the Impostor* foreshadowed Pushkin's *Boris Godunov* and is given here in full. Comedy proved a more productive outlet for the talents of Russian dramatists, and in the person of Denis Fonvizin achieved a distinction it was not to realize again until Aleksandr Griboedov's *Woe from Wit* in 1823. A translation of Fonvizin's first successful comedy, *The Brigadier*, is included in this volume in its entirety.

As the eighteenth century set the stage for the blossoming of Russian literature in the nineteenth century, so in its own way did the activity of the writers of the first half of the eighteenth century prepare the way for the dynamic growth of literary art that remains one of the positive achievements of Russian culture in the age of Catherine. It is to the literature of that period—the first distinctly major period in the history of Russian literature—that this second volume is devoted.

H. B. S.

A Word About Transliteration

Several methods of transliterating Russian are commonly
used. None of them is perfectly adequate. The one chosen
for this book is something of a compromise between the
transliteration scheme adopted by the Library of Congress and
that used primarily in learned journals in the Slavic field.
Preference for one system of transliteration over another
is largely a personal matter and of no great consequence as
long as the method chosen is used consistently. The reader
who knows Russian can readily adapt himself to any transliteration table while the reader who knows no Russian will
have some idea of the pronunciation of Russian words. For
the transliteration in the present book it should be pointed
out that ' after a letter just indicates that it is palatalized
(*n'*, for example, is pronounced like the *n* in "canyon"); *ë* is
pronounced "yo"; *è* is pronounced like the "e" in met (a back
vowel) unlike the unaccented *e* which is pronounced "ye" (a
front vowel). Names of rulers and Russian terms well known
in English are given in anglicized versions and are the only
exceptions to the method of transliteration adopted for this
book.

3. The Reigns of Catherine II (1762–1796) and Paul I (1796–1801), (continued)

1. The Letters of Ernest and Doravra

FËDOR A. ÈMIN

Fëdor Aleksandrovich Èmin is one of the more curious figures of Russian eighteenth-century literature, largely because so little is known about him. We possess no definite information about his nationality and origin or the date and place of his birth. Èmin himself claimed that he was a Turk, but evidence points to the fact that he was born in the Ukraine. According to some accounts he was educated in the Kiev Academy. For inexplicable reasons, he fled to Turkey, where he converted to Islam. With several languages at his command, he traveled far and wide and saw much of Europe, Africa, and Asia. Finally, under the name of Mehmed Èmin, he presented himself to the Russian minister in London and expressed his desire to be reconverted to Russian Orthodoxy. This done, he went to Russia where he found employment first as a language teacher in the Cadets Corps, and later, as a translator. Soon he began what proved to be a productive literary career. He wrote more than twenty-five books, including seven original novels, the satiric journal *Hell's Post,* of which he was sole author, and a three-volume *History of Russia* (which goes only as far as the year 1213 and is devoid of any scientific character).

Èmin's place in the history of Russian eighteenth-century prose fiction rests on his original and translated romances, which are genetically related to the popular tales of the seventeenth and early eighteenth centuries, and his sentimental epistolary novel *The Letters of Ernest and Doravra* (Pis'ma Ernesta i Doravry, 1766).

Èmin's most successful original romance, *Inconstant Fortune, or the Adventures of Miramond* (Nepostoiannaia fortuna, ili pokhozhdenie Miramonda, 1763), became one of the most popular Russian novels of the eighteenth century and went through three editions. With his philosophical novel *The Adventures of Themistocles* (Prikliuchenia Femistokla,

1763), the first of its type in Russia, Èmin moved in a new direction.

His crowning literary achievement remains, however, the four-part *The Letters of Ernest and Doravra*. One of the earliest manifestations of sentimentalism in Russia, the novel echoes to some extent Rousseau's work *La Nouvelle Héloïse*, which was published some five years earlier, in 1761. Unlike Rousseau's famous epistolary novel, however, the pair of lovers do not have to bridge the gulf of class distinctions. In a break with convention, both Ernest and Doravra belong to the same class, the nobility. The problem is that while of noble origin Ernest is poor. Doravra, on the other hand, is wealthy. The conflict springs only partially from this circumstance; there is the added complication of the hero's being married.

For all the moving sensibility of the tender love of Ernest for Doravra and the plainly sentimental "flight" to Mother Nature, who has the power to heal the hero's spiritual wounds, *The Letters of Ernest and Doravra* cannot be regarded as a wholly sentimental work. Traces of classicism are still to be discovered, notably in Ernest's deliberations on the conflict between "duty" and passion and the ultimate triumph of the former, which brings to mind analogous situations in the tragedies of Sumarokov. Attributable also to classicist literary practice are the weighty didacticism of the novel and the satirical thrusts against injustice, favorites, repression, powerful despotic nobles, and so on.

Artistically, *The Letters of Ernest and Doravra*, as all of Èmin's novels, is weak, particularly in terms of its prolixity, feeble composition, clumsiness of style. When the far more elegant and polished works of Karamzin appeared, Èmin's novels rapidly began to lose their appeal. Yet there can be no doubt that their author was highly regarded in his own day. One of the longest entries in Novikov's *Plan for a Historical Dictionary of Russian Writers* is devoted to him. Novikov mentions that in Èmin's early works the style was not "sufficiently pure, but in his later ones this changed considerably; and his satirical writings have a great deal of pungency in them." The entry closes with a poem addressed to Èmin that includes the words: "Those eyes have closed,/ Which saw right through the heart;/ Those lips have closed,/ Which censured passion."

Èmin's son, Nikolai Èmin, continued in his father's footsteps by writing two epistolary novels, *Rose, A Half-True and Original Novel* (Roza, poluspravedlivaia i original'naia povest', 1786) and *The Game of Fate* (Igra sud'by, 1789). The sentimental element in these works is still stronger than in those of Fëdor Èmin, and enables us to trace the ascendancy of full-blown sentimentalism in the Russian novel in the second half of the eighteenth century.

The epistolary literature that began properly with Èmin and continued to be cultivated throughout the second half of the eighteenth century in works of Fonvizin, Radishchev, Karamzin, and others was of no small impact on Russian literature in the first half of the following century. We can see traces of it in Pushkin's *Eugene Onegin*, in several stories of Gogol' (for example, *The Notes of a Madman* [Zapiski sumashedskheogo]), and especially in the novel that launched Dostoevskii's literary career in 1845, *Poor Folk* (Bednye liudi), so evidently a descendant of *The Letters of Ernest and Doravra.*

The translation of excerpts from Èmin's novel follows the text in A. V. Kokorev, *Khrestomatiia po russkoi literature, XVIII veka*, 3rd edition, Moscow, 1961.

Part One
    Letter 1 (From Ernest to Doravra)

Having passed the greater part of my best years in constant mishap, I finally arrived in this city in the hope that here I would find the peace I sought. But when are the hopes of the unfortunate realized? Without relatives, without friends, and without benefactors a poor person has a woeful and hardly bearable time living anywhere until his ability opens up the path to him of some prosperity. I confess in all sincerity that sometimes I grumbled about the cruelty of my fate. Once in a while I senselessly railed against this land in which I could not obtain what I desired. And sometimes, forgiving the country, I cursed the people who were incapable of feeling the misfortunes of others. Such madness is common to almost all people who are well brought up, enlightened, and then unhappy. Discovering in themselves certain merits and yet sunk in the most bitter poverty, they direct their thoughts to the highest level of prosperity. And when their aspirations are denied the longed-for success, they then complain about their lot in life, about the country they are in, and about the people with whom they have intercourse. What strange and irrational judgments impatience arouses in an enlightened person! Why blame and hate people who know nothing of our honesty, of our merits, our aspirations and abilities? Have there been so few dishonest men and frauds wandering the whole world over who received great boons because of their boldness, but finally by their ingratitude and more often their laziness gave cause for despair to the benefactors who accorded them—unworthy people—every possible assistance? Are people guilty for not now hastening to place their faith in the righteous after they had been deceived so many times by liars, and especially at a time when truth itself places on its holy face the mask of contrived pretense so unpleasant to it?

Such observations as well as habitual bad luck enabled me to endure patiently the poverty coming from want. I then began to forget my origins, my upbringing, and the happiness for which it seemed my birth had destined me. I constantly opined that although nature honors us as the rightful heirs of its true beneficence, the fate governing all nature frequently refutes this right, however, and does what it pleases, assigning to a poor person someone else's happiness, and to a happy person someone else's poverty.

All these considerations curbed the ferocity of my poverty and out of necessity I began to philosophize. I determined to make a place for myself in the lowest stratum of society, thinking that the less I was in human society, the more would I find what I need for my sustenance, and that way I would be able to live peacefully. My decision was indeed sudden and I realized it soon enough by becoming the servant of a certain gentleman; but still sooner did it begin to make me unhappy with the life I had thought earlier would be peaceful. I was not disturbed by the fact that I had to do the most menial labor. But I could not, without emotional upset, listen to frequent abuse, indecent both to nature and my situation at the time, because I was guilty of nothing before my master other than the fact that I was the servant and he the master.

It was then I realized that a well-bred person cannot soon

forget what he was before and that he could never live peacefully amidst vulgarity, no matter how poor he might be. One
has to be born a farmer in order to lead peacefully that life
envied by all philosophers. But to a noble person reduced to
such a life by misfortune no pleasure is afforded by waters
flowing out of limpid springs and rippling over clean stones.
Green meadows, fields decked with various flowers, thick,
quiet forests where neither the sun's heat nor cruel winds can
disturb the country dweller, can never be a cozy place to such
a person. The bleating of innocent sheep would offend his
ears, and pure milk, the most tender nourishment of all shepherds and shepherdesses, would only upset his stomach. Wherever he turned, he would find despondency everywhere. His
thoughts would strive for the happy position he once knew,
and what others call the pleasures of village life he would
regard as the most bitter misfortune that ever befell him in
his life. The reason for this is our false pride, which, once it
has taken root in our nature, is extremely difficult to extirpate.
Abandoning my cruel master, I rented a corner in a district
beyond the city, situated by a river. I bought a rod, went fishing, and this way managed to provide myself with food for
several days.

The month of April came. Liberated from the cruel tyranny
of winter frosts, the trees began to blossom; the branches
began sprouting their leaves, and my well-being, which had
been frozen above all by cruel fate, also bloomed. I was received into the imperial service with a decent rank and corresponding remuneration. I had the opportunity to come to
know your parent and to see you. But as soon as my eyes
met your glances that same moment they became more limpid,
for never before had they seen anyone as clearly as they saw
you. Enlightening my gaze you also enlightened my mind,
and it learned that in you it found that significance which was
worthier than all its previous observations. My mind, agreeing
with my eyes, communicated something of the same to my
heart, which suddenly grew anxious, began throbbing, grew
crestfallen, emitted several sighs, and until now finds itself in
this sorrowful situation. Do you not know, madam, what a
malady your glances have caused in me? The power of your
eyes should be known to you. And if you know the name of
the malady you have brought me, do you not know the means
of curing it?

Letter 2
    (From Doravra)

Yesterday I dared inquire what reasons brought you to our state. But I noticed in your account the kind of caution that is not always common to truth. Nevertheless, I do not doubt— nor should I—the veracity of your words; I shall only say to you that in your letter the occurrences that happened to you in this city are described more clearly, more plausibly, and more sensitively. The description of your story here is filled with moralizing judgments that also illuminate your mind, and it is for that reason that I read through your letter two or three times. I regret exceedingly that my glance caused you some sort of malady, and if you yourself do not know with what you are ill, then how can you ask me about the name of your weakness? A doctor cannot treat a patient until he discovers the cause of his illness. Be assured that I am unable either to name or treat your ailment. But I shall tell you what course you should pursue. One must avoid whatever becomes a cause of harm to us. I myself shall do everything in my power not to look at you, since my glances are so dangerous to you. . . .

Letter 5
    (To Doravra)

I would expiate my insolence with death if I were to love another, and not Doravra. But whosoever loves this person who is filled with all the holy virtues will never know what it is to have a base heart. Were I of weak spirit I would end my suffering in despair, but the heart that has ventured to worship Doravra should possess greater strength and constancy. Pay heed, pay heed, sanctuary of virtue, temple of courtesy, gentle Doravra, to the unhappy lover's resolve of which your long silence and cold treatment of me is the cause. When you rewarded me for my love with just a single letter, you did so in order to render my unhappiness endless. I am leaving here for far-off lands. I shall bury myself in a desolate cave, and your letter, which I shall never remove from my eyes, will be to me a book of all statutes. In it will be inscribed my destiny. In it will be recorded my past, present, and future suffering, and with it I, an unfortunate, shall go to the gates of eternity.

I feel the burden of your indignation more than my strength can bear. But believe me, loveliest Doravra, purest being, that I shall not rail against the punishment decreed me. Having discovered his error, the criminal sentenced to death by the law humbles himself before the decision that deprives him of his life. He respectfully bends his neck before the fatal blade and uncomplainingly meets this death that separates him forever from the life so dear to him. Such is the power of consecrated justice that those who lose their lives because of it reverentially esteem the law. In like manner do I respectfully, humbly, and reverentially esteem the torture you mete out for my boldness. I am going out of this city in whatever direction the cruelty of my fate points the way. Having shed abundant tears, I shall leave this place where the life of my soul remains. You have come to take possession of my being; forgive the insolence to which I have confessed and for which I have been punished most severely, but fairly. Be not indignant with me, incomparable beauty, model of courteousness and virtue. Forget the error of my ways and know that the love that devours me may be worthy of punishment but not scorn. No one takes anger at a person sentenced to death; indeed, all have pity on him. And you, heavenly beauty, following the example of worldly justice, pity the unfortunate one whose last letter you are receiving this day, who can in no way cause you further grief, and who is going into eternal incarceration carrying with him the cruelest memory of your charms, a memory that never will cease tormenting all his thoughts, all his feelings, all his being. The vessel that will carry me away from here is already prepared for the journey. The helmsman is delighted that the journey from which he hopes for profit already lies before the bow of his ship. All seafarers take pleasure in the exercise of their trade; I alone, standing on the shore, am torn by my emotions. I tremble from fear that I shall not depart from this city this day. Wherever I turn my thoughts they encounter sorrow. Ahead of me—the eternal and terrible separation of my soul from its soul; behind me—contempt for the purest desire that promises me nothing save continual languor. O you, cruel fate! You, hapless love, companion of my misfortune, follow after me wherever I may go and finish the evil that I am beginning to become aware of now at the time of my departure.

Part Three
   Letter 1 (From Ippolit to Ernest)

. . . Come to us, dear Ernest; complete our happiness by your presence. . . .

Here Nature in its tender blossoms and its little green leaves manifests its joy and life. Here roses, seeing us who admire them, turn red, as though embarrassed. Fair lilies, which do not have so pleasing an appearance, smile pleasantly, like their own delicate color, when they behold the roses' natural shyness. The vegetables of our gardens afford us more satisfaction than the finest and most skillfully prepared foods gracing splendid tables. Here the pleasant zephyr, as though in his own dwelling-place, takes the different flowers into his embrace and frees them from the heat of the burning sun. The pleasant singing of innocent birds takes the place of music that not everyone can have and that does not please everyone. Here everyone knows how to amuse himself; the hours of work and rest are known to all. Here harmony, the happiest aspect of man's life, is not perturbed by any obstacles. The industrious farmer aroused not by a clock beating on a wall or the call of servants, but by the light of dawn, prepares for his labors. His wife and children ready for him everything that he needs, and he knows not that confusion to which magnificent houses filled with armies of servants are liable. The plow, which brings beads of perspiration to his brow, not only does not disturb him but brings him so much joy that he often complains to himself about the shortness of the day that causes them to part—he and his plow; and as evening draws on he looks at the sun as if complaining that it was shortening the work on which he trusts for his good fortune. If at noontime the sun disturbs him by its heat, he takes refuge in thick bushes that abound on all sides and in them he rests so peacefully that the sun cannot reach him either with its heat or its rays because of the great thickness of the bushes. He dines in this pleasant shade; the green grass serves him in place of a tablecloth; simple food, and frequently even plain bread, give him more pleasure than savory dishes.

The pure waters flowing from limpid springs are more pleasant to him than expensive drinks. Once he has finished eating, he resumes his work. Laboring with great satisfaction, he sings different songs at a time when a nobleman living in a great city, sated by savory dishes and costly drinks, rests following his afternoon meal on soft down and, lying in it, tortures himself with his passions: he cannot see someone he wants to; a contemporary of his lives better than he does; he is troubled but he himself knows not why, and amid splendor seeks the cause of his anxiety.

O happy village life that knows no such troubles! Happy are those inhabitants whom heaven never destined for splendor, and satisfies and delights instead with the fruits of their own labors. But do not think, dear Ernest, that there are no unhappy people among village dwellers. Happy are those who find themselves under the command of scrupulous masters and whose owners live together with them. Such village dwellers make every effort to please their masters with their greatest zeal, and their masters in turn, seeing their zeal and labor and the benefit therefrom accruing to them, love their subjects and do not burden them. But how much unhappier are those poor devils whom fate has entrusted to the authority of such people who not only do not know what a good serf is, but who do not even know what a human being is. Inheriting great villages after their fathers' deaths, some of them give themselves over to extravagance and finally so ruin their peasants that they can no longer be of use either to them or to themselves. I have seen many unscrupulous neighbors of ours who refused to believe the stewards of their estates that there was nothing more to be taken from the peasants, and went themselves to their villages, where they tortured their poor serfs with continual beatings until they paid not to be beaten further; I regarded such landowners as tyrants. . . .

2. The Comely Cook, or The Adventures of a Debauched Woman

MIKHAIL D. CHULKOV

The first part of Chulkov's major attempt at a novel, *The Comely Cook, or The Adventures of a Debauched Woman* (Prigozhaia povarikha, ili pokhozhdenie razvratnoi zhenshchiny), appeared in 1770. The remainder was not published, probably because of the censorship, and has since been lost. The edition of 1770 was not reprinted. An extensively emendated version of the work was published only in 1890 and again in 1937. The most recent publication of the complete extant text appears in the two-volume collection *Russian Prose of the Eighteenth Century* (Russkaia proza XVIII veka, ed. G. P. Makogonenko, Moscow-Leningrad, 1950).

Although primitive in some respects, *The Comely Cook* is the best Russian eighteenth-century specimen of the European "rogue novel" with a "fallen woman" as its heroine. In this respect it may be placed in the same tradition as Daniel Defoe's *Moll Flanders* (1722) and, to a lesser extent, *The Fortunate Mistress* (Roxana, 1724).

What Chulkov's work might have been in its complete form is impossible to say, and there is little point in speculating. On the basis of the extant first part, however, as quantitatively deficient as it may be for a novel, especially an eighteenth-century novel, one can find the basic elements of the genre to which it lays claim.

The structure of the work, like *Moll Flanders*, is episodic. There is unity only of character; the reader simply passes with the central character through a series of episodes or adventures. The conventional first-person narrative technique is used, as in Defoe's novels. While this permits the reader a directness of association with the central character, the device is not exploited to its fullest capacity—either by Chulkov or Defoe, and the character remains psychologically undeveloped. The emphasis falls heavily, almost uniquely, on incident, on the raw material of plot; the time is still too early for psychological probing of character.

Chulkov's Martona, like Moll, is a vain woman, without moral conviction, naïve and somewhat cynical at the same time. Both heroines develop a certain practicality (as well as cynicism) about life through personal misfortune and disillusionment, but in each case the practicality concerns an essentially bad life, a life of self-seeking personal advantage.

Social conditions as motivating forces are not without significance in either Chulkov's or Defoe's work, but the situations of the heroines are not identical. Martona takes the easy way out, becomes a "loose" woman as the result of her husband's death and her inability to find adequate employment. Society shares in her guilt. Moll, unlike her distant relation, starts off life with the distinct disadvantage of having been born in prison, the daughter of a criminal mother. In a sense, she is lost before she begins life. With Martona this is not the case. However, neither heroine shows any desire—even in the slightest—of rectifying her situation or of rebelling against her environment; each accepts the condition of her life and simply tries to find within its boundaries as much material comfort as possible.

Neither author dwells in any substantial way on the emotional makeup of his central character. Yet, despite the brevity of Chulkov's work, Martona compares favorably with Moll in this respect and perhaps even surpasses her somewhat.

In the Russian original, Chulkov's work is written in a simple language, closely approximating colloquial speech. Typical in view of his lifelong interest in folklore is the introduction of a folk element in the novel. This takes the form principally of proverbs by which Martona either rationalizes her actions or which appear at significant turns in her fortune. Chulkov's prose style for all its simplicity is at times extremely careless (particularly in the matter of sentence construction), making occasionally for awkward and clumsy reading.

The translations of the complete first part of *The Comely Cook* and of Chulkov's story *A Bitter Fate* are based on the texts in *Russkaia proza XVIII veka*, Vol. 1, ed. G. P. Makogonenko, Moscow-Leningrad, 1950.

To his Excellency, State Chamberlain and cavalier of various orders, my most gracious Sire,

I shall not give his name here in order to avoid falling into error. Books are inscribed to people according to their contents and the temperament of those to whom they are presented. I have seen many such books which were offered to distinguished people but instead of augmenting their virtues they served but to satirize them. Thus someone who wished to bestow praise on his patron but had no understanding of praise or the required moderation succeeded only in scolding him quite stupidly. In order then to spare myself this and besides knowing not the worth of the book which I have written, I am not inscribing it to anyone personally. The title of excellency embellishes a person; therefore I placed it here for the embellishment of my book although my wish was not to embellish it with excellency, but only with the letters from which this word is composed and printed. The following letter I address to each and every Your Excellency and Most Honorable general, chamberlain, and cavalier whose fine qualities, indulgence, and grace I wish to praise indefatigably from the sincerity of my heart.

Your Excellency, Gracious Sire!

Everything that exists in the world is perishable. Consequently, this book of mine which is being inscribed to you is also perishable. Everything on earth is mutable. Thus, this book exists now, will endure for a certain time, finally putrefy, disappear, and will leave everyone's memory.

Man is born into the world to behold glory, honor, and wealth, to taste of joy and pleasure, to experience woe, grief, and sorrow. Similarly, this book has come into the world in order to receive its measure of praise, controversy, criticism, indignation, and abuse. All of this will vanish with it and finally it will turn into dust, just like the person who praised it or who cursed it.

On the pretext of a book, my wish has been to entrust myself to the protection of Your Excellency—the desire common to all people who do not have in their possession the portraits of rulers. Deserving people are promoted. Therefore, your intelligence, virtues, and indulgence have elevated you to this high position. It is natural to you to show grace to the indigent, and I am disposed to earn it in all zealousness. Who you are society will learn only when it will have the good fortune to benefit from your favor.

> Your humble servant,
> The author of this book.

I think that many of our sisters will accuse me of immodesty, but since this vice is natural for the most part to women, not wishing, therefore, to go against the law of nature and be called modest, I shall indulge in it willingly. The world will see, and seeing will understand; once having understood and weighed my actions, let it call me whatever it pleases.

Everyone knows that we won the Battle of Poltava, where my poor husband was killed in action. He was not of the gentry, had no land, and as a result I was left penniless. Although I bore the title of a sergeant's wife, I was still poor. I was nineteen at the time, and my poverty, therefore, seemed to me even more unbearable. I did not know how to deal with people then and had difficulties in finding myself a position. And so it happened that I became loose, because nobody finds any employment for us.

It was then that I acquired the following proverb: "Sew yourself wide sleeves, widow, so you will have some place to put all the lies about you." The whole world toppled over on me and hated me so much in my new existence that I did not know where to rest my head.

Everybody was gossiping about me, covered me with shame, and blamed me for things I did not even know of. I was driven to tears because of it, but an honest old woman who was well known to the whole city of Kiev, where I was living at the time, took me under her wing and felt so sorry for me that the next morning she found an attractive young man for my entertainment. At first I tried to resist, but in two days I followed her advice willingly and completely forgot the sorrow I had felt without relief for two weeks after my husband's death. This man was not so handsome as young, and I was comely enough; as they say, "A bee is attracted to a pretty

flower." He was the butler of a certain gentleman and spent
his money freely because it was his master's and not his own.
It was, in a way, a testimony of his love for me and served as
a kind of perpetual guarantee. In a short time practically all
the shops discovered that I freely bought whatever I needed
and all sorts of knickknacks, and our home constantly grew
in possessions and increased in wealth.

I knew very well the proverb that "wealth breeds respecta-
bility." And so I took myself a servant and began to be a
lady. Whether I knew how to order people around or not I do
not know myself; besides, I had no need to think about such
trivialities—it was enough that I did not want to do anything
myself and was driving my servant like a fool drives a
donkey. Mister Butler desired to boss others no less than
myself. He therefore employed a boy to serve him when he
called on me, and since he was constantly with me the result
was that our bossing did not cease for a moment and we
screamed at our servants as much as we wanted, as the proverb
says: "What more do you want when the fool has his way."
Our conduct was such that "we hit with a bat and paid with
a ruble."

The more clothes a woman has, the more she has the desire
to walk about the city, as a result of which our sisters get
spoiled and get into trouble. I was content with everything
and whenever a bright day came along I could be found
promenading. Many people got to know me and many desired
to become acquainted with me.

Once, close to midnight, some man knocked at our door,
more as if he were trying to break than to walk in. We did
not let him in; however, our strength was limited and Mister
Butler was not with us at the time. Therefore I sent the servant
to open the door. My old woman was ready to greet the man
while I hid myself, thinking that perhaps it was Paris who had
come to fetch Helen, because I was a desirable woman in the
city; or at least that is what I thought about myself.

They opened the doors and two men entered our guest
room. One of them seemed to be the servant and the other
the master, even though the latter was dressed worse than
the former. Without saying a word, the one I thought was
the master sat at the table, and after a while took out a
snuffbox all covered with diamonds. The old woman immedi-

ately noticed it, as a result of which her fear turned to joy and she ceased to consider these people enemies of our breed. This handsome young man asked her whether Martona (which was my name) lived here, to which the old woman replied, "I do not know, but I will ask my master."

And so she came running to me, saying that I should come and show myself and that the golden snuffbox convinced her of some happiness; then she added the proverb: "I am not without eyes and I see what is good for me." In such cases I was not amiss myself. Luckily for me I was not yet undressed, and so I appeared in front of my new Adonis with a solemn mien and a noble manner, and to tell the truth, though I was not greeted as Venus, I was still met as an average goddess. As the proverb says: "They greet you by your clothes, but bid you leave by your brains." From the first he seemed to be so tender that to please him I would gladly have left my butler, and when he made me a present of his snuffbox, I felt that it was mean to have anything to do with a peasant. Judging by the present of gold and diamonds, I came to the conclusion that this man was no one ordinary, and I was right. He was a gentleman, and by no means the lowest. Our first meeting was an auction; we did not discuss anything else until we closed our deal. He was bidding for my charms, and I was yielding them for a good sum of money. Afterward, we gave our mutual pledges with love as mediator and my landlady as witness. Since such contracts are never registered with the police, it remained binding with us without any official notarization. The gentleman was supposed to visit me often, and I agreed to accept him anytime; on this we parted.

After his departure Venus was not so much pleased with the golden apple as I was with the snuffbox given me as a present. Turning it over in my hand as many times as I wanted, I showed it to the old woman and the servants for the hundredth time, and when I was saying something I would point at everything with it. And when this excessive joy allowed my brain, which was inflamed by the gift, to calm down along with all my limbs, which were tired from the wild gesticulation, I put the snuffbox on the table next to my bed and fell asleep. However, in my dreams I could vividly imagine it, as the proverb says: "Who never saw the new is happy even with the shabby." To tell the truth, the snuffbox was somewhat beaten up; but to me it seemed to be new because I never had such things and never dreamed that I would have them.

At ten in the evening my old beau came. I must admit that my conscience did not allow me to get rid of him that soon, but I did not desire his company and so pretended to be ill. However, I forgot to remove the precious present from the table, and as soon as he saw it he took it into his hands and, looking at it for a while, asked me where I got such a thing. I told him that I had bought it.

"Wait, my dear," he said to me, "I'll handle you differently. This snuffbox is my master's and he lost it in a card game last night, as he himself told me, so it would have been impossible for you to buy it so soon. Some spendthrift gave it to you. Until now I thought that I was the only one, but now I see that the whole town takes turns visiting you. I'll show everybody how splendid you are. I'll go immediately and bring the horses and take away everything you've got! Go and get it from someone else and give me back every last thing of mine."

Having said this he went out, leaving me in a terrible fright. We did not know what to do next; we had nowhere to go, and there was nobody to offer us protection because such people as I was then do not have friends, the reason for it being our own unsurpassable pride. And so I was awaiting an unavoidable grief and a parting with our possessions. I did not rely yet on my new lover, and thought that when he saw me poor he would undoubtedly leave me. Everything was foreboding ill luck, and I was ready to die rather than part with the possessions that I cherished and loved so much.

Half an hour later, to my greater grief, my new lover came. What was I to do? I was in a mess then; my ruin was approaching, and here was a new man witnessing my misfortune and my abuse. Seeing me all in tears, he would not leave me alone and began to question me. I answered him nothing and threw myself on the bed. At that time the butler came into the house and, as he approached my room shouted, "I'll get even with you!" But seeing the man standing at my bedside he took off his hat and was so scared he was unable to say a word. My new lover asked him with whom he had had a fight and why he had come here. His cowardice did not allow him to express himself coherently, and so he lied twice or thrice, without further ado, and when the master yelled at him to go home, the whole affair was at an end.

Instantly I felt as if a tremendous load had fallen from my shoulders and it seemed to me that the horrible cloud of my misfortune had passed me by so fast that it did not have a chance to hide the sun. It was not difficult for me to guess that I had exchanged the servant for the master, and I knew full well that the anger of a butler is not dangerous when his master is siding with me. I had to change my disposition now completely, that is, to change my fright to indescribable happiness, and since I have often read the book *Women's Wiles* and made an effort to learn them, such a metamorphosis was not difficult for me. I began to groan a little, as if suffering (as I have learned to do), and I told Sveton (for so my new lover was called) that I had some sort of an attack. And here is where I discovered his good disposition and kindness toward me. In a moment he sent for the doctor, who was completely unnecessary to me, although he did come, for Mr. Sveton was quite capable of relieving me of the greatest fever even with a single word. From that time on, he assigned two of his people to my service, and the same day sent me as a present a silver dinner set or, plainly, dishes; and for the first time, as I sat down to eat with the old woman, who, to tell the truth, did not know how to face a setting like that or how to hold a spoon in her hand (I was somewhat smarter), I repeated the following proverb to myself: "Until now Makar was digging ditches, but now Makar is a mayor." Happiness never gives an account of its deeds; if it pleases it can make a governor out of an ass or transform an owl into a mayor's friend.

My Adonis was a worldly man and really knew how to act in matters of love. In the morning he would send me his butler and my ex-lover (whom he did not know as such) with presents. The butler would bring me a big load of ladies' garments and bow before me as if I were a lady and not his former mistress, and when I asked him to sit down, he would reply very politely that it would be too much of an honor for him. It was indeed strange for me that one night changed me into a lady and mistress over my former master. I accepted the gifts with a serene and noble look, as was fitting for the mistress of a nobleman, and taking out of my pocket a half-imperial gave it to the butler, who accepted it and, sighing quite honestly, asked me afterward to hear him out in private, and when I stepped into another room he knelt before me and said:

"My lady! I am no longer the same person who intended to take everything away from you. I am giving it all to you; please have it in the spirit of the proverb: 'Money is iron and cloth is perishable, but our skin is most precious to us.' I only beg of you one favor—don't tell my master that I knew you. In gratitude for this I'll be on your side and I'll help you ruin him."

I must admit that no matter how unscrupulous or money-crazy I was, the butler's diligence regarding his master seemed to me low. However, benevolence was equally unknown to me, and so in two words I and my former lover decided to ruin his master. However, we did not have the chance to accomplish our intentions, for as the proverb has it: "Shrove-tide does not last forever; there comes Lent." What prevented it, that the reader will soon discover for himself if he is not already bored reading my adventures.

For a week I enjoyed the dignity of Venus, and would never have exchanged my lot for anything in the world; but as everyone knows, Lady Luck does not smile permanently; nobody is more fickle than she. Thus my fortune slipped and my life entered another path. Sveton received a letter from his father, who asked him to come because he was feeling very weak and was despairing of his life. This letter plunged my lover into such pensiveness that he did not know what to do with me. His father's illness made him feel very sad, but the thought of parting with me surpassed his sadness. The tenderness of his love gave way for a time to different plans, but his thoughts began and ended with me; I was the object of his greatest concern; I alone could comfort him in his grief, and he was willing to lose his father just so long as he did not have to part with me.

"A good horse is not without a rider, and an honest man is not without a friend." Seeing his great sorrow, Sveton's neighbor suggested the following idea to him: for Sveton to go together with me and, after bringing me there, leave me in his village, which was only six versts away from Sveton's. This friend would then write to his brother about receiving me and putting me up, saying that I was a relation of his wife and that Sveton could visit me whenever he wanted to without any hindrance. No sooner said than done, and for this good advice my lover gave his friend a ring worth five hundred rubles. The same day we got ready, and left. My landlady did not want to go with me, so I left her in the place, rewarding her as bountifully as was fitting for the mistress of a nobleman. I parted with her without tears because I did not know what gratitude was and thought that one could live in this world without it.

In the middle of our trip Sveton declared to me that he was married but that he had been so only a while. He tried to assure me that he did not love his wife because parents often marry their children, not to whom the children want, but reach an agreement among themselves and force the children to it. This frequently results in a lack of understanding between husband and wife. Sveton assured me that this is what had happened to him. This news, however, cost me many a pill, and I lost so much weight in two days it was as though I had lain in fever for a whole month. I was not sad that I was losing my lover, but I was scared of something that was much worse than a love separation. I could part, or rather I felt that I was capable of parting, with three lovers in a single day more easily than enduring the welcome with which well-born wives regale our sisters for the robbery of their husbands. My heart intuitively felt such a gathering storm, and I would gladly have agreed to return home rather than to follow Sveton. However, to my misfortune, he was so much in love with me he did not even want to hear about it, and kept on assuring me that his wife had to be obedient to him and accept as good whatever pleased him.

Such a song would have been pleasing to me in the city, but here the closer we were getting to the country, the more my fear increased, as the proverb says: "The cat knows whose meat it ate up." I was finally brought to the appointed place, where I was accepted with great joy because the brother of the man who wrote the letter was truly convinced that I was indeed a relation of his sister-in-law. I thanked Sveton for his companionship on the trip and remained there content with everything.

The next morning, while it was still dawn, my lover came to visit me. He made me very happy by saying that his father had completely recovered and that we would soon leave for the city again.

"My wife wants to accompany me," he added, "but as two times two is four it will not be difficult to change her mind, and she will remain here."

Thus, getting ready again for a trip, we saw each other often, and to tell the truth, Mr. Sveton was more in my company than he was at home, which was the ultimate result of my misfortune.

His spouse was not slow in suspecting her husband, and finding out about my presence from his servants, who had been told expressly to say nothing, she sent for the landlord of the house where I was staying, and without any further delay she found out what I was worth and agreed with the landlord to find out for a fact what he already suspected anyway because, as the proverb says: "You cannot hide an owl in a sack" and "You can tell the bird by its wings."

Once, as Sveton and I were alone and we succumbed to human weakness and began making love, the doors of the closet, which, to my misfortune, was situated in my room, opened and a woman stepped out of it and said, "Good luck, friends!"

My lover jumped off, and I jumped up. He left the room, and I collected about ten slaps on my cheeks. That was only the beginning; the end I will not tell you out of self-respect. It is enough to say that in a short time I was all alone in a field without a thing and without a guide. It was very painful to me, and I truly felt the misfortune that surrounded me from all the sides, but what was there to do? "The bear is wrong who ate the cow; but the cow is wrong, too, for going deep into the forest."

I did not know the woods and fields that surrounded me. They were not lovers to me; they were not attracted to my beauty, and did not give me anything. Thus I found myself in extreme poverty. Toward evening I reached some village where I was forced to exchange my silk gown for peasant dress. My conscience would not let me travel in a gown, but neither was I used to wearing peasant's clothes. Outfitting myself so with patience and the peasant's costume, I continued my route. Nothing extraordinary happened to me on the way, except that out of the important poor people I was one important poor person, but not everyone reads such stories with pleasure. The rich fear poverty and the poor are bored with it. And so, the comments on my travel I shall put aside and relate only what may be of interest to the reader.

According to the markings in the calendars I arrived in Moscow on Wednesday, and this day is designated among us as the ancient pagan god Mercury's. Mercury was the god of knavery, and so, as if with his help, I was appointed as a cook to a secretary. Some gay fellow might say: "From the frying pan into the fire." However, one can often be mistaken. The secretary was a religious man. He never went to or rose from bed without a prayer; before dinner and supper he always read prayers and always washed his hands; he never missed a Sunday mass, and during the twelve big religious holidays he would go and pay his respects to others or himself receive them from petitioners. Every morning he would kneel for two hours in prayer while his wife would accept bribes of all types in the front room. When they sat down to drink tea, their young son would bring him a register where all the people who visited him that morning would be entered by name along with the amounts of their contributions, according to which he would decide how things should be settled for each person. At that time I found out that all the servants of the secretary indulged in bribery as well as their master. When he went to his office, his mate looked over the gifts, took a lot for herself, and divided the rest among her servants. In a week I received about eight scarves, without mentioning the pretzels and apples we consumed every day.

At the beginning, the secretary's wife took a liking to me for the reason that "one fisherman sees another fisherman at a distance." She was a woman who would give in easily, and was more unfaithful to him than faithful, which I must add her husband did not demand from her because it was more important to him to keep after his profit than his honor, for he thought that even without honor his house could be prosperous, like the horn of plenty. Besides this commendable talent, his spouse stocked different kinds of spirits, of which there was never a shortage, with the result that she was sober only when she rose from her bed in the morning. I, however, did not indulge myself in this vice and could not be her companion in it; but in all her other activities I was her confidante. I would have completely forgotten my fortunate position if I had not been reminded of it by an illiterate clerk who lived there and was employed by the secretary as a copyist. I was quite surprised to find out that illiterate people can fall in love; I always thought that love does not enter scribes' hearts. He was funny in his position as a clerk, but he was even funnier as a lover. He discovered love, but he did not know from which end to grasp it and how to approach it. First of all, he began to wink and nod his head at me; I knew what he was after and endeavored to make fun of him. Desiring first to test his mind I gave him three riddles to solve: who is the wisest person in the city, who is the most learned, and who is the most virtuous of all.

The next morning he told me the following:

"I can not find anyone wiser than our secretary, who decides all cases without delay and always reports on them in order. There is no man of higher learning than a certain attorney who knows almost all the legal codes by heart and very often puts the judges to silence. Who is the most virtuous that I do not know, and I think that many of the clerical profession would give you the same answer because it is so seldom that we hear about virtue."

When I heard this I smiled, and he continued to speak: "Do you think that poets with their commas and dots are the wisest men of all? If they worked in our office they would forget about their dots if they could not earn their bread with them. The other day, I do not know how, they brought us an ode by someone named Lomonosov. None of us in the office could make anything of it. What more do you want— the secretary himself told us that this was some kind of delirium, and not worth copying."

That is the way my lover talked about learned people. I gather that he would not even have given the best of them a job as a copyist. Realizing soon that his mind was not exactly to my taste and that I did not like him for that, he decided to please me with presents. And for that reason he began to work at his job with diligence, and I must admit that, considering his income, he did give me very nice presents. That is because for every copying job he would ask triple the price, and they say that this is the way they do things: when a scribe is under a secretary's protection he always gets triple for everything. At this time I grieved for Sveton, and comparing him sometimes to the scribe, I wept bitterly. This, however, was due to the fact that I was stupid. Nowadays our sisters do not behave in that fashion; they always like to get rid of a nobleman as soon as possible so as to find another shortly and begin prospering anew. Therefore, in the whole of our country you cannot find one who is as faithful as I am because, unlike them, I do not desire three or four lovers at the same time.

With the help and efforts of the scribe I began to wear better dresses, and those who came to call on the secretary's wife began to look at me more sweetly than at her, which greatly displeased her, and so she dismissed me from my job.

Leaving this house I felt little regret, because I was not parting with anyone and therefore losing nothing. The next day a procurer came to see me, and from the expression of his face I saw that he had found me a decent position, which was also profitable for him because the better the job, the higher his commission. He told me to dress up the best I could because where I was going to live it was my face that was required, and not my services. I must say that I knew how to dress myself as long as there was something to get dressed in. Having done a good job of prettying myself up, we set out, and when we arrived at the designated place he asked me to wait at the gate and went himself to inform the owner of my arrival and ask him whether I could enter. He came out very soon and asked me to follow him. When I entered the room I saw a man of advanced age who had long curly moustaches and an eagle-like nose. He was a retired lieutenant-colonel of a hussar regiment. He was sitting in his chair and counting silver coins. After seeing me he rose slightly, said, "Hello," and asked me to sit down. He told his servant to warm us some water for tea, and began to talk to me. "I am a widower, madam, and it is already eight days since my wife died. I am already old and am finishing my seventh decade. Therefore it is hard for me to take care of my household. I need a woman of your age to look after my pantry, cellar, kitchen, and bedroom. I am really already too old to drag myself about all these places every day. I cannot rely on my servants; true, I do have a cook, but she is already over forty, and therefore she is not as handy as a young woman would be; she can overlook a lot of things. As far as the salary is concerned, I am not going to discuss it now; I will express my gratitude according to the services rendered. I am not going to live forever, and when I die I do not know whom to leave everything I own to, because I am stranger here and I have no relatives. And if my housekeeper were to please me, I would make her the heiress of all my possessions. I heard, madam," he said, "that you are looking for a position like that. If you like, please stay in my house; I will be very happy if you do and I have no doubts that you know all about running a house."

I was not so stupid as to decline a proposition like that. I liked the old man's property and I immediately endeavored to please his finances. When I agreed to accept his proposition, he gave the procurer five rubles in silver and something from his household goods out of gratitude for securing him a housekeeper to his liking; the latter I could observe from the colonel's eyes and from his generosity.

I told him that I had to go and get the little there was of my belongings, but he did not want to agree to that, saying that I did not need anything.

"Here are the keys to my wife's closet, madam; her dresses will fit you. You can use them as you wish; there will be enough of them."

Thus within one hour I took over command of the house and everything that went with it, and two hours later I was in command of the owner himself, who did not spare any time in confessing that he was so much in love with me that if I left him now he would not be able to live any longer without me. My greed for clothes did not allow me to waste much time, and I immediately began to search the chests, in which I found a great number of quite nice clothes, and most of all pearls, which I had never seen before and had never worn. Overjoyed with this acquisition, and forgetting all the rules of decency, I began to restring the pearls according to my taste the very first day, and the hussar colonel, putting on his glasses, helped me in my labors by selecting the largest pearls and handing them to me as he kissed my hands. When dinner-time came we dined together, had supper together, and after supper I was together with him.

Our days went by in great joy on the part of my lover. To tell the truth, I myself was not dissatisfied either; my wealth made me happy, as the proverb says: "Even though gold does not speak, it does a lot of good." However, his old age was somewhat troubling to me; yet I bore it patiently as a generous and steady woman should. By the way, I was not permitted to leave the house except to go to church, and that only during the twelve main religious holidays. That seemed to me to be somewhat unkind, for a woman of the age I was at the time does not require as much food as walks; besides, I was pleased with things, and to a satisfied person house arrest is worse than the most gruesome prison. We lived at the time not far from St. Nicholas's Church. During one holiday I decided to go to mass, and dressed myself as splendidly as I felt like and, under the supervision of my ancient lover, went to church and stood where all the noble ladies usually stand. And since I was escorted with great respect by the colonel, nobody dared to push me aside or bother me, for my dress and the respect paid me by my lover made me a great lady. And in order not to lose people's respect I looked at every one proudly and did not speak a word to anyone.

Next to the choir on the right stood some kind of a young man; he was very good looking and not badly dressed. During the whole mass he did not take his eyes off me, and at appropriate times would make such signs as are understood only by us and by jealous husbands or lovers. My old man noticed all that and, without waiting for the mass to end, asked me very politely to come home with him. This seemed to me very inappropriate, and I did not agree to do as he requested. My lover, fearing lest he infuriate me, was compelled to stay to the end; however, he did not leave my side and stood next to me all the time. I noticed, and think that others could not help noticing also, that the face of my lover was constantly changing. Sometimes it seemed that he was as white as a sheet, as if he were getting ready for an attack, or it was fevered and turned redder than crimson; at times his face was covered with cold sweat. In other words, he seemed to be in such confusion as though he were a madman. At the end of the service he took me so firmly by my hand that I was forced to remind him of my pain. His hand was trembling so badly that I was in motion from it. And so in such indescribable disorder we came home.

As soon as we entered the room, the colonel said to me:

"Yes, madam, indeed I know little about a woman's beauty and charm; you are more beautiful than I ever thought you were, for which I beg your forgiveness. To say truthfully—you are a Russian Helen, and what they say about Venus I do not care to believe. Every fledgling tries to become a Paris and sell his eyes for you. God forbid I should follow the fate

of the unfortunate Menelaeus. However, I will resist an
intruder to the limit of my strength. I have intelligence, power,
and wealth, but what does it matter at all, my beauty, if you
will not feel the same kind of love I have for you?"

With these words he threw himself onto his knees in front
of me with tears flowing down his cheeks. And so I was
forced to play the role of a passionate mistress. I raised him
up from his knees and as a sign of assurance kissed him on
the lips and said:

"My dearest, is it possible that I would be unfaithful to
you and would deceive you at the very beginning of my passionate love? Only death will part us. But even in the grave I
will recall your respect. To please you I renounce all the men
in this world, and none of them will entice me. Be calm, my
dearest! Your faithful and truthful mistress Martona begs you
to do so with tears in her eyes."

Having heard this, my toothless Adonis calmed down
somewhat; however, the glances of the young man cost him so
dearly that he went to bed without eating. Within the following half hour he woke up five times, and sometimes screamed
"Forgive me" with all his strength, or "Halt," or "I am lost,"
for he imagined that I had been abducted or had betrayed
him.

A few days later a man came to our house and asked the
colonel to take him into his service. The old man at first
refused, but the man tried his best and praised himself as
much as he could. Taking out his papers, he wanted to show
them to him, saying that no honest man in this world had as
many letters of recommendation as he had. His words seemed
to me quite convincing, because if a person has devised a plan
to save his head then he has to apply himself diligently to it
in order to get what he wants. So I took his letters of recommendation and while looking through them found a letter
addressed to me. I took it out carefully and hid it in my
pocket and, returning the letters of recommendation to the
man, told him to come by next morning and that in the
meantime we would think over whether we would employ
him or not.

Even though I was not inclined to be unfaithful to my
lover, our inbrn inconstancy, however, did not give me
peace, and I went to another room, opened the letter, and
found the following declaration:

My fair lady!

To fall in love with someone is not within our power. Everything that is beautiful attracts our feelings and mind. You are beautiful, and therefore you have conquered my heart from the first moment I saw you in the church. It seemed to me then that your beautiful eyes spoke for your heart. And having convinced myself of that I dared to declare myself to you, undoubtedly hoping that even if you have not fallen in love with me, perhaps you do not hate me altogether.

An admirer of your beauty, Akhal'

I do not know if there is anyone who could boast that he has always preserved his virtue and while trying to do so denied himself the best and most natural pleasures. I always had the opinion that everything in this world was inconstant; when the sun is in eclipse the sky is continuously covered with clouds; the year has four seasons; the sea has a low and high tide; the fields and mountains now are green, now are white; birds shed their feathers and philosophers change their theories—pray tell, then, how can a woman who is born to changes love one man until she dies? I must laugh at some husbands who boast of their wives' fidelity; I believe it is better to be silent about matters that are under the complete control of women. I never belonged to the sect of the Stoics and did not at all follow their theory, therefore I did not wish to refuse anyone who asked indulgence of me. The next morning, when the servant came whose eyes assured me of his cleverness, I gave him the following reply:

"I am ready to do anything I may be asked, but the colonel does not wish to employ you. I think, though, that you have no need of him, because you can find the road to happiness without him."

"True," said my lover, "there are a lot of people in Moscow; if not in my house, you can get a job in another."

The servant was satisfied with the answer and went away grateful.

Our life is founded on anxieties. So it was that I got busy; the handsomer Akhal' seemed to me, the more I desired to betray my gray-haired Cupid. I did not feel any gratitude toward him at the time when a new love was growing in my heart—very rarely is a woman endowed with such a virtue.

I was one of those beauties who think that they do not owe anything to anyone in this world, and therefore they give away their graces to whomever they please.

First of all, I disclosed the secrets of my heart to our cook. It seemed strange to me that without any promise of reward she was ready to help me, and that convinced me that anyone is ready to serve a rich person whether the services are for a good or ill purpose. From then on we spent time in inventing all sorts of possibilities of arranging meetings with Akhal', and I must say one suggestion was better than the other. My advice was good but my confidante's was still better. We decided that the best thing to do was to dress up Akhal' as a woman for a while and introduce him to me as such; thus we could see each other without difficulties. We could not think of any other way because I was kept so strictly in this house that they rarely let me even come close to a window.

"A sheep likes salt, a goat freedom, and a fickle woman new lovers." We did not want to wait longer, and my helper ran the next day in search of my new lover; even though she did not know his address she found him very soon; as the proverb says: "The tongue leads even to Kiev." Akhal' greeted her with great joy and gave her presents worthy of a lover. She told him about our plans, to which he immediately agreed and gave her a letter addressed to me in which he tried to convince me that in order to please me he would go to the bottom of the ocean.

True enough, he immediately carried out what I desired of him. In the house where he lived he told the landlord that he decided to go to the country for a while and was leaving tomorrow. He would leave his servant and part of his belongings, and asked the landlord to take care of them. When the morning came he took what he needed and went to Iamskaia. Later—I am not sure which—he either sent his boy or went himself to the city and bought for himself and for his boy an extensive feminine wardrobe. They dressed themselves this way and got ready to execute a new kind of comedy. He sent his servant to look for rooms and to say that they came from another city to meet his sister. They found quarters, rented them, and moved in.

Our cook ran over to see them, and settled the matter. When she came back she told me that Akhal' would pretend to be my sister and would send his servant dressed up like a girl. She told me what their names would be and how I should greet this would-be girl when I saw her. And so I awaited with great joy the fulfillment of my wish.

It was already toward evening when our servant informed me that some girl was asking for me. Hearing this, the colonel asked to have her shown into the room: he was very zealously observing all my actions. The cook winked at me slyly, and I knew immediately that this was Mercury sent by my Jupiter. As soon as he came in, I yelled as loudly as I could:

"My dearest, how come you're here? Did Mother arrive?"

"No ma'am," he answered me; "Mother stayed home, but your older sister is here. You did not write to us for a long time, and so she came to see you."

After this he came close to me, kissed my hand, and did all as required by the social code. I asked him whether every one at home was in good health and other things, to which he replied as skillfully as if he had been training for at least ten years how to cheat people. I asked him where they were staying and where they intended living, to which he replied, Not far from our home. Since it was already late I decided to postpone the meeting with my sister to the next day, and asked my keeper to send his servant to my sister with my greetings and to invite her to have supper with us the following day. [I said:]

"Although it is impolite to deliver messages through a servant and actually I should have gone myself to greet her," I told him, "since she has not completely established herself, I might cause her unnecessary disturbance. Besides, among close relatives the social graces can be overlooked."

Thus the first entry was well performed, and our servants went off to my sister.

I must admit that I never enjoyed myself so much as when I was finally able to deceive my vigilant supervisor so successfully. However, the boy was so skillful in his masquerade that if I had not known better I would have been convinced myself that he was a girl. At this time my old man regained his senses and began to ask me about my family, which never before entered his head, because except love he had nothing else on his mind. I told him all about my family so well that neither he nor I were actually able to determine what my origins were; besides, I did not give him a chance to continue a conversation that obviously would not have brought me much gain. I then began to praise the good qualities of my sister, on top of which I added that she was beautiful and a great deal more charming than I.

"Do not fall in love, my dear," I continued saying, holding him by the chin, "I am afraid you might fall head over heels for her and then leave me."

"Let the world turn against me," he replied with a firm and assuring voice, "I am the type of man who loves to his death; I do not belong to today's fickle lovers who are ready to change their mistresses every day and even then look for an occasion to deceive them. No matter how beautiful she may be, she no longer has a chance of enchanting me, when you, my dear, love me from the bottom of your heart. I must admit to you that very seldom have I met a woman like you; you are so faithful that I think you would never even think of deceiving me, and to tell you the truth it would be a sinful thing."

After such a recommendation from him I assured him that I was more constant than the universe, which he truthfully believed, and regarded me in such high esteem that he was ready to go up to his ears in water if it would have pleased me.

During the night, and all the next day I thought of nothing else but my meeting, for the sake of which I spared no efforts to increase my beauty. The time came and my sister arrived. Our meeting was not of relatives but of lovers, and after we threw ourselves into each other's arms it was quite an effort to separate us.

Pleasantness followed pleasantness and one kiss another. My sister pressed me to her heart and kissed me quite often on my bosom, to which I replied in a like fashion. Even an experienced arithmetician would have been unable to add up all our kisses without making a mistake. We were such model sisters that I doubt you would have found in the whole world such a pair. During supper we did not eat a thing and were completely satisfied just looking at each other. With every passing moment I was discovering more new charms in my sister, and it seemed to me that she experienced a similar feeling toward me, and I felt that we could sit like that, without food, just looking at each other the rest of our lives. My old lover confessed that he regarded us as some kind of a "wonder," because he said he had "never seen such a passionate love between two sisters. Putting it quite plainly, one could take you for lovers, and if one of you were dressed in a man's clothes, nobody would believe that you were sisters. I praise your virtue and honest hearts; here indeed are relatives who deserve every respect."

"We have not seen each other already five years," said my sister; "we parted while still infants, and therefore it is not surprising, sir, that we cannot look enough at each other. There are only a few of us left; Mother and the two of us, and after our father's death we were left orphans."

"Then your virtue is even more praiseworthy that even in poverty you do not forget each other and love each other to such an extent that I cannot even explain it. You do not even look alike, but that again happens; not always do children of the same father take after him. I also had a brother who did not look at all like me."

In this way our supper came to an end. My old man drank more then usual and tried not to pay attention to what did not even enter his mind. The woman's dress was so becoming to Akhal' that nobody could have suspected him. However, I liked my sister so much that I did not want to let her go home and asked her to stay over. Akahl' did not want to agree to that in order to force the old man into inviting him himself, and when I appeared to be unhappy that she did not want to accept my invitation, then the colonel began and, of course, persuaded her. Out of respect to his guest he gave his bed up to us and, wishing us a good night, went to another room.

My conscience did not bother me because I thought that there are people in this world who are much bolder than I, and who could do much more harm in a moment than I could in three days. All one has to do is to let himself be ruled by vices, and they will seem much more pleasant than virtue.

So it was that my sister and I spent the night in all kinds of pleasure, and in the morning we parted at dawn lest anyone get wise to our scheme. I went to see my lover, and, apologizing for my sister, said that she had to leave so early because there were some matters to which she had to attend. The same day we had supper at her house, and when we came back home my lover praised her to high heavens and did not know how to compliment her enough. In this manner we visited each other every day and everything was going along for us in the best of order. The old man was happy that I was deceiving him with such skill, and I was grateful to him that he allowed himself to be deceived without giving a sign that he knew what was happening. Akhal', on the other hand, considered himself fortunate that he got from me without much labor what sometimes one does not receive even with two years' effort and that he was dealing with a person whom he could deceive easily and who did not care to notice that he was being deceived.

I know that at the present time a lover's fidelity is the kind of a guest who comes to you and says "hello"—and at the same time has on the tip of his tongue "farewell." A lover is faithful as long as he does not see goodwill from the person he loves. He then sighs and groans all the while on his knees, pretends to be crying, and swears the kind of fidelity one can see only in theatrical performances. But when he receives all he wants from her, then out of the weakness of the human memory he forgets all his promises in a matter of seconds and no longer entertains even the slightest notion of them. This I have experienced myself, and not once. However, now I want to talk about my love with Akhal', and my other experiences I will get to in order. In a while he convinced me that my life was disastrous and my doom could come soon; besides, it was also sinful. I knew all this very well myself, but without any means of changing it, I unwillingly remained in the same state.

"My fair lady," he told me, "I will devote my life to you till death us part and I flatter myself with the hope that I shall never be deprived of your favor. You gave me your heart, and I am happy, and to show you how grateful I am to you I contemplate matrimony with you, that is, if you are willing. I am of noble descent, and even though I am not rich I do not consider myself to be poor. I have neither mother nor father; thus I live the way it pleases me. Nobody can prevent me from marrying you. And so if you agree to it, give me your word and we will start getting ready. You would have to go away from this city in order to prevent all sorts of complications. My village will be your refuge, and the position of your husband your defense and protection. Then nobody will have the right to demand you from me. And so, your life undoubtedly will be happy."

It was not necessary to ask me again, for I knew the difference between something good and something bad, and I also knew how to choose something advantageous as opposed to something harmful. Therefore, I accepted his proposition willingly, and it seemed to me that he was extremely happy with my decision. And even though I was wise to other people's tricks, I could not see his hypocrisy, and this time I found out that no matter how smart and tricky a woman may be, she can always be outwitted by a male, especially when she is passionately in love with him.

Our pact was soon closed and we got engaged. From then on, I began to call my sister my husband and he me his wife. The next day Akhal' told me that for my stay with the colonel I deserved a good salary, but if the colonel would not agree to this my husband suggested that I should appropriate everything that was under my supervision, and by doing this I could enter my marriage with a clean conscience. My betrothed husband in the form of my sister was always in my presence or I in his, and therefore it was not difficult for us to filch my old lover's things. We were especially enthused about his pearls and money because those things are easier to handle and to store in a chest or a valise without arousing anyone's suspicion. When we decided finally that we had taken enough and that if we could not live comfortably the rest of our life on the things we took, then we could live at least two thirds of it quite pleasantly, we began to get ready for our departure; and with the aid of money everything goes easily. The horses were ready and my husband was on his way, agreeing to meet me at a certain gate.

At night, when my lover was enjoying himself in his sleep, I quietly got up and left the house. I reached the place where the horses waited for me, got into a carriage, and was off after my husband. However, to my misfortune, without suspecting it I met the same fate as the unhappy Fillida. My Demofont cheated me and left me without telling where he went. And thus I came to the sad conclusion that he needed my lover's things more than me and that he was more enchanted with the pearls and gold pieces of my lover then he was with my beauty.

When I inquired at the gate I was told that the man by the description I gave them did not even pass this place and that nobody saw him. After crying a little I was forced to return, but did not know whereto; therefore I settled in

Iamskaia in an inn. The true Fillida was not upset with Demofont when he deceived her, she only felt sorry; but I was so angry that if he were in my power and I had the strength I would have torn him in two; but no matter how much I wanted this I could not help myself. My own life was more important to me than his scoundrel's existence, and therefore I began to think about myself. Doubts, fear, and despair were constantly tearing me to pieces, and I did not know what I should undertake next. I was convinced that out of his immense love for me the colonel would forgive me my sins, but the shame of admitting my infidelity, stupidity, and gullibility did not allow me to go and see him. I was ready to suffer any kind of poverty rather then admit that I was fooled.

Whether I experienced some kind of remorse, that is for the reader to guess, I believe, but in order to relieve his doubt sooner, I would like to add that even corrupt women are not left without a sense of fairness, and were it not for fickleness and frivolous luxury they would be more virtuous than a moneylender or a miser. For the sake of my old man I overlooked annoyance and danger and decided to go to him in penance, hoping the while that my skill would help me deceive him if he was very much in anger.

Thus I went to him filled with fear and little hope for a happy outcome. As soon as I entered the courtyard, his manager, who met me there, gave me such a slap in the face that I began to see stars. Such a respectful greeting did not foretell anything good from the meeting, and I was ready to accept all misfortunes from my angered fate because it was already impossible for me to get away. I ran immediately to search for the colonel because I hoped to find more indulgence in him than in his servants. I came across him in his bedroom, where he was in bed, surrounded by a number of physicians. As soon as he saw me he yelled out so loud that he scared everyone who was there. Then he jumped up from his bed and, embracing me, began to sob bitterly. When he came to a bit, he said the following:

"Is this not a dream that has made my desires come true? Is this not a pleasing hope that deceives my mind? My beautiful Martona! Is it you I have in my arms? Are those your lips that I kiss now? Is it your beauty that I see now before me? Is it you, tell me, my beautiful, or have I lost you forever already?"

It is hard to say when my sorrow turned to joy. I embraced him with the utmost sincerity and shed the tears I had already stored up from the time the manager slapped me; when the latter was readying his blow he did not warn me to step aside, and so my tears were flowing like a stream. My lover took this for sincere penance on my part for the crimes I committed against him. However, I told him that I left him only for the reason that I wanted to find out his faithfulness to me and whether he would have grieved had he lost me. To this the colonel replied that not only did he grieve but he was ready to go to his grave because of it. And so I again acquired his former feelings of love and from all his servants their former respect. What I took from him and gave to the man who cheated me he did not even mention, for he felt that I was even dearer to him than his own life.

From that time on, my lover began getting ready to die, for after I left him he ran all over the place searching for me, and desperate and in great grief, out of his senses; and besides, without his glasses he was not cautious, and fell down the staircase right from the first step and broke his sacrum, as a result of which his weak health was getting worse from day to day. I was so mad at the manager that I tried to get even with him every moment, and when I told my lover how undiplomatically he treated me the colonel could hardly breathe after such information. Refusing to accept any explanations from the manager, he punished him quite severely and ordered him to be sent away from the house without payment for his services, which made me extremely happy.

A good deed never remains without reward; sooner or later someone must pay for it. As soon as the dear colonel left this world, I was immediately taken into custody and thrown into a dungeon. After the death of my lover his sister appeared. During his lifetime he never even let her into his house and did not want to hear her name mentioned. The manager got into her good graces and told her everything that went on in the house of her brother. She then decided to demand an accounting of me by court action, which seemed to me to be worse than death itself.

They threw me into a dark cellar without giving me anything to rest on during the night. I was given food twice a day, and this consisted of bread and water, which forced me to fast quite strictly—a thing which never even entered my head before. Such a withdrawn life knocked all the amorous thoughts out of my head. I thought neither of physical adornments nor about the seduction of lovers, and I remained in such a condition for two or more weeks. Every day I shed as many tears as my eyes could hold, and I was terribly sad over things.

One night when I was lying on the floor, my head resting on a stone, the doors of my cell opened and Akhal' entered with another officer. Seeing me in such a miserable condition, he felt sorry for me and asked the officer who had come in with him to take me somewhere else and to take better care of me, until he freed me completely from my confinement. I thanked him, and he kissed me and said that he had to free me. So pitying me, both of them left. No more than a quarter of an hour passed when they took me out of that hell and put me in a decent room where a bed, table, and chair stood ready for me. It is hard to say how glad I was then and how much I thanked Akhal' in my thoughts from the bottom of my heart. I threw myself onto the bed, and not having rested for a long time I slept over half a day. The officer on duty, as I found out later, came to visit me about four times, but having found me fast asleep he did not disturb me. He told me this himself and addressed me with such a respect that I knew that he had fallen in love with me. I was right about that. He was on duty for a whole week and stayed with me all the time; and when the replacement came, he asked him to let him stay another week. At that time Akhal' and he joined forces and freed me from prison. They took me from this place of judgment and put me up with some old woman who was not too badly off and on the very first day equipped me with everything I needed. My face and manners convinced her that I did not sell my charms cheaply and did not shortchange myself; and so she tried more zealously to please me and comfort me.

Ill luck is easier forgotten than good fortune, especially among those people who share my trade. It took me three days to recover; my face acquired its previous beauty, my body became voluptuous, white and tender as before, and there were no signs that I had been in prison and had been completely run down. Everyone thought that I was only now beginning to share my charms with the opposite sex.

For some four days my liberators did not come to me, I

had no idea why. Finally they came together, and seeing me in my previous condition or even better they completely melted and tried to outdo each other in front of me. Akhal' was closer to me and therefore allowed himself more liberties, and Svidal' (that was the name of the other) was extremely polite and tender, for he was afraid to upset me in the slightest way and thus sought a place in my heart with tenderness. Owing to my previous friendship with Akhal' I could not forbid him to behave as freely as he did. Svidal' interpreted this behavior on my part as my preferring Akhal' to him. Thus my task was to reassure Svidal' at an opportune moment that I really preferred him in every respect to his rival.

It is hard to share an inheritance, but to share a mistress is impossible without a quarrel. Akhal' always took advantage of me before the other, and unwillingly I had to obey him; and no matter how I tried to convince Svidal' that I loved him more than Akhal', he did not always believe me and began to be jealous, and jealousy, as everyone knows, does strange things to people and the outcome is usually bad. I found out soon enough that it is hard for our sisters to have dealings with military men, and especially when they are burning with jealousy and do not want to share their catch. One evening all three of us sat at a table and formed a triangle; we were playing omber. According to the rule of the game no one is allowed to see what the next partner has in his hand. Akhal', however, completely disregarded this rule and very often came close to me. Svidal' at first told him very politely not to peek at my cards. But later he got angry and said that Akhal' was quite impolite and that he was forcing himself on a lady against her will. Finally they quarreled. Akhal' told him that he had complete control over me and that Svidal' should not mind other people's business when nobody asked his opinion, to which Svidal' answered that they should consult me as to who has greater power over me. They asked me this question, but I gave no answer and begged to have them stop quarreling; but my words did not help and they had a big argument that almost led to a fight right there in front of me. Svidal' went away and left me with Akhal', who was very happy that he triumphed over his enemy and ordered me very sternly not to be friendly with Svidal' and not to let him inside my house. This command was very upsetting to me. However, I pretended that I agreed with him and would carry out his order.

I discovered on this occasion that Akhal' loved me terribly and that it was not anger but love for me that guided his actions at the time.

A half an hour later Svidal''s servant came, bringing Akhal' the following letter:

DEAR SIR!

I have been insulted by you, and you know how an offense to honor is repaid. Please do me the favor of appearing tomorrow at ten in the morning in the Maria grove where I will expect you, and if you do not come be prepared for me to deal with you as they do with common criminals.

Sincerely, your SVIDAL'

When he read this letter Akhal' became pale, evidently afraid because he was quite inexperienced in duels and this was the first time this had happened to him. However, he gathered what was left of his strength and told the servant that he was ready to satisfy his master as it pleased him. He stayed with me just for a short while and, without any love ceremonies, left home quite confused and scared. I must admit that this forthcoming duel scared me as much as my landlady. We did not know what to do next or where to run or hide, because I have already experienced how pleasant it is to sit behind bars. All night long we cried and did not sleep a wink. I was afraid that something bad might happen due to this encounter, and from the bottom of my heart I worried about Svidal', which convinced me that I had fallen in love with him. Two unexplainable passions tormented my heart and did not give me peace for a moment, and when the said hour came when the duel was supposed to take place I lost consciousness and fell onto my bed, where I remained for the next two hours or more. All the household people stood next to me and cried, feeling sorry for me and fearing that I myself would perish. In a word, our house was filled with crying and sobbing and I was beside myself. Although my conduct was not the best on this occasion, I have no doubt that many virtuous people felt sorry for me and wanted to help me.

Shortly after eleven Akhal' came running into my room, grabbed me by the hand, and pulled me out of bed. He could hardly hold back his breath and was trembling from fear. Throwing himself before me on his knees he said:

"My lady! Without considering your position I have loved you greatly. My poverty was the reason for my cheating you in the past, but after leaving you I discovered that without you I cannot live in peace. Therefore I came back to Moscow and when I found out that you were in trouble I tried to help you as much as I could, and at last succeeded. Finally I decided to keep my promise and marry you, but cruel fate is depriving me of this pleasure. This very minute I must leave Moscow and all Russia. I am a miserable man and must suffer a cruel torture. Farewell, my beauty, forever—I have shot Svidal' to death!"

When I heard these words I fainted, and fell onto my bed. He kissed my hand and went away in a hurry with great tears and sorrow, thinking that I fainted because we were parting.

From this incident I discovered what the passion of real love was like. When I heard that Svidal' died, the blood turned cold in me, my throat became dry, my lips parched, and I could hardly breathe. I thought that I had lost everything in the world when I found out that I lost Svidal'. The loss of my own life did not seem important to me at all; I was ready to follow him to hell if necessary. All the misfortunes that I could think of could not equal my own grief. Springs opened in my eyes and tears flowed down my cheeks in streams. I could see him very vividly before me; all his charms, tenderness, and politeness were constantly before my eyes. I began to rave mercilessly and an unappeasable grief was devouring my suffering heart. I feared no ruin any longer; I was ready to go through any kind of torture and to die without fear, just to pay back Svidal' for his lost life, because I was the cause of it, I, the most wretched creature on earth.

My landlady came to me many times and suggested that the best thing for me would be to leave the city, but I did not fear my own ruin as much as I grieved Svidal''s end.

I spent that day and the following night in racking anxiety, and utterly despaired of my life. The next morning I lay in bed in great confusion, thinking of the dead Svidal'. Suddenly he stood before me and, rushing to me, began to kiss my hands. With what strength I had I started screaming and then fainted. All the members of the household ran up to me and assured me that Svidal' was standing before me alive and not dead and that it was not an apparition but reality. I felt inside me how difficult it was for me to pass from extreme grief to extreme joy, and for a long time I could not. Jumping out of bed I threw myself into his embrace, but even then I could not believe that he was alive and with me. In such cases, however, assurance comes soon. He began to speak and convince me of his love, and the dead never express themselves with such passion. And thus I discovered that he was indeed alive and loved me as much as I did him, or perhaps less—we did not measure it and we made no bargains as to our feelings. The ecstasy we experienced I shall not describe, for it would be superfluous to go into all the details of the words, actions, and movements that occur in the delirium of love. Many have already found out from their own experiences that after a while passion completely leaves the excited man and he completely forgets all that he said as a lover, just as a sick person after a fever or a madman after regaining his sanity.

From the beginning of the world there has been only one obligation, and this forces us to be good, but since it is not appealing to everyone, we have arbitrarily made up different kinds of obligations which commit us to all sorts of things. Of all these obligations I chose one according to which I asked my lover how he escaped death. He answered me in these words:

"True love is always combined with jealousy, and united they made me shrewd and clever. First of all, I was looking for a way to quarrel with Akhal', and when I succeeded, in order to revenge myself, I decided to duel with him, but in this instance I had a wonderful thought in mind. I was only worried that he might refuse to fight. Yesterday I was waiting for him in the grove at the appointed hour, and as soon as he arrived he left his carriage fifty paces from the place and he came to me. Taking out my sword I told him to get ready, which he did with great cowardice. Giving him a way out and wishing to cheat him better, I asked him whether he would prefer dueling with pistols. He gladly agreed because he was an exceptionally good shot. I then took from my pocket two pistols that I had ready without bullets, which he could not notice in his fright. I gave him one and kept the other myself; withdrawing a certain distance we gave each other signs to start, and shot both at the same time. I fell and pretended that I was dead. My servants, as they were told to in advance, came running up to me howling and screaming. Thinking that I really was shot, Akhal' ran to his coach and the very same evening left town."

After this tale we both began to laugh and after laughing we thanked fate for being so kind to us. And so I became Svidal"s completely, and he was more delighted with this than a conceited general who has just taken an enemy fortress; and Akhal' at that time I thought was driving his horses and getting away from what he considered his ruin.

My lover read somewhere that Cupid gilded his arrows and with such cunning conquered all the human race. That is why in the present age every heart wants to be pierced with a golden arrow, for in the event of poverty beauty itself does not allure very much. And so, in order to secure our mutual passion, he designated me an annual salary of two thousand rubles, not counting presents and my other fancies. Besides, he promised to give me a thousand rubles as a gift if I bore him a son and he looked like him. So I began to pray to God, for it seems that I had forgotten that heaven was not obliged to bless our transgressions, even though we might have begun them with a prayer. This wealth did not make me happy because I had already seen enough of it. However, I decided to be more careful in the future and to keep something for a rainy day. I set aside a box where I hid gold coins so that in case my luck changed for the worse I would have something to rely on.

At that time destiny granted me a girl friend. She was a merchant's wife but the daughter of a nobleman. A clever woman, she knew how to pretend that she was very wealthy while she was only of modest means. The way she managed her affairs people thought her to be a modest and sensible housekeeper who did not want to show how rich she was. The merchant married her not because she was from a good family or rich, but only because she was beautiful. He was very much in love with her, yet slept in a separate room out of a desire to preserve his honor and even more his life. His wife was clever and capable of any tricks; he was more frightened of this than of a plague, and the first month after their marriage would gladly have left her. She was one of those women who wrote novels with introductions in verse, and because of this a large number of clever young people gathered about

her. For the sake of knowledge and art they visited her always
during the absence of her husband, and the most talented
sought rich rhymes for her. So busy was she with her versify-
ing she very seldom slept with her husband.

When I came to see her for the first time I found her quite
magnificent. She was sitting in her bed surrounded by a great
number of learned people out of whose pockets papers with
notes were protruding, and each of them would read in turn
their compositions before the assembly, relying on the taste
and judgment of the hostess. I was not surprised that polite
gentlemen consulted her opinions, but it was strange to me
that she would discuss every single work and praise or attack
it as she pleased. And when her husband entered, every one
got up, showed him respect, and tried to get into his good
graces, as if all those people were really his true and sincere
friends. The wife and I got along nicely and without any further courtesies because we were both of the same trade. At
the beginning of our friendship, for the first hour and a half
we spoke about so many things, a whole school would have
been unable to learn all of it in a week. I found out what kind
of a person she was and she found out a great deal about me.
We got to know each other quite well and called each other
sister until the time came for us to quarrel.

The next day I was at one of her parties and witnessed all
sorts of performances. Her house appeared to be a habitation
of love, and all the people walked about or sat in pairs. The
strangest thing I saw was an old man who was trying to convince a thirteen-year-old girl to marry him. While he was
persuading her with words he was also luring her with apples
and oranges, which he kept taking out of his pocket and giving
her with great politeness, but not understanding his intentions
she devoured them as voraciously as if she had never seen
them before.

In a corner sat a lad talking very modestly to a grandmother. I wanted to praise this young man for having respect
for his elders and for leaving all the silly entertainment in
order to please his grandmother. The hostess convinced me,
however, that this was a lover with his mistress. The young
man was assuring her that he was very much in love with her,
and avoiding chronology, which is very unpleasant to old
coquettes, was saying to her:

"My lady, you are very pleasant; you have none of the

fickleness and vices attractive to youth. Mature age has its own merit; you will be the harness of my youth."

He wanted to marry her in the hope that this toothless Grace would live no longer than a year, and her ample dowry would make the young man very satisfied.

A tall potbellied fellow was freer than the rest of them for the reason that when the need arose he served the hostess to her great satisfaction. He laughed so loudly that he could drown out a bass fiddle. He played cards with some maiden who was as heavy as a skeleton. This was his bride, whom he chose out of his great wisdom to be his bedmate.

An officer covered all over with gold was circling around a judge's wife and tried to teach her how to multiply. Elsewhere a beauty was after some pensive dandy, offering her services. In the middle of everything sat a short poet who kept on shouting poems from a tragedy he had composed; sweat was streaming from his brow while his wife was wiping an infantry officer with a white handkerchief. In a word, I found here a school of love or a licentious house. The hostess, however, had an advantage over everyone; no matter with whom a man started his love he had to finish with the hostess, because she was a woman deserving of every praise and loved her mate from the distance. Svidal' came to fetch me, and after saying goodbye to everyone I went home.

I began to think about women now. Many of us are extremely fickle, which is why some learned men and all the philosophers generally hate us. Thinking it over, however, I decided that their scorn does not really mean a thing, because for women's charms even the philosophers made fools of themselves. Socrates was our arch enemy; however, he could not avoid marriage, and as retribution for his contempt for us he had the most willful wife, who devoured his heart as rust does iron.

For a servant I had a clever and obliging Ukrainian fellow. He was capable of all kinds of tricks, as for example: he could swallow knives and forks, let pigeons out of eggs, pull a needle through his cheek, close his lips like a lock, etc., which led people to the conclusion that he was a sorcerer. One morning this fellow told me that the maid of my friend confided in him a certain secret, namely, that for the last half a year her mistress was looking for a man who would help her get rid of her husband but so no one would notice it, and for this service she was prepared to pay a hundred rubles. So she asked my servant to attend to the matter.

"I did not refuse," he continued, "and I want to serve her."

I was frightened when I heard of his intention and told him that I did not agree to it and that I would tell it to everyone. When I said that, he smiled and said:

"You are not very experienced in this world, my lady, and you think that people become their own enemies willingly. I know that it is hard to be responsible for something like that and therefore I am not going to let myself in for any trouble. I intend to act out a comedy for which performance I hope to collect a hundred rubles, and the innocent merchant will remain alive. My first act I will start tonight; please let me go there."

I let him go. However, I decided that it would be best for me to be present while the comedy was played and to tell Svidal' all about it just to make sure no harm came of it. No sooner said than done.

My servant came with fifty rubles, which he had received for making poison, because he told them that poison which begins to act in a week is quite expensive. Svidal' asked him what he intended doing.

"To make poison," he replied, "and you'll see that I'm not the worst apothecary. Once I make it up I'll drink a glass in your presence so that you will not fear any evil consequences."

And so he began to cook different herbs, and prepared his poison in an hour or two. When we asked him how much it cost him, he said about six and a quarter kopecks. Pouring it into a container he drank it and said that if this mixture were put into beer the person who drank it in five days would have such a fit of anger for half an hour's time that he would be ready to beat up everyone in his house or anyone he happened to come across. Afterward he would feel no ill effects. We believed him and let him take his concoction to my friend. He gave her instructions on how to act when the drug took effect. Five days later, as we were told afterward, the merchant had an attack of madness and jumped at everyone in the house so that they had to tie his hands and put him to bed. My friend summoned her relatives to witness her grief. I, too, was asked to come. Svidal' also wanted to see it, and so we both went. When we came the poison had already ceased working and the merchant had regained his senses. However, everyone insisted that he was completely out of his mind. He contended that he was of sound mind, but nobody believed it and did not want to untie him. Finally he began to beg to be freed, but out of pity for him nobody wanted to do it. Then he began to curse everyone, saying that this day the whole world had surely lost its sanity. His friends and relatives tried to talk him into being sensible, and his wife, who was sitting opposite him, cried and told the people to hold him more strongly. He gnashed his teeth at her and was ready to cut her in two.

His wife assured everyone that he was already hopeless and therefore wanted to examine before witnesses the number of banknotes and other papers he had. When they tried to take his keys for this purpose, the merchant began shouting, "Help! Robbery! Plunder!" etc. Many of the people present suggested that he should be fumigated with incense and that the sign of the Cross should be made over him every minute in order to expel the evil spirit which, unseen, was torturing him terribly. The poor merchant did not know what to do next. Tears came to his eyes and he began to weep bitterly. Everyone was sympathetic to his tears but nobody wanted to free him because his wife and the rest of the household said that if he were freed he would cut everyone to pieces and that one should not trust him because he had completely lost all his senses. There was nobody who could save him, and so he begged for a priest. They sent for him immediately, and when he came everyone went out of the room and they were left alone.

Half an hour later the priest left the room and told everyone that he found the merchant completely sane and with all his faculties.

"You are not doing right," he said, "untie him; I assure you he is not mad in the slightest."

And so he left their house, perhaps making fun of their stupidity. Everyone present immediately wanted to follow the priest's advice. Only the wife opposed the priest's order and begged everyone in tears to leave her husband bound. However, no one listened to her and he was freed. A man as bitter as he was will, of course, forget all decency and will attempt to revenge himself on his enemy. The merchant jumped at his wife and, pulling her by the hair, threw her onto the floor. All the people, as many as there were, threw themselves on the merchant, and in spite of his resistance and pleas tied him up and put him back in bed, saying:

"You won't deceive us any more; rest peacefully because you're all excited."

Seeing no other way of freeing himself, the merchant grew silent and stopped raving over his misfortune, thinking that if he were quiet for a certain length of time people would come to their senses and be convinced of his sanity. Thus he decided to submit to raging fate.

It was already dinnertime, but the host was still in his hempen fetters. He was finally obliged to admit that he had been really losing his mind but that, thanks to his fate, had returned to his senses. He then swore that he would not harm anyone, and thus was freed. It was amusing to see how he walked about his room immersed in thought and how everyone was afraid to approach him and walked around him at a distance. What did he think when everyone was convinced that he was hopelessly insane? Finally the table was set and everyone took his place, but there were neither knives nor forks next to the plates, for they feared that he might take advantage of the situation and stab someone. At that very moment guests arrived. They were informed already in the anteroom about the host's misfortune, and so when they entered the room they stopped at the doors and said, "Hello, sir!" But they were scared to come closer, and once they were seated looked at him in astonishment as though he were a real fool. Anger was written on his face, and he was ready to get even with his wife right then and there but he was afraid of being tied up again. He was curious, however, to learn about his destiny, but no sooner asked, "Why did you decide that I was insane?" when everyone immediately rushed to tie him up, thinking that he was about to have another fit. I really felt sorry for him that, although his own master in the house, he could not say a word to his wife or servants.

With the permission of the hosts Svidal' left the table for an hour, and as he was leaving said that he had a servant who was a master storyteller. "Perhaps to drive away unpleasant thoughts it will please you to listen to one of his tales." The host was very grateful to Svidal' for this proposal and thanked him with tears in his eyes. Svidal' called our Ukrainian and told him to tell a story, and on the way taught him what to say and how. The servant had to carry out his master's command perfectly, and told a tale that surprised everyone, including myself, because I never would have thought of it. Svidal' did it only out of pity for the poor host, about whom he felt very sorry.

A Tale

"A certain wealthy merchant, reaching ripe age, without mother or father, decided to marry. He did not look for a dowry, but for a virtuous beauty who knew everything that would make her a sensible mother, a good housewife, and a spouse worthy of love. However, since it is very difficult to find a woman with such qualities he came across the daughter of some secretary who was pretty enough and knew how to keep a young man from falling into want. By the way, she was not without a dowry and brought with her a handsome estate that consisted of invalid promissory notes, longstanding claims, and the hope that she would inherit the estate of her uncle—who was presently on business in Siberia—if he died before getting married, without issue, and without having left a will . . ."

At this point the host turned to the servant and said, "It could not be a better time." And then he said to Svidal', "My dear sir, but this is my life story, and the most talented author could not have described it more vividly."

"Please do listen," said Svidal', "its conclusion will be very pleasant to you, but quite the opposite to your wife. However, vices are always punished publically, and I am doing this out of pity for you. I know that you are not insane; be master in your own house and order her to sit and listen."

My friend wanted to get up and leave, but the host ordered her to stay, saying:

"If you have done something evil, let your parents listen to it too; they are here with us now. Do continue," the host said to our servant, "I owe a lot to your kind master and I see that my insanity is coming to the surface now, for which I am very happy."

"The marriage took place and she got tired of her husband after a few weeks. This natural loathing for her husband she began to remedy with some rhymesters who visited her at any time of the day. Although her spouse regarded such visits suspiciously, he did not dare to tell her about it because noble blood was flowing in her veins and he was afraid of dishonoring her. She finally made the acquaintance of a lady named Martona who had as a servant a Ukrainian named Oral'. This servant knew all kinds of tricks and was considered a sorcerer because of it. The wife of this merchant made the servant agree to poison her husband, and promised him a hundred rubles. Oral' then betook himself and told it to his mistress, who feared the consequences and asked him what kind of poison he was going to make. The servant explained to her that he had no intention of performing such a godless act and that he just wanted to make a fool of the merchant's wife and collect the money promised him. And so, when he concocted the poison he first drank a glass of it before his lady's eyes, which was real proof that the poison was harmless. Getting fifty rubles from the merchant's wife for making the poison, he spent only six and a quarter kopecks on it and then delivered it to her. The wife gave it to her husband in the hope that he would die; but since he suffered only a fit they tied him up and put him in bed. And the conclusion to my tale was made by you, sir. You know it, and so do your guests; thus I shall not continue."

After these words the host jumped up from his seat, kissed the servant on the top of the head, thanked him for saving him, and gave him four hundred and fifty rubles, saying:

"Instead of a hundred rubles have five hundred now for your virtuous act. As concerns my wife, I shall quote a rule given to us by righteous people: 'Avoid evil and do good.' I do not wish to revenge her lawlessness. If it pleases you, my lady," he said to her, "I will buy you a village in your name: you will go there and live happily. I do not need you and I do not intend to live with you any longer, and because I do not want to dishonor you, I shall never tell anyone about my misfortune."

Thus ended the comedy in which the leading actor was my servant, who was quite satisfied with the way everything went. The merchant really intended to buy his wife a village and send her away, and he thanked my lover for exposing her. And so we parted that evening, not knowing that it was to be forever.

Our whole life consists of spending time. Some people spend it in work and labor useful to society, others in idleness and nonsense unmindful of the fact that luxury and idleness are

like the two nipples of corruption—under the guise of sweetness they pour into our soul and body a harmful plague, bringing poverty and fatal diseases. However, everyone in his spare
time likes to engage himself in love.

Svidal' was always free of all civil duties, and I had no
responsibility whatsoever. Thus we were idle people, or rather
lazy, and so we did not let an hour or a minute pass by without
making love.

After some time passed I received a letter of the following
contents:

My LADY!

Nature brings a man into the world so that consequently,
after diverse trials, no one can avoid his predestined fate.
Fortunate is the man who dies happy and, feeling no remorse, leaves this world without regrets. But I, the most
wretched of mortals, having deprived my friend of his life,
and myself, because of that, of my mistress, am now for the
same reason losing my life. . . . Unbearable torment! Fear
grips me when I am about to inform you of my calamity.
I took poison and am ready to die, which I expect to happen soon. May I dare ask you to condescend to let me see
you for the last time. My servant will tell you where I am.
Expecting you with impatience—

AKHAL'

Although scorners of wisdom and intimates of Venus, our
fops say that compassion is not at all a trait of the weaker
sex. However, I insist that in this case they are as knowl-
edgeable as philosophers in proving what a kiss is. Having
read the letter I felt a great sorrow in me. His ill deed against
me was completely forgotten and I could only vividly remember Akhal''s good deeds. I was crying that he was about to
die, and felt sorry for him as does a sister for her own dying
brother who gave her a good dowry but is leaving no inheritance. I sent immediately to inform Svidal' about what had
happened. Without losing any time he came to me and told
me to get ready to go to Akhal''s so we could still find him
alive. And so both of us got ready very fast and we went
together, and Akhal''s servant was our guide.

The place where Akhal' was staying was twenty versts away
from Moscow. When we were getting closer to it Svidal' left

the coach and told me to go on by myself. He wanted to come later, and asked me and the servant not to tell Akhal' that he, Svidal', was still alive, because he wanted personally to beg his forgiveness for his wicked and inadvertent misdeed.

As soon as I rode up to the house I heard a terrible wailing from the whole household. This was the place Akhal' had bought with my money. I thought that he already had passed away, and my knees began buckling; I was beside myself when I got out of the coach. However, I was informed that he was still alive. When I entered the room I was horrified by the sight. The whole room, including the ceiling, floor, and walls, was covered with black flannel. The bed was also covered with a black curtain on which was placed a white carving. The table was also covered with black, and another one stood in front of it with a cross beneath which lay a human skull and two bones. A lamp was burning before an icon. Akhal' sat behind the table in a black robe and a black nightcap with white trimming, reading a book. As he read he cried bitterly. Having heard that I had come he looked at me in deep sorrow and, crying worse than before, said:

"My lady, you see a man who is leaving this world and is going into the unknown. All kinds of visions are tearing apart my heart and indomitable conscience as the first judge of our deeds shows me clearly that in this world I was vile, for I willingly became a murderer. The soul that I killed with my own hand seems to me to be standing at the throne of justice and demanding my rightful punishment. And so anticipating the wrath of fate I took the matter into my own hands. Sit down, my lady, and I shall tell you my misfortune.

"How I proceeded to the infamous deed, and killed Svidal', I think you have already been informed by someone. Confused in my thoughts I do not have the strength to tell you. After saying goodbye to you, I ran away from my lawlessness and the place that reminded me of my ill deed and threatened me with a just but disgraceful punishment. I could escape the place but I could not escape the pangs of my conscience. It followed me everywhere; everywhere it tormented me and brought me to despair. Finally a terrible fear began to pursue me, and when I fell asleep Svidal' would come, awaken me and, standing in front of me, cry bitterly. I was stricken with horror and I had no peace either during the day or during the night. Wherever I went fear followed my footsteps; my own shadow began to frighten me. Seeing no way of freeing myself, I decided to do away with my own life and give up this world, a world I hated perhaps unjustly but which hated me justly. I returned here, and as soon as I arrived I prepared everything for my departure, drank poison, and consider myself now already dead. In these last moments of my existence I see that I am still happy because I can bid farewell to the woman for whom I lived and for whom I suffered. During my life I insisted that I loved you, and now at my death I repeat it. Here is the deed of purchase for this house which I bought for your money. It is signed over to you. Here is my will—I have no relatives and I am giving you all my possessions. With this I bear testimony that you have always been dear to me."

At these words I was unable to hold back my tears any longer and to keep the secret Svidal' asked me to, and as soon as I began to tell him about it I saw that his face changed, his eyes stopped, a terrible quivering seized all his limbs. He did not say a word and he squeezed my hand very strongly. I thought that his last hour was approaching and the poison he drank was taking effect. For this reason I called for his people to come. From my voice he came to somewhat and began to beg forgiveness if he had offended me. He began to talk very confusedly so that it was impossible to understand either the beginning or end of what he said, and he seemed to me to be at death's door. I begged his servants to find Svidal' and to inform him that Akhal' was already breathing his last breath and that he should hasten to beg his forgiveness. When he heard the name Svidal' he fell into greater confusion; terror gripped him and his feeble mind gave way completely. In a great frenzy he said:

"O horrible shadow! At least in my last moment of life leave me in peace. I know that your revenge is just and your anger rightful and that your murderer deserves any punishment from you. I tremble and I cannot look upon you without great horror. I imagine you in blood without breath and without voice. I have deprived you of all that; I am the cause of everything and therefore deserve the torments of hell. I am prepared to accept all the tortures that you and fate embittered by me desire. I am detestful to myself and for that reason have ended my wretched existence. I feel sorry only that fierce death is slow to tear my tortured soul from my body. I am ready and everything is prepared for it."

All of us who were present tried to give him help. I was crying inconsolably, and his servants were wailing bitterly, too, because he was a gracious master to them. I wanted to send for a doctor, but they told me that under oath they promised not to bring anyone to his home, and as a result I had to take advantage of whatever came to mind. He regained his senses somewhat and begged me not to try to help him because he said "it was no longer necessary to him." At this very moment Svidal' came running into the room. As soon as the practically unconscious Akhal' saw him, he tore himself out of our hands and fell into a horrible frenzy: he beat himself and howled and shouted as much as his strength permitted him. He completely resembled a madman. As much as our strength allowed we restrained him and finally covered him with a blanket so that he could recollect his lost senses somewhat and lose that fright he experienced when he saw Svidal', whom he thought he had murdered, because he believed and imagined that his crime was the greatest in the world.

3. *A Bitter Fate*

MIKHAIL D. CHULKOV

A Bitter Fate (Gor'kaia uchast') was included in the last part of Chulkov's collection *The Scoffer*, which appeared in 1789. It is undeniably one of his more interesting stories, and claims the distinction of being the first narrative prose work in which the hero is a peasant. At the root of the work is a true happening—the multiple murder—described in the second part of the story; the tale of the peasant Sysoi Durnosopov functions as something of a frame in which the grizzly events are presented. Apart from the sensational element of the story, the narration is dispassionate and free of any moralization on the part of the author. The picture of peasant life is realistically grim but provides a welcome contrast to the idealization of the peasant so characteristic of Russian sentimentalism (as, for example, in Radishchev's *Journey*, Karamzin's *Poor Liza*, and Kniazhnin's *Misfortune From a Coach*).

"Peasant," "plowman," "tiller of the soil"—all these names, according to writers of old—and the most recent ones are in agreement with them—designate the principal nourisher of the Fatherland in times of peace, and a firm defender in time of war, and they assert that the state cannot dispense with the tiller any more than a man can live without a head! But whether this is true or false we have no time to consider here, and besides, such deep questions do not belong to the domain of entertainment. We can say that the hero of this story, the peasant Sysoi Fofanov Durnosopov, was born in a village far removed from any city, raised on bread and water, and swaddled in bands that, in their fineness and softness, compared not unfavorably with matting. A corner of a peasant hut, stifling in summer and filled with smoke in winter, served him as his cradle. Until the age of ten he went barefoot and with-

69

out a cloak, putting up equally with the unbearable heat of summer and the unendurable cold of winter. Horseflies, mosquitoes, bees and wasps, rather than the rich food of the city, puffed and swelled his body. Until twenty-five, now dressed somewhat better than before, that is, in bast sandals and a gray cloak, he turned up the earth of the fields in clods, and in the sweat of his brow and with relish consumed his traditional food, bread and water. He intended to marry, and sent the matchmaker to many of the village girls, but none of their families would have him, for he was extremely impecunious, unresourceful, and, to put it bluntly, a ninny.

Envy and hatred are the same among peasants as they are among cityfolk, but since peasants are purer in heart than town dwellers, these vices are more quickly detected than in the subtle politicians who dwell at court and in the cities. Such village citizens are called "cannibals"; these, holding the destinies of the other peasants in their hands, grow rich at their expense. Lending out money at interest, they "hitch" the others up to their businesses as oxen are hitched up to a plow. Whenever there are several, or even one of them, the whole village is populated by poor wretches, with the "cannibal" the only person among them who is well off. In order that his debtors should complete the sowing, harvesting, and haymaking of his fields before their own, they must always be delayed in their own work; when they have delayed too long, they will have nothing to harvest, and thus they will remain eternally in debt to the "cannibal," who takes no loss but rather an increase from this, for the whole village comes to labor for him as if to do *corvée*.

These "cannibals," because of the many shortcomings in the peasant life of Sysoi Durnosopov, determined to send him off to the army as the conscript due from the local estate, and so they brought him to town, where for the first time in his life Sysoi beheld straight streets, rectangular walls, and people diversely costumed and dressed in different colored clothing. But he had little time to gape, for soon he was brought to the recruiting center. Taking his measure, they called out, "Too short!" and the physician cried "Legs too thin!" And so they dismissed him without shaving the nape of his neck, and all this they did for the specific information of their "suppliers," who were thus given to comprehend the incident at their leisure, for it was not the first time that an experience of this sort had occurred with them. The next day, earlier than the day before, Sysoi Durnosopov was again delivered to the recruiting center: on his crown was set some "hush money," but how much I cannot say exactly; to each of his legs a paper ruble was bound, all of which, in a single night, brought him up to the proper height and thickness of calves. They shaved his forehead, and Durnosopov was acknowledged a model recruit; this stirring scene took place in a former provincial government office. The examiners refused to take anything for the recruit in kind, but demanded money for his food and clothing, to which demand no rejoinder was possible; some money was paid out for him and the bargain concluded on the spot.

At that time our army was serving abroad, and Sysoi was sent off with some other recruits, outfitted by the charity of his community, for no clothing or food was ever issued him by his commander, whom he did not see once during the entire journey; that officer caught up with his men a mere hundred versts or less before they reached the army. Of five hundred men not more than fifty reached the army; the rest ran away or died, or both. The commanding officer handed in a report stating that, for lack of a command, the recruits had run off at various times. They held a court-martial, but all the same the recruits were reassigned without clothing or equipment, for nothing had been found on their commander at the time of his arrest, and rumor had it that he had concealed everything in a remote place in the event of a strict sentence by the court.

Sysoi mastered the manual-at-arms and served as a model soldier in some three assaults, earning praise from his commanders, but in the last of these battles he lost his right arm, so that he could do nothing that required its use. For this reason he was soon discharged and left free to return to his former dwelling place. He soon set out, putting all his movable property into a knapsack and hanging the latter over his shoulder. Many are of the opinion, and assert quite justly, that this knapsack was no burden to him on his journey, for he had nothing in it besides a shirt, a necktie, and ten kopecks in copper, which he spent for food along the way.

His journey from the army back to his place of birth was scarcely so glorious as Prince Bova's from the realm of Tsar Dadon to the domain of Kirbit Verzaulovich, the father of

Milokrasa Kirbitovna,[1] nor so memorable as the ride of the celebrated knight Peter to the domain of the fair Queen Magdalene of Naples,[2] and so in consequence it need not require such a detailed description; it is enough to state that he got there only through the kindness of charitable people.

At dawn in winter, on Christmas Day, he arrived in his parish in time for matins and went along with the others to church, where he hoped to see his father and mother. But they were not in the church, and in answer to his questions his relatives told him that they had seen them the evening before, and had no idea why they should be absent on such a high feast day.

After matins Sysoi and many of his relatives went to his father's home, but, knocking underneath his windows and on the gate, they could not arouse anyone to open. They went to the village elder, and respectfully inviting him along with other peasants, broke down the gates and, going into the yard with a lighted taper, they saw the following in order. In front of the porch a ram was hanging, half skinned, and beside it on the railing of the porch steps there lay a bloodstained knife. In the middle of the yard the father was hanging in a noose that had been made fast to a crossbeam, choked to death. The hut was open, and sticks of wood, partly charred, were scattered over the floor. The mother was lying in the middle of the room, her head gashed in with an ax that lay beside her, covered with blood. Behind a curtain in the hanging cradle a three-month-old baby girl lay, dressed in swaddling clothes, her throat slit. In the stove a four-year-old boy was found dead, the hair on his head all singed and his skin cracked by the heat. In the front corner on a bench lay the father's best clothes, and on the table the mother's holiday dress, brought out from the closet and laid out, as peasants are accustomed to doing.

Seeing all this, the discharged soldier broke into tears, followed by several of his female relations. And indeed how could it be otherwise? For any village inhabitant, seeing a father, mother, brother, and sister suddenly dead, can hardly help but show pity and begin to wail according to the custom and style of the country. The groaning made by the wailers in

---

[1] In the Old Russian tale of *Bova Korolevich*.
[2] In the Old Russian tale of *Peter of the Golden Keys*.

the hut brought the whole village on the run. Old and young expressed their sympathies, and the little children were terrified—in a word, the entire village was absorbed by the amazing occurrence.

A case incomprehensible not only to villagers but even to many who reside in the city was expounded by the peasant men and women of the village in many different ways, according to village wit and reasoning powers and without observing any of the rules laid down by the liberal arts. One man said that it was the work of bandits, who had no time to carry off the clothing. Another reasoned, more justifiably, that a hearth sprite had fallen into a temper and had settled scores with the family just as a supernatural power might be expected to. Old women were more inclined to believe the latter explanation; they said a prayer and asked their old men if it were not a sin to touch the dead. And the wisest heads, calling the town clerk and the elder, wrote out a report with all the details and sent it to the city.

In consideration of such a great feast day all the judges and secretaries were away from the city, in the villages belonging to the neighboring landowners, and the clerks left on duty declined to accept the report. Thus only in six weeks could the court convene to consider it, and one of the members be dispatched to the scene to examine the evidence. But since the bodies of the dead were already buried, the official sent for the inspection reported that, "On inspection and after search it appeared that the peasant, drinking himself to intoxication on the eve of the holiday, murdered his family, and himself, falling off the porch, was struck and killed." On delivering this report, he added, "The peasants belong to the state, so that no suit is possible." And so it was resolved that, "This report is to be referred to higher authority, and the case withdrawn from the register of unsolved cases, marked as solved, and filed in the archives."

Thus this unusual occurrence was settled by the authorities on the basis usually followed in complicated cases that ought rightly to require more wit and penetration from our judges. But our courts' lack of enlightenment and their laziness have buried matters even more important than this in a fog of ignorance.

But when scholars of the time heard of the matter, they pondered the apparently insoluble case and determined to investigate it insofar as it was still possible to do so. After a reasonably thorough investigation they concluded, tentatively, on the following. The four-year-old boy, in a deep sleep and upset by a nightmare, had gotten out of bed, taken the knife that peasant children are often given to play with when their mothers or fathers lull them to sleep and, under the influence of his dream, had cut the throat of his baby sister in her cradle. Coming to his senses and realizing that he had acted badly, he hid himself in the stove. The father and mother, arising in time for church, first made ready their holiday garb; then the father went to skin the ram. His wife started to light the stove, paying no heed to the children, since they were sleeping, as she supposed and heard, peacefully. Putting on wood, she lit the stove. The foolish boy dared not stir from terror, but when the fire was growing hot, the dry wood suddenly kindled and flared up, the unbearable heat reached him and he cried out; the mother, rushing to the bed, could not find him, and realized that he must be in the stove. She called out to her husband, and herself took to pulling the logs out of the stove and scattering them about the floor. Meanwhile the boy had suffocated. The peasant ran into the hut with his customary eternal weapon, the ax, which he had ready, probably, for cutting up the ram. Supposing that his wife had burned his son alive in the stove, and acting in haste and fear, and therefore in hot temper, he unreasoningly and violently struck his wife on the head a blow that cost her her life. Turning soft with grief and struck dumb, the peasant did not know what he should do; he beheld two dead bodies in front of him and, looking into the cradle, he found yet a third. Despair struck this unreasoning man, a despair that would have shaken even a more enlightened and magnanimous man not a whit less; moreover, he was seized by fear of shame and conscience, as well as by the threat of harsh punishment for so much lawlessness, all of which he was unceasingly compelled to ascribe to his own doing. All this caused him to lose his reason, and so fear, grief, and despair led him to hang himself. Thus the scholars of the day pityingly resolved the case, and their solution was acknowledged by many at the time to be the correct one, for indeed, no one was able to give another explanation of this amazing occurrence.

The unfortunate soldier, burying his whole family and devoting the remains of the estate to the funeral, was left the sole heir of his father's house, without cattle or grain, no very great quantity of either having been found by him. And what is even more important and even more painful to a poor man —he lacked a right arm, without the use of which he could hardly be taken for a whole peasant, or indeed even for a proper half of one.

4. *Poor Liza*

NIKOLAI M. KARAMZIN

Karamzin's best known fictional work and a classic of Russian sentimentalism appeared for the first time in the *Moscow Journal* in 1792. So successful was the story that pilgrimages were made to the pond near the Simonov Monastery outside Moscow in which the unfortunate Liza drowns herself in the story. Not only that, but young lovers carved their initials and various tender sentiments in the trees surrounding the pond (it has been pointed out, however, that from about 1799 the inscriptions become somewhat less reverent), and there were even instances of suicides.

The plot of *Poor Liza* (Bednaia Liza)—the seduction by a young nobleman of a girl of lower social origins—was among the most conventional in European sentimentalism. What is characteristic of Karamzin's treatment of it is the subordination of the element of social conflict to the ethical problem and the avoidance of a completely negative character in the young man, Èrast.

Although Liza herself can hardly be accepted as a realistic portrait of a peasant (particularly if she is compared with Aniuta, for example, in Radishchev's *Journey*), Karamzin has introduced an element of psychological analysis, which was virtually unknown before in Russian literature. The emotions experienced by a young girl in love for the first time are handled faithfully and with some delicacy. Èrast and his milieu, which were of course more familiar to Karamzin, appear more convincing, without any of the pastoral aura that still clings to Liza herself. In a certain sense, Erast may be regarded a precursor of the soul-weary romantic heroes of Russian literature, of Pushkin's Eugene Onegin or Lermontov's Pechorin. The impact of Liza's pure emotions on her jaded young lover in the early part of the story, which is traced with no little skill, easily brings to mind the early relationship between Tatiana and Onegin in Pushkin's classic.

Following the pattern of most of Karamzin's narrative

A portrait of Nikolai Karamzin.

prose, *Poor Liza* is presented as a first-person narration strongly emotional in coloration. The author frequently addresses his readers directly and expresses his own subjective opinions about the principals. However, unlike a great deal of sentimentalist fiction dealing with this or similar themes, Karamzin avoids a concluding moral and the eventual (conventional) triumph of good over evil.

The popularity of *Poor Liza* created a fashion for this type of fiction, and numerous imitations appeared, among them *Poor Masha* (Bednaia Masha) by A. Izmailov, *Unfortunate Liza* (Neschastnaia Liza) by P. Dolgorukov, *Poor Lilla* (Bednaia Lilla) by A. Popov, the *Story of Poor Maria* (Istoria bednoi Marii) by N. Brusilov, and others. Pushkin also wrote a version of the story, in a parodic vein, under the title "The Lady Rustic" (Baryshnia-krest'ianka). It was included in his *Tales of Belkin* (1830) cycle. The present translation[1] follows the text in N. M. Karamzin, *Izbrannye sochineniia*, ed. P. Berkov and G. Makogonenko, 2 vols., Moscow-Leningrad, 1964.

Perhaps no inhabitant of Moscow knows as well as I the environs of this city. For no one is out as often in the fields; no one has wandered more on foot, aimlessly and without plan—wherever my nose led—through meadows and glades, over hill and dale. Each summer I find new, pleasant locales, or find new beauties in the old.

But the most pleasant place for me is there by the gloomy, Gothic towers of the Si . . . nov Monastery.[1] Standing on the hill, to the right, you can see almost all Moscow, that frightful

---

[1] *Poor Liza* was translated into English as early as 1803. It was included, together with several other stories, in a book of translations from Karamzin entitled *Russian Tales by Nicolai Karamsin*, translated by a John Battersby Elrington and published in London in 1803. The following year, 1804, brought another book of Karamzin's stories in English. The translations are identical to those in the publication of 1803. The translator signs himself only as "a Dane," and dedicates the work to Mr. A. de Gyldenpalm, the Danish *chargé d'affaires* in London.

[1] The Simonov monastery, founded c. 1370.

mass of houses and churches that strikes the eye as a mighty amphitheatre: a magnificent picture, especially when lit by the sun, when its evening rays ignite the innumerable gilded cupolas and the innumerable crosses rising up to the sky! Misty, dark-green, flowering meadows spread out below. And beyond them, over yellow sand flows the clear river, ruffled by the light oars of fishing skiffs or gurgling under the rudder of freight barges, which sail from the most bountiful parts of the Russian Empire and supply hungry Moscow with grain. On the far side of the river you can see an oak grove, along which numerous herds graze. There young shepherds, sitting in the shade of the trees, sing simple, doleful songs and thus hasten along the summer days, so monotonous for them. Farther out, the gold-capped Danilov Monastery[2] shines in the thick green of ancient elms. Still farther, almost on the horizon's edge, the Sparrow Hills[3] turn blue. To the left appear vast, grain-laden fields, woods, and three or four small villages, and in the distance, the village of Kolomensk[4] with its tall castle.

I visit the place often and almost always greet spring there. And I go there in the sullen fall days to grieve along with Nature. The winds moan frightfully in the walls of the deserted monastery,[5] among the graves grown over with tall grass, and in the dark passageways of the cells. There, leaning against the rubble of gravestones, I hear the dead moaning of times devoured in the abyss of the past—moaning from which my heart shrinks and trembles. Sometimes I enter the cells and imagine those who lived in them—sad pictures! Here I see a gray elder on his knees before a crucifix, praying for speedy release from his earthly bondage; for all his pleasures

[2] Founded in the second half of the thirteenth century by Prince Daniil, the son of Aleksandr Nevskii.

[3] Vorob'ëvy gory, in Russian; the high ground southwest of Moscow. It is now called Lenin Hills.

[4] A village to the south of Moscow. The castle referred to was probably the four-story one built on Catherine's orders in 1767 on the site of an older wooden castle erected in the time of Tsar Alexis Mikhailovich, in the 1660's.

[5] In 1771 the Simonov monastery was placed under quarantine and vacated because of an outbreak of plague in the Moscow area. It remained uninhabited until the mid-1790's. During Napoleon's invasion of Russia it was sacked in 1812.

in life have disappeared, all his feelings have died, save those of illness and feebleness. Over there a young monk—with a pale face and languishing gaze—looks out at the field through the grating of his window and sees the joyous birds sailing freely in the sea of air—he sees, and bitter tears stream from his eyes. He pines, fades, and wastes away—and the cheerless tolling of the bell heralds for me his untimely death. From time to time I examine on the portals of the temple the representations of the miracles that took place in the monastery: there fish fall from the sky to sate the inhabitants of the monastery, besieged by numerous enemies; here an icon of the Blessed Mother turns the enemy to flight. All this refreshes in my memory the history of our Fatherland—the sad history of those times when the rapacious Tatars and Lithuanians plundered with fire and sword the environs of the Russian capital, when hapless Moscow, like a defenseless widow, looked to God alone for aid in her bitter misfortunes.

But most often I am attracted to the walls of the Si . . . nov Monastery by the memory of the deplorable fate of Liza, poor Liza. Ah! I love those objects that touch my heart and force me to shed tears of tender grief!

About a hundred and fifty yards from the monastery wall, by a birch grove, in the middle of a green meadow stands an empty cabin with no doors, no windows, and no floor. The roof has long since rotted and caved in. In this cabin thirty years or so ago lived the beautiful, dear Liza with her old mother.

Liza's father was a rather well-to-do settler, for he loved work, tilled the land well, and always led a sober life. But soon after his death, his wife and daughter grew poor. The lazy hand of a hired man worked the land poorly, and the grain ceased to thrive. They were forced to rent out their land, and for a pittance of a sum. And what is more, the poor widow, almost constantly shedding tears over the death of her husband—for indeed peasant women know how to love!—from day to day became weaker and weaker and finally could not work at all. Liza alone—who was fifteen years old at her father's death—only Liza, sparing neither her tender youth nor her rare beauty, worked day and night; she wove flax, knitted stockings, gathered flowers in the spring and picked berries in the summer and sold them in Moscow. Observing her untiring daughter, the sensitive and good mother often pressed her to her weakly beating heart, called her the grace of God, her provider, a joy in her old age, and prayed to God that He reward her for all she was doing for her mother. "God gave me hands in order to work," Liza would say, "you fed me at your breast and watched after me when I was a child: now my turn has come to watch after you. Only do stop grieving, stop weeping; our tears will not bring dear father back to life." But often the tender Liza could not hold back her own tears. Oh! She would remember that she once had a father and that he was no more; but to soothe her mother she tried to hide the grief in her heart and appear at ease and gay. "In the next world, dear Liza," the bereaved old woman would answer, "in the next world I will stop weeping. There, so they say, everyone will be happy; I am sure I'll be happy when I see your father. Only, I don't want to die now—what will become of you without me? Whom can I leave you to? No, God grant you will get settled some-where first! Perhaps a good man will turn up soon. Then, having given you my blessing, dear children, I shall cross myself and peacefully lie down in the damp earth."

About two years had passed since the death of Liza's father. The meadows were covered with flowers, and Liza had come to Moscow with lilies of the valley. A young, well-dressed man with a pleasant appearance greeted her on the street. She showed him the flowers—and blushed. "Are you selling these, Miss?" he asked with a smile. "I am," she answered. "How much are you asking?"—"Five kopecks."—"That's too little. Here's a ruble for you." Liza was amazed, then dared glance at the young man. She blushed even more, and casting her eyes to the ground, she told him she would not take the ruble. "Why not?"—"I do not need any extra."—"I think that beautiful lilies of the valley, plucked by the hand of a beautiful girl, are worth a ruble. But since you will not take it, here is five kopecks. I would like to buy flowers from you all the time; I would like you to gather them only for me." Liza gave him the flowers, took the five kopecks, bowed and wanted to go; but the stranger held her by the arm. "But where are you going, Miss?"—"Home."—"And where is your home?" Liza told him where she lived; she told him, and left. The young man did not want to hold her back, perhaps because the passers-by were beginning to stop and stare and snigger at them.

When she arrived home, Liza told her mother what had happened to her. "You did well by not taking the ruble. Perhaps this was some sort of bad man. . . ."—"Oh, no, Mother! I don't think so. He had such a good face and his voice . . ."—"Nonetheless, Liza, it is better to live by your own labors and to take nothing as a gift. You have yet to learn, my dear, how evil people can harm a poor girl! My heart is always in my throat when you go into the city; I always place a candle before the icon and pray to God to protect you from all evil and harm." Tears came to Liza's eyes; she kissed her mother.

The next day Liza gathered the very best lilies of the valley and again went with them to the city. Her eyes were searching quietly for something. Many people wanted to buy flowers from her; but she answered that they were not for sale, and she kept looking first to one side and then to the other. Evening came on; she had to return home, and the flowers were cast into the Moscow River. "No one shall have you!" said Liza, feeling a certain sadness in her heart. The following evening she was sitting near the window, spinning and singing sad songs in a quiet voice, when suddenly she sprang up and cried, "Oh! . . ." The young stranger was standing under the window.

"What's the matter?" asked her frightened mother, who was sitting beside her. "Nothing, Mother dear," answered Liza in a timid voice, "I just caught sight of him."—"Of whom?"— "That gentleman who bought flowers from me." The old woman looked out the window. The young man bowed to her so respectfully, with such a pleasant appearance, that she was unable to think anything but good of him. "How do you do, my good woman!" he said. "I am very tired. Would you have any fresh milk?" The obliging Liza, not waiting for an answer from her mother—perhaps because she knew it already—ran to the cellar, brought back a clean earthenware pot covered with a clean wooden plate, snatched up a glass, washed it and dried it with a white towel, poured and handed the glass through the window, but she herself kept looking to the ground. The stranger drank—and nectar from the hands of Hebe could not have seemed to him more delicious. Anyone can guess that afterward he thanked Liza, and thanked her not so much with words as with his glance. Meanwhile the good-hearted old woman had managed to tell him of her grief and her comfort—of the death of her husband and of the fine qualities of her daughter, of her love for work, tenderness, and so forth and so on. He listened to her attentively, but his eyes were—is it necessary to say where? And Liza, timid Liza, glanced at the young man from time to time; but lightning does not flash and disappear in a cloud so quickly as her blue eyes, having met his glance, turned to the ground. "I would like your daughter to sell her work to no one but me," he said to her mother. "Thus she will not have reason to go into the city often, and you will not have to part with her. I myself can stop by from time to time." At this point, a joy that she tried in vain to hide sparkled in Liza's eyes; her cheeks flamed up like the sunset on a clear summer evening; she stared at her left sleeve and plucked at it with her right hand. The old woman eagerly accepted this offer, suspecting no evil intentions in it, and assured the stranger that the cloth that Liza wove and the stockings she knitted were exceptionally fine, and wore better than any others. It grew dark, and the young man now wanted to leave. "But how shall we address you, good and kind sir?" the old woman asked. "My name is Èrast," he answered. "Èrast," Liza said softly, "Èrast!" She repeated this name five or six times, as if trying to learn it by heart. Èrast said goodbye to them until the next time, and left. Liza followed him with her eyes, while her mother sat lost in thought, and then, taking her daughter by the hand, she said: "Oh, Liza! How good and kind he is! If only your betrothed would be like him!" Liza's heart skipped a beat. "Mother, dear mother! How could that ever be? He is a landowner, and among peasants . . ." Liza did not finish her sentence.

It is time the reader should know that this young man, this Èrast, was a rather wealthy nobleman with a decent mind and a good heart, good by nature, but weak and frivolous. He led a dissipated life, thought only of his own pleasure, sought it in worldly amusements, but often could not find it: he was bored and would complain of his fate. At their first meeting Liza's beauty made an impression on his heart. He read novels and idylls; he had a rather lively imagination, and often transported himself in thought back to those times (real or unreal), when, if one is to believe the poets, everyone wandered carefree through the meadows, bathed in clear springs, kissed like turtledoves, rested under the roses and the myrtle, and spent all their days in happy idleness. He felt that he had found in Liza that which his heart had long sought. Nature is calling me into its embrace, to its pure joys, he thought, and he decided—at least for a while—to abandon high society.

Let us return to Liza. Night had fallen—the mother blessed her daughter and wished her sweet dreams; but this time her wish was not fulfilled: Liza did not sleep well at all. The new guest in her soul, Èrast's image, was so vividly before her that she awoke almost every minute, awoke and sighed. Even before the rising of the sun Liza got up, went down to the banks of the Moscow River, sat on the grass and, lapsing into a despondent mood, gazed at the white mists that churned in the air and, rising upward, left behind sparkling drops on the green cloak of Nature. Silence reigned all about. But soon the rising luminary of the day awakened all creations: groves and hedges came to life; birds fluttered about and began to sing; and the flowers raised their heads to drink in the life-giving rays of light. But Liza kept sitting despondently. Ah, Liza, Liza! What has happened to you? Up to this time, awaking with the birds, you were gay along with them in the morning, and your pure, joyous soul shone in your eyes, just as the sun shines in the drops of heavenly dew; but now you are lost in thought, and the universal joy of nature is foreign to your heart. Meanwhile a young shepherd, playing his pipes, was driving his flock along the banks of the river. Liza stared at him and thought: If only the one who now occupies my thoughts had been born a simple peasant, a shepherd, and if only he were now driving his flock past me: oh! I would bow to him with a smile and I would say to him pleasantly: "Hello, my dear shepherd boy! Where are you driving your flock? Here, too, the green grass grows for your sheep; and here the crimson flowers blossom, from which one can plait a garland for your hat." He would glance at me with a tender look— perhaps he would take my hand. . . . A dream! The shepherd, playing his pipes, passed by and with his variegated flock vanished behind a near hill.

Suddenly Liza heard the sound of oars; she looked toward the river and saw a boat, and in the boat—Èrast.

Her heart began to beat faster, and not from fear, of course. She stood up and wanted to go, but she could not. Èrast jumped out onto the bank, approached Liza, and—her dream was partially fulfilled; for he *looked at her tenderly and took her hand*. . . . But Liza, Liza stood with her eyes cast down, with flaming cheeks, and with a fluttering heart—she could not take her hand away from him—she could not turn away when he came close to her with his rosy lips. . . . Oh! he kissed her, kissed her with such ardor that the whole universe seemed to her to be blazing on fire! "Dear Liza!" said Èrast. "Dear Liza! I love you!" And these words resounded in the depths of her soul, like heavenly, exquisite music; she scarcely dared believe her ears and . . . But I must put down my brush. I will say only that at this moment of ecstasy Liza's shyness disappeared—Èrast learned that he was loved, loved passionately by a new, pure, and open heart.

They sat on the grass, and in such a way that not much space remained between them—they looked into each other's eyes, said to each other: Love me! and two hours seemed to them only an instant. Finally Liza remembered that her mother might worry about her. They had to part, "Oh, Èrast!" she said, "will you love me always?"—"Always, dear Liza, always!" he answered. "And can you swear to this for me?"—"I can, dearest Liza, I can!"—"No! I don't need an oath. I believe you, Èrast, I do. Could you ever deceive poor Liza? Would this not be impossible?"—"Impossible, impossible, dear Liza!"—"How happy I am! And how Mother will be overjoyed when she learns that you love me!"—"Oh, no, Liza! There's no need to tell her anything."—"But why?"—"Old people are often suspicious. She would imagine something bad."—"That could never happen."—"Nonetheless, I ask you not to say a word to her about this."—"All right; I must obey you, although I would rather not keep anything from her." They took leave of each other, kissed for the last time, and promised to meet every evening, either on the bank of the river or in the birch grove, or somewhere near Liza's cabin; only, they had to see each other without fail. Liza left, but her eyes turned back a hundred times to Èrast, who remained standing on the bank, watching after her.

Liza returned to the cabin in a completely different mood from that in which she had left. A heartfelt joy manifested itself on her face and in all her movements. He loves me! she thought, and was carried away by the idea. "Oh, Mother dear!" Liza said to her mother who had just awakened. "Oh, Mother! What a beautiful morning! Everything is so gay in the fields! The skylarks have never sung so well; the sun has never shone so brightly; and the flowers have never smelled so pleasant!" The old woman, leaning on her crutch, went out into the meadow to enjoy the morning Liza had described in such delightful colors. Indeed, it did seem to her exceptionally pleasant; her dear daughter with her joyousness had brightened all Nature for her. "Oh, Liza!" she said, "everything of the Lord God's is so good! I have lived to threescore years on this earth and I still cannot look upon the Lord's works enough. I cannot see enough of the clear sky that seems like a high tent, nor of the earth that every year is covered with new grass and new flowers. The Heavenly King must have loved man very much when He furnished this world so well for him. Oh, Liza! Who would ever want to die, if only there were a few times when we would have no grief? . . . Obviously it has to be this way. Perhaps we would forget our soul if tears were never to fall from our eyes." But Liza thought, Oh! I would sooner forget my soul than ever forget my dear friend!

After this, Èrast and Liza, fearing lest they break their word, saw each other every evening (after Liza's mother had gone to bed) either on the bank of the river or in the birch grove, but most often in the shade of the century-old oaks (about a hundred and seventy yards from the cabin), oaks that overshadowed the deep, clear pond that had been dug in ancient times. There, through the green branches, the beams of the silent moon oftentimes silvered Liza's light hair, which was ruffled by the zephyrs and the hand of her dear friend; often these beams caught in tender Liza's eyes a sparkling tear of love, which a kiss from Èrast never failed to dry. They embraced—but chaste, shy Cynthia did not hide from them behind a cloud; their embraces were pure and sinless. "When you," Liza said to Èrast, "when you tell me, 'I love you, my friend,' when you clasp me to your heart and gaze at me with your tender eyes, oh! then I feel so good, so good, that I forget myself, forget everything, everything except—Èrast. It's a wonder, a wonder, my friend, that I could have lived quietly and happily before I knew you! Right now I can't understand it; now I think that without you life is not life, but sorrow and boredom. Without your eyes the bright moon is dark; without your voice the singing nightingale is tedious; without your breath the breeze seems unpleasant." Èrast was carried away with his shepherdess—as he called Liza—and, seeing how much she loved him, he seemed more amiable to himself. All the sparkling amusements of high society appeared worthless in comparison to those pleasures with which the *passionate friendship* of a pure soul nourished his heart. With revulsion he thought back to the despicable sensuousness with which he had sated his feelings before. I shall live with Liza as brother with sister, he thought; I shall never misuse her love and I will always be happy! Foolish young man! Do you know your own heart? Can you always answer for your actions? Does reason always rule your emotions?

Liza demanded that Èrast visit her mother often. "I love her," she would say, "and I want what is good for her; it seems to me that seeing you is a great blessing for anyone." And in fact the old woman was always happy when she saw him. She loved to talk with him about her late husband and tell of the days of her youth: how she met her sweet Ivan for the first time, how he fell in love with her, and how he lived with her in such love and harmony. "Oh! We could never gaze at each other enough—right up to the hour when cruel death cut him down. He died in my arms!" Èrast listened to her with unfeigned pleasure. He bought Liza's work from her and always wanted to pay ten times the price she asked. But the old woman never took any extra.

Several weeks passed in this manner. One evening Èrast waited a long time for his Liza. Finally she arrived, but she was so sad that he became frightened; her eyes were red from tears. "Liza, Liza! What has happened to you?"—"Oh, Èrast! I have been weeping!"—"Over what? What is it?"— "I must tell you everything. They have found a husband for me, the son of a rich peasant from the neighboring village; Mother wants me to marry him."—"Are you willing?"—"You cruel thing! Need you even ask? And I am sorry for Mother; she weeps and says that I don't desire her peace of mind, that death will torment her if I do not marry while she is still alive. Oh! My mother doesn't know that I have such a dear friend." Èrast kissed Liza and said that her happiness was dearer to him than anything in the world; that after her mother's death he would take her into his home and he would live with her never to part, in the country and in the thick forests, as in paradise. "But you can never be my husband!" said Liza with a quiet sigh. "Why not?"—"I am a peasant girl."—"You insult me! Most important of all for your friend is the soul, a sensitive, pure soul—and Liza will always be nearest my heart."

She threw herself into his arms—and this was to be the fatal hour for her purity! Èrast felt an unusual excitement in his blood—Liza had never seemed so delightful—her caresses had never touched him so strongly—her kisses had never been so inflamed—she knew nothing, suspected nothing, feared nothing—the blackness of the night fed desire—not a single star showed in the sky—no ray of light could illumine the error. Èrast felt himself trembling—Liza did too, not knowing the cause—not knowing what was happening to her. . . . Oh, Liza, Liza! Where is your Guardian Angel? Where is—your innocence!

The error took only a moment. Liza did not understand her emotions; she was astonished and kept asking questions. Èrast was silent—he searched for words and did not find them. "Oh! I am afraid," said Liza, "I am afraid of what has happened to us! I feel as if I were dying, that my soul . . . No, I cannot say that! . . . You are silent, Èrast? Are you sighing? . . . My God! What is this?" Meanwhile lightning flashed and thunder rolled. Liza began to tremble all over. "Èrast, Èrast!" she said, "I am frightened! I am afraid that the thunder will kill me like a criminal!" The storm raged menacingly; rain poured from the black clouds—it seemed that Nature was lamenting the loss of Liza's purity. Èrast tried to calm Liza, and he took her to the cabin. Tears rolled from her eyes as she parted with him. "Oh, Èrast! Assure me that we shall be just as happy as always!"—"We shall, Liza, we shall!" he answered. "God grant it so! I can do nothing but believe your words: after all, I love you! Only, in my heart . . . But enough of this! Farewell! Tomorrow, tomorrow we'll see each other."

Their meetings continued—but how everything had changed! Èrast was no longer able to be satisfied only by the innocent caresses of his Liza—only by her gazes filled with love—only by the touch of a hand, by kisses, by pure embraces. He wanted more, more, and finally he was unable to desire anything—and whoever knows his own heart, whoever has pondered the nature of its tender pleasures, will certainly agree with me that the fulfillment of *all* desires is the most dangerous temptation of love. Liza was no longer for Èrast that angel of purity who previously had inflamed his imagination and delighted his soul. Platonic love had given way to those feelings of which he could not be *proud*, and which were no longer new to him. As concerns Liza, having given herself to him completely, she lived and breathed for him alone, and like a lamb she submitted to his will in everything and found her happiness in his pleasure. She saw a change in him and often said: "You were gayer before; we were more at ease and happier before; and I was never before so afraid of losing your love!" Sometimes in parting he would say to her: "Tomorrow, Liza, I cannot meet you; some important business has come up." And each time Liza sighed at these words.

Finally she did not see him for five days in a row, and was greatly disturbed; on the sixth day he came with a downcast expression and said to her: "My dear Liza! I must say farewell to you for a while. You know that we are at war; I am in the service; my regiment is going on a campaign." Liza grew pale and almost fainted.

Érast caressed her; he said that he would always love his dear Liza and that upon his return he hoped never to part with her again. For a long while she was silent; then she burst into bitter tears, grasped his arm and, gazing at him with all the tenderness of love, asked, "You cannot stay?"—"I can," he answered, "but only with the greatest ignominy, with the greatest blemish on my honor. Everyone would despise me and shun me as a coward, as an unworthy son of my fatherland."—"Oh! Since that's the case," said Liza, "then go, go wherever God wills! But they might kill you."—"Death for the Fatherland is not terrible, dear Liza."—"I shall die just as soon as you leave this earth."—"But why think like this? I hope to stay alive, I hope to return to you, to my friend."— "God grant, God grant it so! Each day, each hour I shall pray for it. Oh! Why do I not know how to read or write! You would inform me of everything that happens to you; and I would write to you—of my tears."—"No, spare yourself, Liza; spare yourself for your friend. I don't want you to weep without me."—"You cruel man! You would think to deprive me of even this comfort! No! I shall cease weeping after we part only when my heart dries up."—"Think of that pleasant moment when we shall again see each other."—"I shall, I shall think of it! Oh! If only it would come soon! My dear, kind Èrast! Remember, remember your poor Liza, who loves you even more than herself!"

But I am unable to describe all that they said on this occasion. The next day was to be their last meeting.

Èrast wanted to bid farewell to Liza's mother, who could not hold back her tears when she heard that her *kind, handsome gentleman* had to go to war. He forced her to take some money from him, saying: "During my absence I do not want Liza to sell her work, which we agreed belongs to me." The old woman showered him with blessings. "God grant that you return safely to us," she said, "and that I shall see you once more in this life! Perhaps my Liza will find herself a desirable bridegroom by that time. How I would thank God if you could come to our wedding! And when Liza has children, you know, sir, that you must be their godfather! Oh, how I want to live until then!" Liza stood alongside her mother and did not dare to glance at her. The reader can easily imagine what she was feeling at this moment.

But what feelings she had then, when Èrast, embracing her for the last time, for the last time clasping her to his heart, said: "Farewell, Liza! . . ." What a touching picture! The sunrise, like a crimson sea, inundated the eastern sky. Èrast stood under the branches of the tall oak, holding in his arms his pale, despondent, bereaved friend, who, bidding him farewell, said farewell to her own soul. All Nature attended in silence.

Liza sobbed—Èrast wept—he left her—she fell—she got up on her knees, lifted her hands to the sky and watched Èrast, who was moving away—farther—farther—and finally disappeared—the sun rose, and Liza, abandoned, pitiful, lost all her feelings and consciousness.

She came to—and the world seemed to her doleful and sad. All the pleasures of Nature had disappeared for her together with the one dear to her heart. Oh! she thought, Why have I been abandoned in this wasteland? What keeps me from flying after dear Èrast? I am not afraid of war; I am only afraid without my friend. I want to live with him, to die with him, or to save his precious life by my own death. Wait, wait, my dear! I am flying to you! She was ready to run after Èrast; but the thought: I have mother! stopped her. Liza heaved a sigh, and with bowed head set off quietly for her cabin. From this hour hence her days were days of grief and sorrow, which had to be hidden from her tender mother: thus her heart suffered even more! Her heart found relief only in those moments when Liza, alone in the depths of the forest, could freely pour forth her tears and moan over the absence of her dear one. The sad turtledove would often join its plaintive voice to her moaning. But sometimes—though they were very rare—a golden ray of hope, a ray of solace brightened the gloom of her sorrow. When he returns to me, how happy I will be! How everything will change! Her gaze brightened at the thought and her cheeks became rosy, and Liza smiled like a May morning after a stormy night. About two months passed in this way.

One day Liza had to go into Moscow in order to buy some rosewater with which her mother treated her eyes. On one of the big streets she met a magnificent coach, and in the coach she caught sight of Èrast. "Oh!" Liza cried out, and she raced toward it; but the coach passed by and turned into a court-yard. Èrast stepped out and was about to go into the entrance of a huge house, when suddenly he found himself—in Liza's embrace. He turned pale—then, answering not a word to her exclamation, took her by the arm, led her into his study, shut the door, and said to her: "Liza! Things have changed: I am engaged to marry; you must leave me alone now, and for your own peace of mind forget me. I loved you, and I love you now; that is, I wish all the best for you. Here are a hundred rubles—take them"—he put the money in her pocket—"allow me to kiss you for the last time—and go on home." Before Liza was even able to come to her senses, he led her out of his study and said to the servant, "See this girl to the street."

At this moment my heart is surging with blood. I forget the man in Èrast—I am ready to damn him—but my tongue will not move. I look up to the sky, and a tear trickles down my face. Oh! Why am I not writing a novel, instead of this sorrowful story of something that really happened?

And did Èrast betray Liza, when he told her that he was entering the army? No, he was in fact in the army; but instead of battling the enemy, he played cards and gambled away nearly all his estate. Soon peace was concluded, and Èrast returned to Moscow burdened with debts. There remained only one way by which he could repair his circumstances—marry an elderly, rich widow who had long been in love with

him. He decided on this, and moved into her house, after
having cast a sincere sigh for his Liza. But is this any
justification?

Liza found herself on the street and in such a state no pen
could describe. He, he has driven me out? He loves another?
I am lost!—These were her thoughts, her feelings! A cruel
fainting spell interrupted them for a while. A kindly woman
who was coming along the street stopped over Liza, who was
lying on the ground, and tried to revive her. The poor thing
opened her eyes, stood up with the help of this kind woman,
thanked her and set off, whither she did not know. I can live
no more, thought Liza, no more! . . . Oh, if only the sky
would fall on me! If only the earth would swallow up a poor
girl! . . . No! The sky will not fall, the earth will not tremble!
Woe is me! She walked out of the city and suddenly found
herself on the bank of a deep pond, under the shade of the
ancient oaks, which several weeks before were the dumb
witnesses to her raptures. The recollection rent her soul; a
most terrible, heartfelt torment showed on her face. But
within a few minutes she was lost deep in thought. She looked
about herself, caught sight of her neighbor's daughter (a
fifteen-year-old girl) coming along the road. She called to
her, took the hundred rubles from her pocket and, giving them
to her, said: "Dearest Aniuta, my dear little friend! Take this
money to my mother—it isn't stolen—tell her that Liza is
guilty before her; that I have hidden from her my love for a
certain cruel man—for È. . . . Why know his name? Say that
he has deceived me—ask her to forgive me—God will be her
help—kiss her hand just as I am now kissing yours—tell her
that poor Liza told you to kiss her—say that I . . ." At this
point Liza threw herself into the water. Aniuta screamed,
began to sob, but could not save her. She ran to the village—
people gathered and they pulled Liza out; but she was already
dead.

Thus she ended her life, she who was so beautiful in soul
and body. When we are *there*, in the new life, we will see each
other, and I will recognize you, tender Liza!

They buried her next to the pond, under the somber oak,
and placed a wooden cross on her grave. I often sit here, lost
in thought, resting against the receptacle of Liza's dust; the
pond stirs before my eyes, and the leaves rustle over my head.

Liza's mother heard of the terrible death of her daughter,

and her blood froze from horror—her eyes closed forever. The cabin became deserted. The wind moans in it, and superstitious villagers, hearing this noise at night, say: "There the dead girl is groaning; there poor Liza is moaning!"

Érast was miserable to the end of his life. Having learned of Liza's fate, he could not find any solace, and he considered himself to be her murderer. I made his acquaintance a year before his death. He told me this story himself and led me to Liza's grave.—Perhaps now they have become reconciled!

5. *The Island of Bornholm*

NIKOLAI M. KARAMZIN

Published in 1793, *The Island of Bornholm* (Ostrov Born-gol'm) is one of Karamzin's more effective works of fiction. The awesome but majestic Scandinavian landscape, the medieval Gothic castle with its drawbridge, vaults, and sub-terranean dungeon, the nocturnal setting, the intrusion of dreams, "forbidden love," and the terrible vengeance visited upon the two young lovers, and finally the all-pervading gloom and mystery (which the author cannot bring himself to reveal even at the end of the work) combine to evoke a thoroughly romantic atmosphere. By hints and allusions, by delicate shades and halftones, Karamzin skillfully creates a sense of deepening mystery, of growing suspense. The "truth" of the tragedy is only suggested, never boldly stated, and when he reaches the conclusion of his tale Karamzin tauntingly leaves the reader to resolve the mystery for himself.

Friends! The fair summer is over, golden autumn has turned pale, the foliage has withered. The trees are without fruits or leaves; the misty sky is agitated, like a gloomy sea; the winter down falls on the cold earth. We take leave of Nature until the joyous meeting of spring; we shut ourselves away from snowstorms and blizzards; we shut ourselves up in a quiet study! Time shall not burden us, for we know a remedy against boredom. Friends! The oak and the birch flame in our fireplace; let the wind rage and strew the windows with white snow! Let us sit by the red fire and tell each other tales and legends and accounts of what lies in the past.

You know that I have traveled abroad, far, far from my homeland, far from you, who are so dear to my heart. I have seen many wonders, I have heard many amazing tales; much have I told you, but I could not tell you all that has happened to me. Listen; I will recount—I will recount the truth, and no invention.

England was the farthest point of my travels. "Out there," I told myself, "homeland and friends await you; it is time to calm yourself in their embraces, time to dedicate your pilgrim's staff to the son of Maia,* time to hang it on the heaviest bough of the tree beneath which you played in your childhood years." And so I took passage in London on the ship *Britannia*, to sail home to my beloved land of Russia.

On white sails we scudded along the blossoming banks of the majestic Thames. Already the boundless ocean lay green ahead of us, already we could hear the sound of its agitation; but suddenly the wind shifted, and our ship, in expectation of a more propitious time, was forced to put in opposite the town of Gravesend.

Together with the captain I descended onto the shore, and strolled with a peaceful heart over green fields adorned by nature and industry, places exotic and picturesque; finally, fatigued by the heat of the sun, I lay down on the grass, under a century-old elm, close to the seashore, and gazed at the moist expanse, at the foamy billows that with a dull roar were carried in countless rows toward the isle from the gloomy distance. The dejected sound and sight of the endless waters were beginning to incline me to drowsiness, to that sweet idleness of soul in which all ideas and feelings stand still and become fixed, like a suddenly frozen stream, and which is the most expressive and the most poetic image of death. But all at once the branches rustled over my head. . . . I looked up and beheld a young man, pale, languid—more an apparition than a human being. In one hand he held a guitar; with the other he was tearing leaves off the tree, while he gazed out at the blue sea with motionless dark eyes in which there shone the last ray of dying life. My glance did not meet his, for his senses were dead to external objects; he stood two paces from me, but saw nothing and heard nothing. Unhappy youth! I thought, you are destroyed by fate. I do not know your name or your family, but I know that you are unfortunate!

He sighed, raised his eyes to heaven, and lowered them

---

* In ancient times travelers returning from abroad dedicated their staves to Mercury.—Author's note.

again to the ocean waves; he left the tree, sat down on the
grass, and strummed a melancholy prelude on his guitar,
gazing unceasingly out to sea, while he sang softly the following song (in Danish, a language which my friend Dr. N.N.
taught me in Geneva):

The laws do all condemn
The object of my love;
But who, my heart, could e'er
Refuse your sacred need?

What law is there more pure
Than that of heart's desire?
What call is there more strong
Than beauty's or than love's?

I love—I'll love fore'er;
Curse then my heart's desire,
You souls who know not pain,
You hearts who know not woe!

O Nature's realm most pure!
Your tender friend and son
Is innocent in all.
'Twas you that gave me soul;

Benevolent your gifts
That her did so adorn;
O Nature! You desired
That Lila be my love!

Your lightnings struck close by,
But did not shatter us,
When we embraced and kissed
And our desire did slake.

O Bornholm, Bornholm fair!
To you my heart would e'er
Return and dwell again,
But vainly do I weep;

I languish and I sigh!
Fore'er am I exiled
From shores of you, fair isle,
By the paternal curse!

> And you, beloved mine!
> Yearn you and live you still?
> Or have you ended all
> In roaring ocean's depths?
>
> Oh, come to me, oh, come,
> Beloved shade so dear!
> And I will join you now
> In roaring ocean's depths.

At that moment, impelled by an involuntary inner force, I was on the point of rushing toward the stranger and embracing him, but at that very instant the captain took me by the hand and said that a favorable wind had filled our sail and that we must lose no time. . . . We sailed. The youth, flinging down his guitar and folding his arms, gazed out to the blue sea in our wake.

The waves foamed under our ship's helm; the shore of Gravesend concealed itself in the distance; the northern provinces of England lay dark on the other end of the horizon; at last all disappeared, and even the birds that for a long time had soared over our heads now turned back toward shore, as if terrified at that endless expanse of the sea. The agitation of the murmuring waters and the foggy sky were the only objects left in view, majestic and terrible. My friends! To experience all the daring of the human spirit, one must be on the open ocean where nothing but a thin plank, as Wieland says, separates us from a watery grave, but where the skilled seaman, unfurling the sails, rushes on and in thought already sees the luster of the gold that, in some other part of the world, will reward his bold enterprise. *Nil mortalibus arduum est*; nothing is impossible for mortals, I thought with Horace, my gaze lost in the endlessness of Neptune's realm.

But soon a severe attack of seasickness made me lose consciousness. For six days my eyes did not open, and my tired heart, washed by the foam of the storm waves,* hardly beat in my breast. On the seventh day I revived, and with a joyous if pallid aspect mounted to the deck. The sun was already sinking in the clear azure skies toward the West; the ocean,

---

* In truth, the foam of the waves often did wash over me, who was lying unconscious on the deck of the ship.—Author's note.

illuminated by its golden rays, murmured; the ship flew with
full sail over the breast of the cleaving billows, which in vain
sought to outstrip it. All around us, at varying distances,
white, blue, and pink flags were unfurled, and on the right
hand lay something dark that resembled land.

"Where are we?" I asked the captain.

"Our trip has been propitious," he said, "we have passed
The Sound; the shores of Sweden have disappeared from our
sight. To starboard you can see the Danish island of Bornholm, a place dangerous for shipping; there shoals and rocks
lie hidden on the sea bottom. When night approaches, we
shall anchor there."

The isle of Bornholm, the isle of Bornholm, I repeated in
my thoughts, and the image of the young stranger at Gravesend arose in my mind. The mournful tones and words of his
song resounded in my ears.

They hold the secret of his heart, I thought, but who is he?
What laws condemn the love of an unhappy man? What curse
has exiled him from the shores of Bornholm, so dear to him?
Will I ever learn his history?

Meanwhile a strong wind carried us straight toward the
island. Its fierce cliffs already came into view, with boiling
streams that hurled themselves, roaring and foaming, down
from their heights into the ocean depths. It seemed inacces-
sible from all sides, from all sides walled by the hand of
majestic Nature; nothing but terror appeared on its gray crags.
With horror I saw the image of cold, silent eternity, the image
of implacable death and of that indescribable creative power
in the face of which all that is mortal must tremble.

The sun had sunk in the waves, and we cast anchor. The
wind had calmed down, and the sea scarcely rocked. I gazed
at the island, which with inexplicable force lured me to its
banks; a dark presentment spoke to me: Then you can
satisfy your curiosity, and Bornholm will remain forever in
your memory! Finally, learning that there were fishing huts
not far from the shore, I determined to ask the captain for a
boat and go to the island with two or three sailors. He told me
of the danger, of the rocks beneath the water's surface, but
seeing his passenger's resolution, he agreed to fulfill my
demand, on condition that early the next morning I return to
the ship.

We set out and safely reached the shore of a small calm

inlet. Here we were met by fishermen, a folk crude and rough, raised on the cold element under the roar of ocean billows, and unacquainted with a smile of friendly greeting. Hearing that we desired to look over the island and spend the night in one of their huts, they tied up our boat and led us through a mountain of flintstone that was falling to pieces, up to their dwellings. In half an hour we came out onto a broad green plain on which, as in the Alpine valleys, low wooden cottages were scattered, along with thickets and boulders. Here I left my sailors, and myself went on farther to enjoy for yet a while the pleasant sensations of evening; a boy of thirteen served as my guide.

The scarlet glow had not yet died in the bright heaven; its rosy light was strewn on the white granite boulders, and in the distance, beyond a high hill, it lit up the sharp towers of an old castle. The boy could not tell me to whom the castle belonged.

"We do not go there," he said, "and God knows what goes on there!"

I redoubled my steps and soon approached the great Gothic edifice, surrounded by a deep moat and a high wall. Everywhere silence reigned; in the distance the sea sighed, and the last ray of evening light died on the copper-sheathed tips of the towers.

I walked around the castle—the gates were closed and the drawbridges raised. My guide was fearful, of what he himself did not know, and begged me to go back to the huts, but could a man impelled by curiosity heed such a request?

Night came on, and suddenly a voice resounded; the echo repeated it, and again all was silent. From fright the boy seized me with both hands, and trembled like a criminal at execution. In a minute the voice resounded again and asked, "Who is there?"

"A foreigner," I said, "brought to this island by curiosity. If the law of hospitality is honored as a virtue in the walls of your castle, then you will shelter a traveler in the dark time of night."

There was no reply, but in a few minutes the drawbridge thundered and dropped down from the tower; with a noise the gate opened—a tall man clad in a long black garment came to meet me, took me by the hand, and led me into the castle. I turned around; the boy, my guide, had hidden.

The gate banged after us; the drawbridge thundered up again. Crossing a spacious courtyard, grown over with bushes, nettles, and feathergrass, we came to a huge house from which light was shining. A tall peristyle in antique fashion led to an iron porch, the steps of which resounded under our feet. On every side it was gloomy and deserted. In the first hall, surrounded inside by a Gothic colonnade, there hung a lamp that scarcely cast its light on the rows of gilded columns, which were beginning to fall down from age; in one spot lay fragments of a cornice, in another, bits of pilasters; in a third, whole columns that had tumbled down. My guide looked around at me several times with piercing eyes, but did not say a word.

All this made a terrifying impression on me, composed partly of dread, partly of a mysterious, inexplicable satisfaction, or, to put it better, the pleasant anticipation of something extraordinary.

We crossed two or three more halls like the first one and illuminated with the same lamps. Then a door opened to the right, and in the corner of a small room there sat a venerable gray-haired old man, his elbow propped on a table on which two white wax candles were burning. He raised his head, looked at me with a kind of mournful tenderness, gave me his weak hand, and said in a pleasant voice:

"Though eternal grief inhabits the walls of this castle, still a traveler who seeks hospitality shall always find a peaceful refuge here. Foreigner! I do not know you, but you are a man, and in my dying heart there still dwells a love for men. My house and my embrace are open to you."

He embraced me and seated me and, trying to impart to his gloomy face an aspect of liveliness, he looked like a bright but cold autumnal day that resembles mournful winter more than joyous summer. He sought to appear hospitable, to impart with his smile confidence and a pleasant sensation of intimacy, but the signs of grief of heart that were planted so deeply on his countenance could not disappear in a moment.

"You, young man," he said, "must inform me concerning the happenings of the world, which I have renounced but still not yet quite forgotten. For a long time I have lived in solitude; for a long time I have heard nothing of mankind's fate. Tell me, does love still reign on earth? Does incense still smoke on the altars of virtue? Are the peoples happy that dwell in the lands you have seen?"

"The domain of science," I answered, "is spreading more and more, but human blood still flows on the earth; the tears of the unfortunate still flow; men praise the name of virtue and dispute concerning her existence."

The old man sighed and shrugged his shoulders. Learning that I was a Russian, he said: "We come from the same people as you. The ancient inhabitants of the islands of Rügen and Bornholm were Slavs. But you long before us came to the light of Christianity. Magnificent cathedrals, dedicated to the one God, rose up to the clouds in your lands, while we, in the darkness of idolatry, still brought bloody sacrifices to unfeeling idols. In triumphant hymns you celebrated the great Creator of the universe, while we, blinded by paganism, praised the idols of mythology in discordant songs."

The old man spoke to me of the history of the northern peoples, of the happenings of antiquity and modern times, spoke so that I was forced to marvel at his intelligence, his knowledge, and even his eloquence.

In half an hour he arose and wished me good night. The servant in the black garb took a candle from the table and led me through long narrow corridors. We came to a large room, hung with ancient weapons, swords, lances, suits of armor and helmets. In a corner underneath a canopy stood a high bed, adorned with carvings and old bas-reliefs.

I wished to ask this servant a multitude of questions, but he, not waiting for them, bowed and left; the iron door banged shut—the noise resounded frightfully in the empty walls—and all was silent. I lay down on the bed, looked at the ancient weapons, lit up through the little window by a weak ray of moonlight, thought of my host and of his first words, "Eternal grief inhabits the walls of this castle," and mused of times past, of the events of which this castle might have been a witness; mused, like a man who wanders between graves and coffins, gazes at the dust of the dead, and makes it live again in his imagination. Finally, the image of the mournful stranger at Gravesend came to my soul, and I fell asleep.

But my sleep was troubled. I dreamed that the suits of armor hanging on the wall turned into knights and that these knights came toward me with naked swords and with angry

looks and said: "Unhappy man! How dare you come to our
island? Do not sailors pale at the sight of its granite shores?
How dare you enter the terrible sanctuary of this castle? Does
not its terror resound over all the surroundings? Does not the
traveler turn back on seeing its frightening towers? Impudent
man! Die for your pernicious curiosity!" Their swords clanged
over me, the blows fell on my breast—but suddenly all vanished, and I awoke and in another minute fell asleep again.
Now a new dream disturbed my spirit. I dreamed that terrible
thunder resounded in the castle, the iron doors banged, the
windows shook, the floor rocked, and a frightful winged
monster that I cannot describe flew toward my bed, hissing
and roaring. The nightmare vanished, but I could no longer
fall asleep; I felt a need for fresh air, went to the window, and
found to one side a small door, opened it, and descended a
steep staircase into the garden.

The night was clear, and the full moon shed a silvery light
on the dark foliage of the old oaks and elms that formed a
long dense alley. The murmur of the waves blended with the
murmur of the leaves, stirred by the wind. In the distance the
rocky mountains lay white, resembling a wall of teeth that
encircled the whole island of Bornholm; between them and
the walls of the castle a large wood was visible on one side,
and on the other, an open plain with small thickets.

My heart beat even more strongly with the impression of
the terrible nightmares, and my blood had not yet subsided.
I entered the dark alley, under the shelter of the rustling oaks,
and with a feeling almost like veneration I submerged myself
in its gloom. Thoughts of the druids stirred in my mind, and
I felt as if I were approaching that very sanctuary where all
the mysteries and horrors of their religion were preserved.
Finally the long alley brought me to some clumps of rosemary,
behind which there rose a sandy hillock. I wanted to climb to
its top, from there to behold in the bright moonlight the landscape of the sea and the island, but suddenly I noticed an
opening leading inside the hill: with some effort a man could
enter it. An irrepressible feeling of curiosity impelled me to
enter this cavern, more like the work of human hands than
like a creation of wild Nature. I entered, and felt the damp
and cold, but resolved to go on and, going forward some ten
paces, made out several steps that led up to a wide iron door;
this, to my amazement, was not locked. As if involuntarily

my hand opened it—there, behind an iron grating that held a large padlock, a lamp was burning, fastened to the vaulting; in the corner on a bed of straw lay a pale young woman in a black dress. She was asleep, and her reddish locks, intertwined with the yellow blades of straw, covered her high breast, which scarcely stirred with her breathing. One of her hands, white but withered, lay on the ground, while her head was cradled on the other. If a painter had sought to depict exhausted, endless, and eternal misery, lulled to sleep by the poppies of Morpheus, then this woman could well have served as a subject for his brush.

My friends! Who is not touched at the sight of an unfortunate? But the sight of a young woman, suffering in a subterranean dungeon, the sight of the weakest and dearest of all creatures, persecuted by fate, could endow a stone itself with feeling. I looked at her with commiseration and thought to myself: What barbarian's hand has shut you away from the light of day? Can it be for a heavy transgression? But the gentleness of your face, the tranquil motion of your breast, and my own heart reassure me that you are innocent!

At that very moment she awoke, looked at the grating, caught sight of me, gave a startled sigh, and raised her head, arose and came up to me and lowered her eyes to the ground, as if trying to collect her thoughts, again fixed her gaze on me, and was on the point of speaking, but did not speak.

"If the sympathy of a wayfarer," I said after several minutes of silence, "brought by the hand of fate to this castle and to this cave, can lighten your fate, if his real commiseration can deserve your trust, then demand his services!"

She looked at me with motionless eyes, in which I could see amazement, something of curiosity, irresolution, and doubt. Finally, after a strong inner movement that stirred my breast as if with an electric shock, she answered firmly:

"Whoever you may be, whatever chance has brought you here, foreigner, I cannot ask anything from you but pity. It is not in your power to alter my fate. I kiss the hand that punishes me."

"But your heart is innocent," I said, "and it, of course, cannot deserve such a cruel punishment?"

"My heart," she replied, "may well have been in error. God will forgive my weakness. I trust that soon my life will come to an end. Leave me, stranger!"

She came up to the grating, looked at me tenderly, and repeated in a low voice:

"For God's sake, leave me! . . . If he sent you here, he whose terrible curse still rings eternally in my ears, tell him that I suffer, that I suffer day and night, that my heart is withered with grief, that no tears can ever lighten my sorrow. Tell him that I bear my imprisonment without a murmur, without complaining, that I die his tender, unhappy . . ."

Suddenly she fell silent, thought for a moment, and withdrew from the grating, fell to her knees and covered her face with her hands; a minute later she looked at me again, again lowered her eyes to the ground, and said tenderly and timidly:

"Perhaps you know my story, but if you do not know it, then do not ask me, for God's sake, do not ask! Foreigner, farewell!"

Before going I was about to say a few words to her that came directly from my heart, but my glance still met hers, and it seemed to me that she was on the point of asking me something very important for her heart's peace. I stopped, awaiting her question, but after a long sigh it died on her pale lips. We parted.

Coming out of the cavern, I refrained from closing the iron door, so that the fresh pure air would penetrate into the dungeon through the grating and lighten the unfortunate woman's breathing. The glow of dawn was red in the sky; the birds had awakened; a breeze was blowing the dew from the bushes and flowers that grew around the hillock.

My God! I thought. My God! How miserable to be shut off from the company of living, free, joyful beings with which the endless expanses of Nature are everywhere populated! Even in the far north, among high, lichen-covered rocks, terrifying to the gaze, the work of Your hand is fair, the work of Your hand enraptures the spirit and the heart. And here, where the foamy waves have battled granite crags from the beginning of time, here too Your hand has imprinted the living signs of a creator's love and well-being; here too at morn roses bloom in an azure heaven, here too tender breezes are scented with their aroma, here too green carpets are laid out like soft velvet under man's feet, here too birds sing, sing merrily for the merry man, and sadly for the sad man, pleasing all; here too the grieving heart can relieve itself of its burden of misfortunes in the embrace of a sympathetic Nature! But that poor woman, locked up in a dungeon, is shut away from this consolation; the dew of morning no longer moistens her tired heart; the breeze does not refresh her wasted breast; the sun's rays do not illumine her gloomy eyes; the silent balsamic effusions of the moon do not nourish her spirit with gentle dreams and pleasant reveries. Creator! Why have You given man the destructive power to make one another and himself unfortunate?" My strength gave way, and my eyes closed, under the branches of the tall oak tree, on the soft greensward. My sleep lasted about two hours.

"The door was open, and the foreigner entered the cavern," I heard as I awakened, and opening my eyes I saw the old man, my host: he was sitting in deep thought on a bench of turf, about five paces away from me; beside him stood the man who had brought me into the castle. I went up to them. The old man looked at me with some severity, arose, pressed my hand, and his look became more gentle. We entered the thick alley together without saying a word. It seemed that he was hesitating in his mind and was uncertain, but suddenly he stopped short and, fixing on me a penetrating, fiery gaze, asked firmly,

"You have seen her?"

"Yes," I answered, "I have seen her, but I do not know who she is and why she suffers there."

"You will learn," he said, "you will learn, young man, and your heart will bleed with pity. Then you will ask yourself why Heaven has poured out the full cup of its wrath on this weak, gray-haired old man, a man who loved virtue, who honored its holy laws."

We sat down under the tree, and the old man told me a frightful tale, a tale that you will not hear now, my friends; it will remain for another time. But now I will tell you one thing only, that I penetrated the mystery of the stranger at Gravesend, a terrible mystery!

The sailors were waiting for me at the gate of the castle. We returned to the ship, they raised sail, and Bornholm vanished from our sight.

The sea murmured. In mournful meditation I stood on the deck, my hand on the mast. Deep sighs constrained my breast, and finally, I looked up at the heavens, and the wind blew a tear on my face into the sea.

6. The Rossiad: An Epic Poem

MIKHAIL M. KHERASKOV

In his discussion of epic poetry that precedes *The Rossiad* (Rossiada), Kheraskov mentions that epic poems had been begun in Russian before his own work but that for one reason or another they remained unfinished. He sees himself, therefore, as the first poet in Russian literature to produce a national epic.

Kheraskov's assessment of the development of epic poetry in eighteenth-century Russia was fair. Prior to leaving on his first diplomatic assignment to London in 1732, Kantemir had begun an epic devoted to Peter the Great and entitled *The Petriad* (Petrida). He completed the first canto but then abandoned further work on the project. Lomonosov also had undertaken at one time an epic on Peter to which he gave the name *Peter the Great* (Pëtr Velikii), but it too was destined to remain unfinished except for the first two cantos. Even the homage to Peter by the French poet Antoine Thomas was never completed. For his own attempt at an epic Sumarokov chose the victory of Dmitrii Donskoi (Prince Dmitrii of Moscow, known as *donskoi*, "of the Don," because of his defeat of the Tatars at Kulikovo Field, near the Don River, in 1380), but never got beyond the first page.

In a sense, the only successful epic writing before Kheraskov's works was Vasilii Trediakovskii's *The Telemachiad* (Tilemakhida), a version in dactylo-trochaic hexametric verse of approximately 16,000 lines based on the prose novel *Les aventures de Télémaque* (published first in 1699) by François de La Mothe Fénelon. Although Trediakovskii's metric translation of the French prose original contained many fine lines and generally managed to convey the rhythm of the Homeric epics (and served later as the model for the verse translations of the *Iliad* and *Odyssey* by Gnedich and Zhukovskii, respectively), the deficiencies of the work tended to overshadow its positive aspects, and earned the author little more than the mockery of his contemporaries. No doubt for that reason, and

106

because *The Telemachiad* was principally a translation and had been preceded chronologically by his own didactic poem in alexandrines, *The Fruits of Learning* (Plody nauk, published in 1761, five years before *The Telemachiad*), Kheraskov made no mention of Trediakovskii or his lengthy version of *Les aventures de Télémaque* in his "A View of Epic Poetry."

Kheraskov wrote altogether ten major poetic works: *The Fruits of Learning* (1761), *The Battle of Chesmé* (Chesmesskii boi, 1771), *Selim and Selima* (Selim i Selima, 1773), *The Rossiad* (1778), *Vladimir Reborn* (Vladimir vozrozhdënnyi, 1785), *The Universe, World of the Spirit* (Vselennaia, mir dukhovnyi, 1790), *The Pilgrims, or The Seekers of Happiness* (Pilgrimy, ili iskateli schast'ia, 1795), *The Tsar, or Novgorod Liberated* (Tsar', ili osvobozhdënnyi Novgorod, 1800), *The Storyteller, or The Unknown One* (Bakhariana, ili neizvestnyi, 1803), and *The Poet* (1805). Of these, the three historical epics *The Battle of Chesmé*, *The Rossiad*, and *Vladimir Reborn* established their author's position as the foremost epic poet of eighteenth-century Russia.

Acknowledged as Kheraskov's most outstanding work, *The Rossiad* was begun in 1771 and printed in 1779 by the Moscow University Press, of which the poet was then director. A second edition was issued in 1786, and a third, incorporating a number of changes, appeared in the collected edition of Kheraskov's works in 1796.

Running to a length of over 9,000 lines *The Rossiad* was the fruit of Kheraskov's ambition to create a national epic, which Russian literature still did not possess and the creation of which he saw as his greatest contribution to Russian literary development.

Kheraskov selected as his subject a historical event that, in his opinion, marked a decisive turning point in the fortunes of his country: the seizure of Kazan' from the Tatars by the forces of Ivan IV, "The Terrible," in 1552. Apart from the inherent significance of the episode, this choice must have been motivated in part also by Catherine's determination to wrest the Crimea from Tatar hands, thus eliminating the last vestige of Tatar rule in Russia. Significantly, *The Rossiad* appeared between the first and second Russo-Turkish wars.

The emphatic patriotism spirit of *The Rossiad* should not obscure, however, its ideological aspect. As he asserts in his

historical foreword to the poem, Kheraskov had no intention
of embroiling himself in any controversy over the character
of Ivan the Terrible. His desire was clearly to bypass the
controversial and portray only the heroic. Yet in his depiction
of Ivan, Kheraskov presents the image of an ideal ruler who
does not rule autocratically, but exercises his power in con-
sultation with his nobles. It is difficult to avoid imputing a
political significance to such an idealized portrayal of Ivan in
The Rossiad. The same may be said, conversely, of the equally
idealized portrait of Prince Ivan Kurbskii, who appears the
model of a responsible nobleman devoted to his country's
good. Although greatly shocked by the Pugachëv Uprising
and more conservative politically in the years following that
great upheaval, Kheraskov was nonetheless one of the most
enlightened men of his day and a champion of liberal thought
in the 1750's and 1760's. Highly respected throughout his
career for his moral authority, he concerned himself deeply
with the nature of political power, and recognized the dangers
inherent in absolutist monarchy. It comes as no surprise
therefore, that such a concern is reflected in so markedly
patriotic a work as The Rossiad.

Formally, Kheraskov's epic adheres more or less faithfully
to the patterns of the genre as formulated in classicist poetics.
Its model, as the poet himself infers in his introduction to the
work, was Voltaire's Henriade, which enjoyed a wide circle
of admirers in the eighteenth century. Written in six-foot
iambics, with the caesura after the sixth syllable, the poem
consists of twelve cantos dealing with a single historical
happening, in this case the seizure of Kazan'. The mythologi-
cal references in which the classicist epics traditionally abound
are entirely conventional in The Rossiad, and of no great
significance. The no less traditional element of the supernatural has also been preserved in Kheraskov's poem: the
Russian forces are protected by God, the angels, and saints;
the Tatars, on the other hand, are watched over and guided
by Muhammad, the pre-Islamic Tatar deity known as Kiremet,
sorcerers, and so on. The prophetic dream traditionally
invested with a structural function in the epic appears in The
Rossiad in the form of a dream by Ivan the Terrible that
embraces something of a synthesis of Russian history and
appears to have been modeled directly on a similar dream of
Henri IV in the Henriade.

Traces of the epic poem *Jerusalem Liberated* (Gerusa-
emme liberata, 1575) by the Italian Baroque poet Torquato
Tasso (1544–1595) can also be discerned in *The Rossiad*.
That Kheraskov knew the work is clear from his remarks
about it in the introduction to his poem. The attraction of the
Italian epic was natural: like *The Rossiad*, it too dealt with
the struggle between Christian and Muhammadan. Kheraskov's indebtedness to Tasso resides principally in his weaving
into the heroic fabric of his epic the thread of the knightly-
romantic tradition. Following the example of the Italian
master, Kheraskov similarly focuses considerable attention on
key figures in the enemy camp and their activities. The love
element of *The Rossiad* revolves in fact around the female
commander of Tatar Kazan', Sumbeka. One Soviet com-
mentator, A. V. Zapadov, has presented the plausible thesis
that even here Kheraskov had an underlying political motive.
He suggests in his introduction to the Poet's Library (Biblioteka Poèta) edition of Kheraskov's works that the love
intrigue that gradually comes to assume precedence over
Sumbeka's administrative responsibilities is a veiled criticism
of the conduct of Catherine's court and the position of her
favorites.[1]

The blending of the heroic and knightly-romantic in *The
Rossiad*, the "duality" of the poem, found a parallel also in
the style in which it was written. As expected for the genre,
the "high" style of the Lomonosovian tradition predominates;
the work abounds in Slavonicisms, and is heavily rhetorical.
But elements more appropriate to the "middle" style intrude
from time to time, particularly in the many love scenes.

Popular and highly regarded in its own time, *The Rossiad*
all but fell into oblivion in the nineteenth century, and apart
from its historical importance as the major epic work of
eighteenth-century Russia is read now only as an academic
exercise. The present translation, which attempts to keep only
the meter of the original, has been taken entirely from the
first canto of the poem. It follows the text in M. M. Kheraskov, *Izbrannye proizvedeniia*, Biblioteka Poèta, ed. A. V.
Zapadov, Leningrad, 1961.

[1] M. M. Kheraskov, *Izbrannye proizvedeniia*, Leningrad, 1961,
pp. 34–35.

Historical Introduction

In the most remote times that the ancient historians have made familiar to us, the Russian state was powerful. It was dreaded by its neighbors and esteemed by many nations. In glory, strength, abundance, and victories, according to the position of states at the time, it did not take second place to any European power, while in the expanse of its territory, then as now, it surpassed all others. But after the death of Grand Prince Vladimir[2] the fragmentation of Russia into different parts, into separate principalities; the internal dissension, disorders, and the ambition of the now greatly multiplied princes began gradually to sap its strength. The result was that finally they succumbed to the calamitous yoke of the plunderous Tatar hordes. From that time on, the former glory of Russia was extinguished and was hardly known throughout the world. Thus it lay for nearly three centuries in oblivion beneath its ruins. This lamentable and shameful situation in which the Tatar invasions and power had submerged Russia; the wresting of many of its principalities plundered by her other neighbors; the disorder caused by internal sedition—which was completely exhausting the Fatherland—brought Russia to its complete and utter collapse.

This evil endured to the time of the Tsar Ioann Vasil'evich the First,[3] who on a sudden built Russia anew, prepared it for its autocratical course, boldly and courageously removed the yoke of the Tatar khans, and restored peace within the bosom of his state. But in his time the kingdom of Kazan' was not yet destroyed; the Novgorodians had not yet been entirely subdued; neighboring states did not yet manifest the necessary esteem for Russia. This great change from which this nation passed from weakness to strength, from humiliation to glory,

---

[2] The reference is to Prince Vladimir Monomakh (1053–1125).

[3] The reference is to the tsar usually referred to as Ioann (or Ivan) III (1440–1505). In his account Kheraskov appears to ignore Ivan I Kalita (died 1341), Grand Prince of Moscow (1328–1341), and Ivan II Ivanovich (1326–1359), Grand Prince of Moscow (1353–1359).

from subservience to domination, this important and extreme change transpired in the time of the grandson of Ioann, Ioann Vasil'evich the Second,[4] who is the hero of this poem.

Should not, then, the reign of Ioann Vasil'evich the Second represent the middle level to which Russia, after reaching a disastrous position, began to come to life again, to grow and to regain its former brilliance, which it had lost for nearly three hundred years? When we imagine a state in complete disarray, oppressed by its neighbors, torn asunder by internal dissension, agitated by the disharmony of its polyarchy, subjugated by infidels, plundered by its own magnates, when we imagine all this and picture to ourselves a young monarch accepting the power of autocracy, rooting out the confusion in his Fatherland, restraining the strong and terrible enemies of his authority, bridling the polyarchy, pacifying rebellious insurgents within the bosom of the state, returning the cities wrested by neighbors and adding whole states to his scepter, quelling the pride and disharmony of his boyars, granting wise laws, organizing his army in the most efficient manner, do we not feel esteem for a sovereign of so great a spirit? . . . Such a monarch was Tsar Ioann Vasil'evich!

Foreign writers have composed absurd fables about his severity, yet despite that they portray him as a great man for his many notable deeds. Out of respect Peter the Great himself determined to follow this monarch in wise undertakings. History obscures the brilliance of his glory by certain terrible tales alluding to his passionate nature. Whether or not such tales, so out of keeping with his spirit, should be given credence I leave to the historians for consideration. Moreover, the excessive imperial severity for which he was dubbed the Terrible concerns neither my purpose nor the period with which my composition deals.

By celebrating the destruction of the kingdom of Kazan', together with the collapse of the power of the Tatar hordes, I had in mind the tranquillity, glory, and well-being of the entire Russian state, the renowned deeds not only of the sovereign but of the entire Russian Army, and the restoration of prosperity not just to a single person but to the entire nation. That is why this work has been named *The Rossiad.*

[4] Kheraskov is speaking of Tsar Ioann (or Ivan) IV, "The Terrible" (1530–1584).

I present the young monarch crowned with laurels, this monarch of whom Lomonosov in his short chronicle of Russia affirms that he became terrible only after the death of his first wife and that the disorders of the boyars, like some ferocious storm, agitated his disposition. This is something also that must have occurred long after the seizure of Kazan'. I glorify together with the tsar the loyalty and love of their Fatherland of the princes, nobles, and of all the Russian warriors who served him. Is this event important in Russian history? True sons of the Fatherland, after reviewing in their minds the calamitous situation of Russia at the time, can ascertain themselves whether or not it is a subject worthy of an epic . . . and my poem is obliged to vindicate this.

Publishing this eight-year labor of mine, now corrected for the third time and augmented in many places, I sense its imperfections and inadequacies in comparison with other epic poems. This composition is weak but it is the first in our language; this alone earns the author a certain pardon.

I based the plot of this work on historical truth as much as I was able to discover printed and manuscript information that served my purpose. I also added several small anecdotes furnished me from Kazan' by the former director of university gymnasia in 1770. However, my readers must remember that it is unnecessary to look for historical veracity in an epic poem any more than one should look for poetry in historical accounts. I rejected much, transposed much from one period to another, contrived, shortened, shaped, and constructed. Whether or not I succeeded in my undertaking is not for me to judge. But it is incontestable that epic poems possessing their particular designs are composed usually according to the same rules as this one.

A View of Epic Poetry

In the *Iliad* Homer celebrates the wrath of Achilles over the abduction of his slave girl Briseis by King Agamemnon (a wrath as calamitous for the Greeks as it was for Pergamum), bloody battles, the havoc of those besieging the Trojans, and the havoc of the besieged Trojans. Achilles takes vengeance for his friend Patroclus, who was slain by Hector—he slays the valiant Hector, and with this the poem concludes.

In the *Odyssey* the ten-year wandering of the King of Ithaca, Odysseus, is celebrated, as also his return home and the terrible murder of the suitors of Penelope, which was prophesied by the seer Theoclymenus.

In his incomparable *Aeneid* Virgil sang of the flight of Aeneas from Troy after its razing by the Greeks, his arrival in Carthage, his romance with Dido, and his infidelity to this unfortunate queen. He described further another flight of his, to Italy, where after slaying Turnus he unites with Lavinia, the bride of this respected prince.

In *Paradise Lost* Milton tells of the fall from grace of the first man, the temptation of the forbidden fruit, the triumph of Satan, the expulsion of Adam and Eve from Paradise for their disobedience, and the reason for the ill-fortune of the whole human race.

Voltaire begins his *Henriade* with the murder of Henri III[5] and concludes it with the conversion of Henri IV[6] from one religion to another—but his lovely verses make all this enchanting.

Armida in Tasso's *Jerusalem Liberated*, the beautiful sorceress Armida, is the spirit of this priceless poem; her wiles, cunning, shrewdness, her tenderness, her very cruelty after the dismissal of Rinaldo are delightful, but not edifying.

Let us skim over the *Lusiad* of Camoës[7] and the *Pharsalia* of Lucanus.[8] The first deals with the wanderings of the Lusitanians in Africa, the discovery of some new lands—legends and miracles. The entire poem is a poetic tale in which even the poet himself takes part. But the tale is painted with a vivid brush; it is charming, alluring. It is a gallery of superb pictures, presented in disorderly fashion, but each one of them delights, moves, marvels, and sinks into the memory.

Many call *Pharsalia* a mere chronicle sung in a splendid

[5] King Henri III of France (1551–1589).

[6] King Henri IV of France (1553–1610).

[7] A reference to the Portuguese writer Luis Vaz de Camoës (1524?–1580), whose principal work was the epic poem *The Lusiads* (Os Lusíadas, published 1572).

[8] Kheraskov is speaking of the epic *Pharsalia* (also known as the *Bellum Civile*) by the Roman writer Marcus Annaeus Lucanus (39–65 A.D.).

style; but this chronicle is filled with noble thoughts, animated pictures, penetrating descriptions, and strong expressions. It celebrates the war of Julius Caesar and Pompey. Unfortunately, the song was left unfinished and was not corrected.

I am writing this for those who believe that an epic poem should be a panegyric poem. The epic poem embraces some important, memorable, noteworthy occurrence that took place in the history of the world and that was of great consequence for all mankind. Such, for example, is Milton's *Paradise Lost*. Or an epic poem may celebrate an event that took place in some state and that served the glory of the whole nation, the cause of peace or, finally, its transformation. Such for example should be the poem *Peter the Great*, which, in my opinion, it is still not time to write. Two great spirits undertook to sing of Peter the Great: Lomonosov and Thomas. Both began— but both did not finish.

To this latter category of epic poem Voltaire's *Henriade* and my *Rossiad* must be assigned. I have no wish, however, to compare my weak effort to the masterful epic of Voltaire. Woe to the Russian who does not appreciate how great an advantage, how pleasant a tranquillity, and how magnificent a glory accrued to our Fatherland from the destruction of the kingdom of Kazan'. One must return in thought to those terrible times when Russia was bent under the Tatar yoke; one must imagine the invasions and the insolence of the Tatar hordes that were perpetrated within our state; one must present to oneself the Russian princes groveling before and dependent on the proud and debasing rule of the Tatar chieftains of Kazan'; one must see the rulers of Kazan' dominating not only the cities but also all the villages and even sending their idols to Moscow itself so that the princes they controlled should bow before them; one should read attentively the whole history of the suffering of our Fatherland in the time of its subordination to the hordes, and then suddenly imagine Russia emerging triumphant over its enemies, throwing off the yoke of its tormentors, our Fatherland, crowned with the laurel wreaths of victory, and the young sovereign dictating benign laws to his former lawgivers.

Reader! If in reviewing all these misfortunes of our Fatherland your heart does not overflow with blood, your spirit does not grow excited, and is not led finally to a delightful rapture—do not read my *Rossiad*; it was not written for you but for people who know how to feel, who know how to love their fatherland and to wonder at the notable exploits of their forebears, who have assured the safety and peace of their descendants.

Canto the First

I sing of Russia freed from the barbarians,
The rule of Tatars overthrown and their pride humbled;
Movement of ancient arms, travail, and bloody battles,
Russia triumphant and Kazan' reduced to ruins.
The years of peace from these times had their true beginning,
Which like a bright dawn came to shine over all Russia.
O Thou, that soar higher than all the stars of heaven,
Spirit of poetry, come from those heavenly places,
And pour your rays, O Art, and your illumination
Upon this frail and dark creation I now offer.

Open, Eternity, the gates of habitations
Where earthly vanities all have been cast aside,
Where souls of righteous men are finally rewarded,
Where laurel wreaths and fame are held in light esteem.
Before an altar there bestrewn with stars all over,
Where king and lowest slave stand one beside the other,
Where poor forget their want and sad forget their sorrow,
Where every man is no less equal than the next,
Reveal Thyself to me, Eternity, that I may
Attract attention with my lyre of kings and nations.
The curtain has been raised! . . . There shine before the eyes
    now
The heroes, crowned with brilliant rays of light, resplendent.
'Twas by their bravery Kazan' 's now bloodied moon
Was into darkness thrown and robbed of all its glory.
O you who now rejoice in the celestial places,
Appear before me here—in your past earthly aspects!

By insolent Trans-Volga hordes' despotic power
The eastern part of ancient Russia still was burdened
And on our prisoners the fetters rattled loudly.
Revolts were brewing and new crimes began arising;
Through villages and towns pale fear itself extended;
Woe followed woe and evil made pursuit of evil.
The altars in the churches had no incense smoking;

РОССІЯДА

ИРОИЧЕСКАЯ ПОЕМА.

ПѢСНЬ ПЕРВАЯ.

Пою отъ варваровъ Россію свобожденну,
Попранну власть Татаръ и гордость побѣжденну,
Движенье древнихъ войскъ, труды, кроваву брань,
Россіи торжество, разрушенну Казань.
Отъ круга сихъ временъ, спокойствія начáло
Какъ свѣтлая заря въ Россіи возсіяло.

A

От-

The first page of the first edition of Mikhail Kheraskov's epic
poem The Rossiad, 1779.

Church singing came to cease and winds alone there howled;
Beneath thorns in the field the plow lay idly quiet,
And to the dark woods from their flocks went shepherds
    running.
When daylight cast its bright glance and the North illumined,
It found a prostrate Russia suffering and groaning.
Kazan', which drew the breath of life in its embrace,
Ignoble tribute from her weary hands was taking.
This city, thrown up by the enemies of Russia,
Like some proud mountain to the north was elevated,
And when it raised its head it stood beside two rivers
From where it looked upon the shores of raging Volga.
Under the shade of groves, 'midst many-colored flowers,
'Twas placed by Batu[9] with its gates all northward-facing
Through which he charged straight to the very heart of Russia,
Destroying settlements and setting towns afire.
Seeing from mountaintops the murderings and fires
Where had their dwelling once the ancient Russian Bulgars,
Inflamed with zealous faith for the law proper to it
Kazan', plunged in the darkness of Muhammad's legions,
In tears beheld the blue smoke and the reddish sky,
And unto Russia 'cross the fields its hands extended.
The Russian princes it besought for light and succor
When in her did extend impiety its darkness.
Moved thus to pity for the places native to them
And the anxiety and woe of their own people
The princes, rending all the Northland into pieces,
The bold hordes humbled, pouring out their blood in battle.

But no matter how fought the Russian Herculeses
New heads kept growing back upon the evil Hydra,
And when their stings were grown again in hidden places,
These serpents crept once more into the breast of Russia.
Although upon the ground the dragon's head lay shattered
The ancient venom still had not been quenched inside it.
'Neath ashes hid the fire and frequently erupted;
To Russia's misery its strength it kept on gathering.

[9] Batu-Khan (died 1255) was the grandson of Genghis-Khan, who commanded the Tatar forces from 1237 to 1240. After conquering a number of Russian principalities, he founded the Tatar state or khanate known as the Golden Horde, with its capital at Sarai on the lower Volga.

It came to pass that in Ioann the Second's youthhood
The trampled might of the unruly hordes awakened.
This grandson of a brave grandfather wreathed in glory
Almost let slip Kazan' from hands which were yet feeble.
His spirit had been saddened by the expedition
Which in the previous year he led into misfortune,
Where Boreas himself raised arms against the Russians.
Having concealed Kazan' from them with wings now frosted,
He wrapped himself all up in darkened cloud and storm
And bore resemblance to some dread-inspiring monster.
In empty steppe he howled and in thick forest bellowed;
He circled 'midst the mountains, tore, uprooted, roared;
And then to fertile shores the Volga's currents whirling
From out his icy lips he blew frosts, winds, and snows,
The Russians' blood enflamed no longer seemed to warm them,
So that it could the year approaching boil more hotly.

'Twas after this the young tsar to his capital took flight,
Where he took joy not with the trumpets' blast but pleasures.
O Thou who live in peace high up among the heavens!
Grant me forgiveness for my boldness, mighty Tsar,
In daring to present in darkness your days' morn,
But your bright noon yet still more loudly shall I hail.
Great are you that you calmed the storm around your
      kingdom,
But greater yet that you did overcome the passions.

When it saw Moscow fall asleep, its swords abandoned,
The trembling moon did dare to peek out from the clouds;
It raised its open eyes then smoldering with hatred
From River Volga like some dreadful storm erupted.
Having disturbed the peace the horde tore off its fetters
And moved by anger stirred itself, incited riot,
And there began its head and shoulders to raise up,
And Russia to oppress as it had done before.
Again this dreadful beast did enter Russian cities,
In his train bringing murder, violence, and plunder.
One hand a sword held, but the other—clanking irons;
Walls crumbled all around and steppe and forest suffered.
On the command of the perfidious Sumbeka[10]

[10] Sumbeka was the daughter of the Nogai Tatar murza Iussuf
and the wife of Enalei, the ruler of Kazan' in the 1530's. After

The rivers of Kazan' flowed rich with blood of Russians.
Bearing a torch the scourge of evil now unleashed
In fury put the flame to Moscow's settlements.
Chastisement, blade in hand, did enter Christian dwellings
And martyrs' blood soon cried out to the heavens.
The sadness, cries, and groans of orphans but remained;
Their fatherland turned just to dream this lamentation.

Base greed now harnessed to the chariot of profit
Sowed suffering within the Russian capital.
Where magnates are concerned for personal advantage
Feelings of pity stay there for a long time silent.
Thus Moscow smitten by internal desolation
Inconsolable was by alien misfortunes.

Truth for a time from young Tsar Ioann took concealment;
Deceit, replacing honor, saw to its own interests.
It now did in the guise of zealousness appear,
Made entry, and with every passing day grew stronger.

There flattery showed itself in a pretended beauty
Which in its nakedness and bare of all pretenses
Was dark as night itself, and timid, humble, hasty;
Before the strong 'twas low, before the lowly haughty,
Itself prostrating at the feet of earthly rulers
It sought to be of use to them as just mere buffer.
Thus flattery having changed its natural gall to sweetness
Has lured the careless youth to empty entertainments.
The magnates, zealous only for their own advantage,
Joined forces with it and humiliated power.
And flattery did receive support which it had hoped for
And from the tsar's young face all innocence withdrew.
What did then Truth, pursued by slander's vicious arrows?
Harassed, Truth driven so took refuge in a cave!

In troubled times there once existed mighty nobles
Who for their fatherland great love did truly harbor;

---

her husband's death she married Saf-girei and became the mother
of Utemish-girei who in 1549 succeeded his father as ruler of
Kazan' though he was but two years old at the time. During the
Russian siege of the city Sumbeka and her son eventually went
over to the Russian side.

Who found the power to disdain seductive pleasures
And tears could not restrain in face of plain disaster.
Thus moved by holy law and holy obligation
They did not shun to make complaints before the throne.
Beholding Truth defeated and triumphant evil,
To shield the tsar from lies they did themselves embolden.
Their hair all white with age they gathered 'round the tsar,
Their tears did manifest the sorrow of them all;
Their heads and glances and their hearts so in dejection
They drew, it seems, about the crown a fog of mourning.
The light of virtue shined upon their saddened brows
On which the sovereign could read his own dishonor.
The spirit, they proclaimed, of bravery sleeps within you!
But knowing this himself the monarch heeded not.

Sad was the capital, fair Moscow bent her head,
And sadness like the night had shaded her face over.
Grief crept into her heart and sorrow found her lips;
The splendid places which surrounded her mourned also;
And letting loose her hair misfortune strolled the city,
Her eyes cast downward all into despair conducted.
In agony she beat her chest and cried profusely.
The streets knew triumph not nor did the dwellings peace;
In grassy vales just grief, in groves reigned naught but
    moaning.
Among the city's throngs no wedding songs were heard;
All were arrayed in garb of sadness and as orphans;
Inside God's temples all that could be heard was wailing.
Consumed by a disease to which there was no end,
Moscow then bore resemblance unto stagnant water
Which, suddenly deprived of movement or of freshness,
Turns dull, grows fetid, and breeds poison of itself.
Its people cast into despair, pursued, and wearied,
Were like volcanic fire in Aetna blazing suddenly
Which tosses up thick clumps of trees and wooded hillocks
From mountain summit to the very heavens.
The people have bestirred! . . . Then in their violent fury
From just a spark a brazen rising burst to blazing.
It swept right through the streets and burned in marketplaces,
And Moscow saw the glow of woeful consequences.[11]

[11] A reference to the Moscow fire of June, 1547. Some nobles
sought to cast guilt on the brothers Iurii and Mikhail Glin'skii,

Those in rebellion rose against the evil magnates
Who had endeavored to increase the monarch's sternness
And tried to keep his soul in constant agitation,
So they could plunder Russia bare during the tempest.
The princes Glin'skii[12] were both victims of this rising;
One of them was slain by the insurrectionaries,
The other managed to escape through cunningness
And from the throne began to rage with a new thundering.
Extending o'er the tsar's bright house the cloud of vengeance
This power implacable did arm itself with lightning
And levied its blows at those men and at those places
Where Truth did dare its mouth to open and speak plainly.
To champions of games did go just compensation,
While loyal sons, their eyes tear-filled, fell into silence.

Losing the loveliness which once it could be proud of,
And seeing all around it desolation, conflict,
Grief everywhere and in the breast of Moscow illness,
Its borders jeopardized by bold hordes' frequent raiding,
A throne unsteady 'neath a shade of pomp and splendor,
'Neath foreign rule the Don, the Dniepr, Dvina, Volga,
And now expecting the approach of night eternal—
Russia her tear-filled eyes raised to the very heavens,
She raised her arms outstretched unto the Heavenly Father,
And kneeling humbly did petition the Creator.
She then made move to bare her bosom, faint and wounded,
And with one hand did indicate all Moscow bloodied,
The sea of evil poured about it—with the other.
She then commenced to sob, and not a word could utter.

On rainbowed dawns above the stars there sat supremely
The mighty God who roars in thunders and in tempests;
Before Whom light of day is like the very darkness;
Who animates all things and sets worlds into motion;
Who from the heavens looks upon all equally,
Forgives, treats tenderly, becalms yet fears not to chastise.
Of fire and water King—He knew the voice of Russia

---

who were close to the tsar, and organized a conspiracy against
them. Iurii Glin'skii was killed, but Mikhail escaped to Lithuania,
was captured, arrested, imprisoned but eventually pardoned.
[12] See Note 11.

And seeing the last hour of His children's glory
In one brief moment the days of their sorrow reckoned;
And then determined to extend a hand of sustenance.

The heavens up above her suddenly grew brighter;
A dew with power of restoration then descended,
Besprinkled lightly her unhappy breast and countenance,
And in a moment's time the weary Russia strengthened.
Upon this suddenly a red dawn cloaked the Northland,
And angels, peering at the earth through crystal doors,
Did then compose upon their lyres celestial concert
And sang of the beneficence now crowning Russia.

Then to one of the righteous men in that assemblage,
Who dwelt within the grace of godly emanations
And held a place of glory in the heavenly kingdom,
Who did His praises sing in the angelic chorus,
Almighty God declared: "Approach your hapless offspring;
In darkness let her see the light, extend her counsel.
Appear to Ioann in the person of his nation
That in you he may see all Russia subjugated."

7. Elisei, or Bacchus Enraged: A Poem

VASILII N. MAIKOV

The son of a landowner of the Iaroslav district, Maikov never received much formal education. He did not finish the gymnasium attached to the Academy of Sciences in St. Petersburg and is believed never to have studied a foreign language throughout his life. From 1743 to 1761 (with a four-year break) he served in the Semenovskii Regiment of the Guards. Upon leaving the army with the rank of captain he settled in Moscow, where his first literary works began appearing from 1762. He wrote odes, fables, and a humorous poem in the mock-epic vein entitled *The Omber Player* (Igrok lombera, 1763), which enjoyed considerable success.

From 1767 to 1768 Maikov took part in Catherine's Legislative Commission. When its work ended, he returned to St. Petersburg and in 1770 received an appointment as an official in the Ministry of Defense.

Maikov's most fruitful literary activity came in the years 1768–1775. He became a member of the circle of writers grouped about Nikolai Novikov, and contributed to *The Drone*. His relations with Fonvizin were also quite close at this time. Maikov worked in several genres—ode, verse epistle, epigram, tragedy—but it was with his mock-epic poem *Elisei, or Bacchus Enraged* (Elisei, ili razdrazhennyi Vakkh, 1769–1770) that he scored his greatest literary triumph and for which he is most remembered as a writer.

Following the Pugachëv Uprising, Maikov became increasingly active in Masonic circles. After retiring from his government position in 1775, he went to Moscow and worked closely with Novikov on the Masonic journal *Morning Light*. His last major literary work before his death in 1770 was the pastoral drama with music *A Country Holiday, or Virtue Crowned* (Dereven'skii prazdnik, ili uvenchannaia dobrodetel', 1777), an idealized picture of landowner-serf relations.

A portrait of Vasilii Maikov by the eighteenth-century Russian artist F. S. Rokotov, about 1765.

Maikov began to write *Elisei* in late 1768 or early 1769. The first three cantos must have been known in manuscript form in the first few months of 1769, since we find them parodied in Chulkov's poem *Verses on a Swing* (Stikhi na kacheli) published in May of that year in his own satirical journal *This and That*. The fifth and final canto of the poem must have been done at the earliest toward the end of 1770, judging from the reference to Kheraskov's work on his epic poem *The Battle of Chesmé*, which was published in 1771. *Elisei* was finally brought out in November, 1771.

The European tradition of the mock-epic poem based on a burlesque of Virgil's *Aeneid* began with the *Virgile travesti* of the seventeenth-century French writer Paul Scarron (1610–1660), whom Maikov invokes at the beginning of *Elisei*. The arbiter of classicist literary theory Boileau opposed Scarron's type of burlesque in his *Art poétique* as an offense to the dignity of the classical epic, yet he himself experimented with the mock-epic in *Le Lutrin*. In the eighteenth century the mock-epic was firmly established as a literary genre, and proved capable of producing major works of literature from one end of Europe to the other: Alexander Pope's *Rape of the Lock* (1712), Ludvig Holberg's *Peder Paars* (1719), Voltaire's *La Pucelle* (1755), the Polish writer Ignacy Krasicki's *Myszeidos* (1778) and *Monachomachia* (1778), and Vasilii Maikov's *Elisei*.

The Russian Boileau, Sumarokov, had given his stamp of approval to the two basic types of the mock-epic in his *Epistle II* and left several examples of literary travesty. Prior to Maikov's work, the now forgotten poet Ivan Barkov (1732–1768), who published Kantemir's satires in 1752, was immensely popular at one time for his travesties in the manner of Scarron, but because of their pornographic nature his works were not permitted to be published.

Maikov's technique of travesty differed from Scarron's and from that recommended by Boileau. Its originality (and the source of its appeal to contemporary readers) lay in the presentation of images of "lower" aspects of contemporary reality corresponding to specific episodes in Virgil's *Aeneid*. This introduction of "low" scenes was not sanctioned by classicist literary theory. Consequently, in Western mock-epics such scenes rarely appear. The humor of *Elisei* springs then from two sources: the usual mock-epic disparity, or "tension," between the contents and form and from the contents themselves, that is, precisely from the so-called "low" scenes. Although the primary purpose of these scenes is to evoke humor and not to make social commentary, *Elisei* is by no means wholly devoid of political accents. The romance between Elisei and the directress of a house of correction for prostitutes in the third canto is a travesty of the love affair between Aeneas and Dido in the third canto of the *Aeneid*. Some students of Maikov's work also insist on seeing the episode in *Elisei* as an allusion to the private life of the Empress Catherine. This is a matter for speculation. More obvious, however, is Maikov's intention of attacking through *Elisei* the control of private businessmen (the *otkupshchiki*, or "tax farmers," in the work) over the spirits monopoly and the increase in prices that enriched these entrepreneurs at the expense of the populace. Sumarokov had already dealt with the same issue in several of his fables and in the *Chorus to a Topsy Turvy World*.

The conception of *Elisei* may be if not wholly then in part attributed to the appearance of the translation of the first canto of the *Aeneid* by the poet Vasilii Petrov (1736–1799).

A graduate of the Slavonic-Greek-Latin Academy, and a follower of the Lomonosovian tradition of panegyric poetry, Petrov became Catherine's more or less official court poet from the year 1766. Two years later he was named the empress's official translator and her personal reader.

Most of Petrov's poetry was panegyric and sycophantic. This earned him the esteem and support of court circles but led to his being made the butt of many satirical attacks and parodies by his fellow writers, particularly Sumarokov and Novikov.

Petrov's translation of the first canto of the *Aeneid* under the title *Enei* in Russian was published in 1770 but circulated in manuscript from late 1768 or early 1769. In the Soviet Academy's *History of Russian Literature* (Volume IV, Part II, ed. G. A. Gukovskii, V. A. Desnitskii, Moscow-Leningrad, 1947, pp. 210–211) the scholar A. M. Kukulevich suggests that Petrov's translation of the first canto of the *Aeneid,* especially truncated from the rest of the work, may be read as an allegorical personification of Catherine the Great represented by the figure of the wise and beautiful ruler of Carthage, Dido. The argument is reasonable in the light of the enthusiastic reception of the work in court circles. As further evidence may be cited the fact that the first edition of Petrov's *Enei* was decorated with a small wreath with the monogram of Catherine and the praise lavished on Petrov by the empress in her large French work *L'Antidote*, a polemic against the French astronomer Abbé Chappe d'Auteroche's (1722–1769) *Le Voyage en Sibérie* (1768).

The publication of *Enei* and the resultant acclaim by the court increased the satirical jibes aimed in Petrov's direction. The poet was accused of a high-blown, complicated, often unintelligible style. Malicious epigrams began to circulate, one of which, by Maikov, read as follows: "The power of the Russian language!/ Petrov had just to wish it—and Virgil became a stutterer." Maikov took up the cudgel against Petrov more decisively in *Elisei*. The poem contains several thinly veiled satirical allusions to Petrov and his translation. To many of Maikov's contemporaries *Elisei* appeared not only a travesty of certain episodes in the *Aeneid* but a travesty of its Russian translation as well.

The translation of *Elisei* follows the text in the collection *Iroi-komicheskaia poema*, ed. V. Tomashevskii, Leningrad, 1933.

TO THE READER:
Gracious Reader! I had wanted to write a very large introduction to this poem in which it was my intention to explain in detail the reason that motivated me to this composition. But I judged that however important the reason—even to the point that I might malign* some esteemed person by insisting that he compelled me to it, saying to me: "Have no regard for the critics and write what comes into your head, for you write well," this would little embellish my effort if by itself it would not merit the praise of my gracious Reader. I do know that just on the advice of some respectable person or, lower, on very strictest order, a miserable writer will not ever write anything good, just like a frog—no matter how much it swells itself up it will never be the equal of an ox.

* It is possible to malign anyone, knowing that nobody will be called to a confrontation for this calumny.

Contents of the Poem

First Canto

Enraged by the pride of the tax farmers, Bacchus gets angry at them because the high prices of wine,[1] beer, and mead have reduced the number of drunks. He comes to a tavern where he sees a coachman named Elisei and rejoices that he has found a man who by his appearance seems to him to be the perfect instrument for his vengeance. Elisei, meanwhile, asks a waiter for wine in a beer mug and drinks it all with a single gulp, which strengthens Bacchus's hope all the more. After downing the wine, Elisei strikes the waiter on the head with the mug and causes a row in the tavern. When a district corporal hears it, he enters, has Elisei placed under guard and led to a police station. Bacchus then goes to Zeus to plead for him to release Elisei from jail. Zeus informs him that he has received a petition from Ceres[2] about the decline of activity due to the intoxication of all the peasants. Zeus then orders Hermes to summon all the gods to Olympus for a settlement of the quarrel between Bacchus and Ceres and to go afterward to the police station and free Elisei from captivity.

Second Canto

Hermes comes to the prison and, dressing Elisei in a woman's clothes, takes him to the Kalinkin house[3] where dissolute women were being kept under guard at the time. Elisei wakes up, wonders how he got there and imagines that he is in a convent. In the meantime, the directress of the house rises, awakens all the girls, and distributes work among them. Seeing Elisei, she soon discovers that he is not a woman. She conducts him to her own room where he reveals to her that he is a coachman and then tells her about the battle of the

---

[1] *Vino*, in the original. It could also be used generally with reference to spirits.

[2] In Roman mythology the goddess of the harvest.

[3] *Kalinkinskii dom*, in the original. In old Petersburg a house of correction for prostitutes.

hay mowing that took place between the Zimogorians and the Valdaians.[4]

Third Canto

The conclusion of Elisei's narration. The directress's love for Elisei. The assembly of the gods on Olympus at the command of Zeus. While Elisei prepares to spend the night with the directress, the head of the guard comes on a tour of inspection. Seeing Elisei in a woman's clothing with the directress, he takes him for a wench, but one newly arrived. He asks her where she comes from and why he does not have her name in his registry. Although the directress straightens out the matter, the stern head of the guard does not accept her explanation and orders the would-be wench taken into custody. Hermes then frees him and gives him a Fortunatus cap[5] in which Elisei again returns to the directress, with whom he spends several months. But tiring of her love, he leaves the house. The directress pines over his flight. The commander enters at that time and, noticing the things left behind by Elisei, gets angry at her and wants to whip her; but, appeased by her cunning, he soon returns to peace with her.

Fourth Canto

After leaving the Kalinkin house, Elisei goes to the city; but, growing weary, he lies down to sleep in a forest. He is suddenly aroused by the shouting of a woman whom two thieves are trying to rob. He saves her from them and discovers that she is his wife. She tells him everything that happened to her since she parted with him. He sends her to the city but himself remains behind in the forest, where Silenus[6] appears

[4] A reference to post drivers from the Zimogor'e and Valdai stations in the Novgorod district on the Petersburg-Moscow route.

[5] The hat that makes its wearer invisible. Known as the *shapka-nevidimka* in the Russian folk tradition.

[6] In Greek mythology a satyr and companion and tutor of Dionysus (Bacchus). Classical authors often refer, not to one Silenus, but to several sileni of more or less the same characteristics.

to him and leads him to the home of a wealthy tax farmer
so that he can drink as much as he wants. Silenus then
returns to Bacchus in heaven. Searching for the wine cellar,
Elisei unexpectedly comes upon a bath where the tax farmer
and his wife were then steaming themselves. He drives them
away and, after giving himself a steam bath, dresses himself
in the tax farmer's clothes. Wearing the Fortunatus cap that
makes him invisible, he enters the tax farmer's rooms and
hides himself under his bed. He lies there until the tax farmer,
upset by a storm then passing over, gets out of bed. Then
leaving his hiding place beneath the bed, Elisei lies down to
sleep with the tax farmer's wife. After the storm, the tax
farmer notices the strange movements of his wife in bed and
thinks that some household spirit is squeezing her. He wants
to send the following morning for a sorceress who would drive
this household devil from his house. Hearing this, the coachman fears the arrival of the sorceress and leaves the tax
farmer's rooms in search of the wine cellar, where he hopes
to slake his thirst.

Fifth Canto

Taking himself into the tax farmer's wine cellar, Elisei
rejoices at finding much to drink there. At this point, Bacchus
and his retinue appear to him. After making a shambles of
the cellar, Bacchus and Elisei go off to devastate the wine
cellars of other tax farmers. When the tax farmer awakes the
following morning he sends for the sorceress. Just when she
arrives the housekeeper runs out and tells of the destruction
of the wine cellar. In grief, the tax farmer begs the sorceress
to drive the devils out of his house. Meanwhile Zeus sees
that Elisei is harassing many tax farmers, and so he summons
the gods to him and passes judgment on him. He finally
decides to have him sent into military service, and this is what
became of Elisei.

Canto the First

I sing of the sound of glasses, I sing of that hero[7] who,
drunk, caused dreadful woes in many taverns for the pleasure

[7] A parody of the invocation of Virgil's *Aeneid* ("Arma virum-
que cano . . .") in the Russian translation of Vasilii Petrov.

of Bacchus; he beat up and got drunk wastrels and ox-cart drivers, broke cauldrons, buckets, goblets, bottles, and saucers. The tavern windows suffered the same lot. From the strength of his terrible hands trembled waiters and all the tax farmers, who had no premonition of these woes when they robbed everyone and made themselves rich. O Muse! Keep not silent about this. Speak,[8] or even mutter from inebriation if it is impossible for you to talk plainly.[9] Speak: you truly know the reason why the god of drink, employing so shrewd a strategy, sent this unlikely hero against all tax farmers to destroy his favorite capital.

O you, dear one, beloved Scarron! Leave the sumptuous throne of magnificent Priapus; leave the throng of blaspheming writers; come strum for me your fiddle[10] or balalaika, so that I likewise could begin to hoot and dress up my heroes as barge haulers; so that Zeus would be my twaddler, Hermes a prankster, Neptune like the dumbest ox and, in a word, so that my gods and goddesses should split the readers' sides.

Opposite the quarters of the last company of the Semenovskii Regiment stood a house with wide gates to which it was some distance from Tychok's tavern.[11] This was a public house named Star in which were kept Bacchus's bucket and chariot. This house was designated as Bacchus's capital, and it flourished under his personal protection. In it old Silenus himself sat stretched out. But the breed of evil tax farmers repugnant to Bacchus upset the time designated by him for intoxication when they raised the price of hops. Frightful were the woes that resulted from this. Wine and vodka became costlier, and the same thing happened to foamy beer; and they even began selling sweet mead higher. Then, puffing themselves with pride at the number of their victories, the

---

[8] In the original Russian: *povezhd'*. This is the second-person singular imperative form of the Church Slavonic verb *povedeti*. Petrov often uses the form (which was archaic in his own time) in his *Aeneid* translation; Maikov's use of it in *Elisei* is clearly parodic in intent.

[9] An allusion to the complexity of Petrov's style.

[10] *Gudok*, in Russian; a three-stringed folk instrument akin to the fiddle.

[11] *Tychok* in Russian means "blow," "hit," "wallop." A tavern by this name did exist in the city of St. Petersburg in Maikov's time.

tax farmers in their pride looked with contempt upon
Bacchus, and thought that he should dance to their piping.
But Bacchus thought differently of this: "Am I just to let it
pass?" he began to shout from his cups. "What do I see as
the consequence of all this? Must I deprive myself of my
dearest inheritance? The prices have already been fixed for
vodka and wine. A small tumbler goes for three kopecks and
if in such an unhappy circumstance a drunk would like to
have a little beer instead? Alas, this comes still higher. Neither
beer nor wine will be able to act as they should. Have I not
now suffered a worse humiliation than befell Juno at the
hands of Paris?[12] Am I not able to crush these schemes?"
Now he began to shout, "Fellows, bring the lashes!" But he
thought that this was improper for immortals, though the
matter was truly deserving of his lashes. Moreover, his dignity
did not permit him to make a fool of himself. He then began
to think of another way of avenging the insult he had suffered.
And so he said: "When the too proud Alcyon[13] insulted me
once by disdaining my holiday I gave her fitting punishment;
for the same scorn, Penteus himself also tasted the cudgel,
not only the lashes;[14] and those were not the only ways I paid
back those who upset me when I was drunk." As he said
these things his drunken gaze grew dim. He seated himself
in a wagon and went off to a tavern with unsubdued vengeance in his turbulent thoughts. He approached a crowd of
drinkers who were leaning against a wall. It was then a day
free of all worldly vanities; people were wandering all about
the city although it was scarcely dawn. Drunkards' heads
were spinning from drink, for it just happened to be the
Shrovetide season.[15] Just as mice crawl for groats from dark

---

[12] Paris, the son of Priam, the King of Troy, resolved the argument as to which of the goddesses—Juno, Athena, or Venus—
was the fairest by choosing Venus.

[13] Alcyon, in Greek mythology, was a daughter of Aeolus
and the wife of Ceyx, son of the Morning Star. Both were
changed into birds for the impiety of calling themselves Zeus and
Hera, she into a halcyon and he into the bird of his name.

[14] Pentheus was a King of Thebes who was punished for refusing to recognize Bacchus as a god and prohibiting the celebration
of rites in his honor.

[15] In the celebrations attending the Shrovetide season, mass
drinking was common.

holes,[16] so did all the rabble throng to the tavern from the high mountains that art, not nature, created for the pleasure of working people.[17] There were shoemakers, tailors, and weavers, and mutually contaminated versifiers who were blowing the verses they had written into one another's noses and were peddling their compositions like bast shoes. Many smashed noses could be seen there.[18] One fellow was all black and blue, another was without hair, a third was rubbing his congealed lips, a fourth counted the teeth he still had left from the beating he had suffered at the hands of others. There was also a multitude of all kinds of dolts there; among others there entered the tavern a fair youth, a gambler, drunk, rowdy, brawler and, in short, the local pride then of all Iamskaia Street.[19]

By trade a coachman, his name was Elisei. He wore a plain dark coat and a hat set at a jaunty angle; his whip made of a branch of meadowsweet dangled loosely on his knee. As soon as he entered a tavern he instantly subdued the roar of drunks just as if the sea had drowned them. *Beneath a clear sky he extended his merry course/ And traveled like Neptune along the foamy surface of the waters.*[20] Forgive me, O Muse, for giving way to the desire and singing these two verses without restraint. I admit to you that though they have little sense, their essence broke through cleverly. Perhaps through them I shall receive praise. Henceforth I want to sing my verses so. It seems to me that I am not insulting you when I imitate a school refrain. But if you yourself move the pen of such writers, have you not gone balmy in your old age? Oh! No, I am guilty before you, my dear Muse. Never do you seek union with ignoramuses. Your confidants are known among us. Parnassus today harbors one of them,[21]

[16] A Russian folk saying: *Kak myshi na krupu.*

[17] A reference to street decorations put up for the Shrovetide festivities.

[18] Fist fighting was a popular diversion during the Russian Shrovetide festivities. Sumarokov wrote a fable about this, *The Fist Fight* (Kulashnyi boi).

[19] A district settled by coachmen.

[20] These lines are almost a direct quotation from Petrov's *Aeneid* translation (corresponding to Virgil, I, 154–156).

[21] A reference to Lomonosov, who died in 1765. Maikov juxtaposes him to his imitator Petrov.

while the others now inhabit the earth and are regarded as dwellers of Parnassus. And so I deem it more advantageous to follow their sense and wit.

Having already exerted my too frail strengths, I am following the singers who are dear to me. Whether I reach my goal or stumble along the way, I shall be true to those whose taste I admire and I shall forgive those who slander it. And now I return my thoughts to my tale.

When Bacchus saw the drunken coachman, his heart welled up with joy like a river. In his own mind now he saw his success. Turning to Silenus, he said to him: "Is this not now the summit of good fortune, that I have already found what I intended to seek? That youth seems robust by appearance. On him shall I place the mantle of all my hope. He seems as though born to humble every worker, and in my grief I know that he will not abandon me. I will throw off all the fear that troubled me before. I am already rejoicing, as though I had already been avenged. Does not my victory appear clear to me, when my darling is drunk even before dinner? And if fear still troubles you, just have a look; you can see everything in his eyes. His cheeks seem flushed to me, and if I may say so, he will surpass all bounds and consume more wine than you."

Silenus would have taken this for a joke, had not this drunk convinced him that he measured his brewery by his own barrel. Grabbing an ox-cart driver by the collar behind the bar, Elisei shouted: "Give me wine, or I'll cuff you one! Give it to me, or I'll bloody your nose!" Pointing to a drinking goblet, he demanded: "Pour in three kopecks' worth of anise, or I'll tear the tavern paling down with you." The ox-cart driver began trembling in the face of obvious death, but Bacchus shouted: "Oh, my worthy foster child! I shall end all my misfortunes with you. I shall take a fearful vengeance on the tax farmers with you! The whole lot of them will stop squeezing me when your fist begins fighting together with me. Not rivers, but seas of beer will flow here." So spoke Bacchus, burning with vengeance.

In the meantime, the coachman had already filled his goblet and drunk all of it down to the bottom with a single gulp. After drinking, he struck the ox-cart driver on the head with it. This blow resounded throughout the tavern. Buckets, bottles, and saucers fell from the shelves; fragments of the goblet splattered against all the windows. The boundary between the bar and window was ripped asunder; as rain mixed with hail flies from a cloud, so then did saucer and glass fragments fly to hail Elisei's thunderous victories. And the poor little ox-cart driver plumped down for a nap behind the bar. Frantic, he started calling: "Help! Oh brothers, they're robbing me! They're beating me!" And all the while he lay back end up. This seemed to annoy our hero. In a fury, he stuck a hand behind the bar and seized the ox-cart driver by his pants. If the thin belt holding them up had not broken, my hero, raising him up, would have knocked him on the floor. But fortunately, or miraculously, the belt could not bear the weight, and tearing, to the hero's displeasure, left the ox-cart driver free behind the bar. Since Elisei could raise him no further, he began to scold him in a fatherly way: "Since my fist couldn't instill fear in you, just await, rascal, the punishment you've got coming." As the hero spoke these words, a corporal suddenly opened the tavern doors. He was the head of a police circuit, and hearing the noise in the tavern while passing, though he was no relation to the ox-cart driver whatsoever, he took his side and asked: "What noise is this here? Was there any fighting going on here?" At this, everyone took to his heels, for nobody wanted to answer for what had taken place. But unfortunately the corporal had a sharp eye and saw Elisei standing very boldly. "I see, brother," he said, "it's your work, after all. Wasn't it you, my hawk, who tore the tavern apart?" Then the ox-cart driver opened his mouth in a yawn more boldly still. He got up and approached the corporal without his pants on. "Avenge me!" he shouted. "Avenge me on this ruffian, Honorable Corporal, who attacked me, an innocent person here." This corporal was stern, and had no liking for jokes. "Who hit you? Tell me!" he asked, furrowing his brows. In tears, the ox-cart driver answered him, "This drunk here broke all my ribs." And then, pointing to Elisei: "He caused the state treasury and me loss, and so long as he is locked up I'm ready to endure anything. He cleaved my forehead with a drinking mug, and tore my pants and waistcoat."

Then the corporal suddenly appeared with a dragoon and struck Elisei with a lash like a bolt of lightning. Although the column on the lash was not very thick, it nevertheless beat

stingingly from the corporal's hand. Elisei was dumbfounded
but remained on his feet, at which the soldier grew still
angrier. Never had he seen such a peasant whom his hand
could not knock off his feet. He wasted no time in ordering
the hero bound, and Elisei was forced to surrender without
a struggle. Not that he was lacking in courage or strength;
he simply did not dare to struggle with the police. And so
with his hands fastened with a rope, he let himself be taken
to jail as a prisoner.

Then all ray of hope for Bacchus was extinguished and
he wallowed in a sea of despair. He left the drinking establishment just like an animal smoked from its lair, and not
delaying there even an hour more he went with his uncle to
the heavens. He flew swifter than the Amazon empress who
surpassed the whirlwinds with the speed of a horse. He flew
on winged tigers, like the wind.[22] Dust rose in a column from
under the beasts' thighs. Although dust does not rise from
under the thighs, as everyone knows, this was no simple thing
but something miraculous.

He sped to the heavens and urged on the tigers. A light
wind ruffled his curly locks. Enormous knees were visible on
the outside, and the folds of a chlamys tied together by a
knot, purple morocco to the calves, and Cherkessian boots
exceeded all beauties of attire. His belt was Persian and his
cap made of sable. The raiment was taken from a song the
Volga barge haulers sing after getting themselves good and
drunk.[23] This little song is called the Kamyshen'ka, after the
river that flows as an estuary into the mother Volga. Art
extracts beauty from everything.

[22] There is some evidence that Maikov is parodying here the
first version of Petrov's ode *To a Carousel* (Na karusel', 1766),
which is no longer extant. The poem is believed to contain the
image of dust rising from under a horse's thighs. An echo of it
may be found in Sumarokov's parody of the Maikov ode *A
Dithyramb to Pegasus* (Difiramv Pegasu). Maikov parodies the
image further in his verse *Epistle to M. M. Kheraskov* (Epistola
M. M. Kheraskovu).

[23] Maikov has in mind the well-known folk song from the cycle
about Stepan Razin, beginning:

> Chto ponizhe bylo goroda Saratova,
> A povyshe bylo goroda Tsaritsyna,
> Protekala, prolegala mat' Kamyshen'ka reka . . .

Bacchus finally reached those places where his father always drank. Having been transported there by the service of his animals, he espied his father and mother. Juno was not in a laurel wreath, but in a cap. Zeus was also not seated upon his throne, but on a cock. Placing its head between Zeus's legs, it was shouting, *Cockadoodledoo!* amusing Juno in this way. The lord of high places fell asleep among ripples of clouds and began breaking wind at Juno. The mother of the gods turned her nose away, went up to her husband, ran a tender glance over him, and then said: "Do gods play pranks just like mortals? Or is it that you have quaffed too much nectar, my dear?" Zeus listened to her words in good humor, then pronounced a godly reply to her question: "Your nose is still working, isn't it, Juno?" At these words, he stroked her with his hand. Here Momus[24] joined in the conversation and, humoring them, said derisively: "O our powerful Zeus! I see that you are another Hercules who stayed with Omphale[25] a whole week, leaving important matters behind and spinning on a distaff like a woman. Well, what can I say? The whole world is like that now. It seems that fashionable wives no longer have any husbands. Every day I see this with my own eyes. The husbands are all simpletons, and ruled by their wives." This speech seemed coarse to Juno. She said: "Listen, Momus, the joke is not pleasant to me. You insult many honorable people with it. Is it that you no longer see any intelligent husbands? Listen, poor Momus, to what I shall tell you now. Husbands are obedient to their wives because. True, sometimes wives are to their husbands . . . But . . . what is the point of tossing pearls before swine? Why should I waste my words on a fool? An empty head will not be able to understand them." At this point Momus wanted to defend himself with a gibe, and it was evident that he would be unable to take his leave of them without a quarrel, that he would be cast from heaven by the two of them, but Bacchus prevented this by his arrival.

His eyes filled with tears, he announced: "O thou ruler of all creation! Gaze upon these streams of bitter tears; gaze and

[24] In Greek mythology, the god of mockery and censure.
[25] In Greek mythology, a queen of Lydia for whom Zeus, dressed as a woman, spun wool and did other womanly chores for three years in order to appease the gods.

grieve at my sorrow, Zeus! You rule the entire world with your might and you never leave us in misfortune. With what loathsomeness have I angered you that you have placed tax farmers on hops and delivered wine over to the hands of such tyrants? You were not so severe even in your anger at the Trojans as you seem mad at me now, who never has sinned either in drink or in sleep. I am your blood; I have my life because of you. Recall your beloved Semele.[26] And if the memory of her is still dear to you, bend and do not enter into the affairs of inebriates. Why do you wish to interfere in matters that do not concern you? Your duty, my father, is to drink, eat, and be merry. But now you have obstructed the path to drunkenness. Have you rewarded me as you promised? You once swore that in future years the inhabitants of the whole wide world would drink themselves drunk and that they would stay that way for a long, long time. Has your vow now been changed, Father?"

Then the father of the gods received his son's words and raised his eyes, which were red with wine. After smilingly passing over Bacchus the kind of gaze he had when he and Juno went to bed, he kissed him heartily and replied to him as follows: "I see that your grief saddens you. But you stay here and do not grieve any longer. Put off your petition until morning, for the morning is always wiser than the evening. You see that I myself am a bit drunker than you; you see truly that I am not making this up. Tomorrow I shall summon all the gods to me. I do not decide important matters alone. And I never censure anyone about anything while drunk. If you have to have a real court to settle the issue, my son, the immortals will investigate your entire case. I heard how Ceres once petitioned here, and this was the argument of her petition: almost the whole race of mortals became drunkards and as a result of it there was a great switch to grain. Merchants, scriveners, artists, peasants—all became drunk in turn and forgot us in their drunkenness. Moreover, the smoke from the wine fermentation reached even as far as my habitations and gave my eyes a good smarting. And you yourself remember that my eyes were like saucers. But now, you see, they have become like morels, which is why I wear glasses to this very

---

[26] In Greek mythology, the daughter of Cadmus, King of Thebes, and mother of Bacchus.

day. In her petition Ceres wrote clearly that it was not safe for wine to be free. If it is, then the whole world will get drunk and all activity will cease forever."

Then Bacchus plaintively answered Zeus. "If drinking disturbs activity," he began, "then I shall say no more about it. Let the gods decide between me and Ceres. I can endure it until tomorrow morning. But now I have a still more serious request to make of you. A coachman has been arrested for getting into a scuffle in a tavern. He is a dear confidant and brother of mine. They are now taking him, or have already taken him, intoxicated, to jail, where chains are waiting for him. You can prevent this from happening, my father, and free my friend from the cat-o'-nine-tails. I know that all are indignant at him over there and will give his hide a good tanning with the tails. The police have already become costly to me, and I have a real enemy in them. They simply hate all brawlers and drunks, and offend me much more than you. All the roads to drunkenness are cut off by them. For pity's sake, Father, step in and save him!"

Zeus then summoned Hermes to him, and when he arrived gave him the following command: "Listen to me, my dear son! You know yourself that you were not the only son fathered by me. I have a seraglio bigger than a sultan's. And if I may be bold enough to praise myself now, I have more offspring than all the other gods from continuous pleasures in earlier days. Should I not, therefore, look out for my children? Learn at my side, Hermes, dear, that it is no wonder that I am the father to so many of you. Fortunate, that until now my sacrum has not hurt."

Thus this father of immortals went on with his storytelling and would have spilled out millions more lying words if his spouse had not been present at the time. She raised a scowling glance at him from under her brows, and this way interrupted the empty talk with which he would have heaped Hermes's shoulders full, burdening this intelligent messenger and making him like an ass. But no sooner did he exaggerate something than he himself sensed what he was doing and, ceasing his empty talk, said: "Be obedient to my command, Hermes. Everything is possible for your speed. I am already long familiar with your services to me. This moment now leave the heavenly habitations and heed my word with care; set forth without delay along the road and bring to all im-

mortals as fast as you can this command: Tell them that it is
my desire that e'er the dawn comes up in the sky and begins
to gild the mountains and forests, and Phoebus leaps from
Thetis's[27] couch, an assembly of immortals should appear
before me on Olympus. But if some one of them delays even
a little, he will be turned skyward like an inverted funnel,
or, to put it simply, I will hang him by the heels and he will
swing like a jester amid the gods. He will never be able to
free himself no matter how daring he may be. But I still have
not given you my whole order. Once you have finished doing
everything I have asked, bring aid to this hero about whom
Bacchus humbly besought me. Go ahead and show the experience of all your powers. This hero is the coachman who
was taken to the police for brawling and was locked up for
drunkenness. If you do not succeed in freeing him, you yourself will be put in a cell." Hermes so received Zeus's stern
command. After putting on his wings, he took up his messenger's staff, descended from the highest regions, flew off,
and sought out all the gods, like a hunting dog. With difficulty
he found them in various parts of the universe. And he found
all the gods busy at the time. Pluto and the pagan priests were
feasting on the dead. In Ustiuzhna,[28] Vulcan was forging
a beer mug and evidently thinking about home brew for a
holiday. His wife was in a circle of honest wives who entice
everyone. Cupid was standing guard over swans. Mars was
with Venus, and Hercules, out of boredom, was playing with
children with a long crutch. In many huts old Cybele[29] was
telling everyone's fortunes with beans. Minerva, perhaps just
for amusement, was sharpening bobbins for girls for lace.
Neptune, with his frightfully long beard and trident, or spear,
to express it more clearly, was stirring up a puddle that had
been thawed by the sun and was making great waves in it.
He kept this up until the whole trident broke, which caused
all the young children to laugh, and they began mercilessly
throwing snowballs at the old fellow. This god of children's

[27] In Greek mythology, the mother of Achilles and one of the
fifty daughters of Nereus (the Nereids).
[28] A town in northern Russia, to the south of Lake Onega.
[29] In ancient Phrygian mythology, the goddess of nature; identi-
fied with the Greek goddess Rhea.

games lost his patience, grew angry at them, and began boiling
with rage. He wanted to tear their souls out of them right
then and there, but their fathers stepped forward and gave
his ears a good warming. They kept shoving the god of water
on all sides, saying to him with every blow: "Don't be angry
that you've been received so inhospitably. In the old days you
were received in honor, but now it is not surprising that you
are not. We were baptized in God's grace and are more enlightened than our ancestors; no longer will we continue to
respect a god as stupid as you." So shouted all the Orthodox
peasants. Hermes, taking notice of this, went away faster and
a little while later came upon other gods. Bellona[30] was
chasing peg-tops on the ice with a stick. Hermes came across
Apollo, who was also not in idleness. He was taking a marvelous exercise for himself: there he was chopping wood at a
peasant's. Sticking out his tongue like a tired dog and panting,
he repeated the blows in trochaic rhythm. Now and then,
however, an iamb and dactyl appeared. All around him there
was an assemblage of all sorts of little scribblers who were
mumbling to each other, I have no idea what. It seems that
they were observing his blows and, after listening to all the
strokes of the ax, all of them went home, as though they were
experts. After their return, they were all proud of themselves
just as if they had studied in the Spasskii School.[31] Not knowing which meter went with which verses, one of them considered himself a Russian Homer.[32] Another began comparing
himself to Virgil, though he himself barely knew the alphabet.[33] A third was boasting to all of his gift, and regarded
himself no less than a Pindar.[34] That they spoke nonsense
this way is not surprising; what is surprising, though, is that

[30] In Roman mythology, the goddess of war and sister of Mars.

[31] A common name for the Slavonic-Greek-Latin Academy in
Moscow. Maikov is making a thinly veiled allusion to Petrov,
who not only graduated at the Academy but later taught poetics
and rhetoric there.

[32] An allusion to the poet Trediakovskii's translation of
Fénelon's *Télémaque* (Tilemakhida).

[33] Maikov is referring to Petrov, the Russian translator of Virgil.

[34] Also a reference to Petrov, who wrote a number of panegyric
odes. The ancient Greek poet Pindar (522?–443 B.C.) is recognized
as the founder of the panegyric genre.

people read their poetry, poetry that, after the first glance, is
worth nothing to those who know better, poetry that is more
dangerous to hearts than bane. Now I exclaim: "O times!
O customs! O education, father of all vices, when will your
end appear to us?[35] And will such days arrive quickly when
fools will cease glorying? No, fate it seems speeds my short
age faster than enlightenment can improve those mores that
cannot distinguish nonsense from good. Or is it that they no
longer expect the resurrection of the deceased and do not fear
to be tortured for having no regard for Lomonosov? They
will suffer, even should they apologize, if they have compared
a famous singer to a hack. But it seems that this is enough
vengeance for them if their ravings and rantings carry no
weight in this world. The glory of a famous poet is not
lessened because some fool does not praise him. All the
detraction becomes a joke to him. But it seems a sin to me
to go on about these shameful people. The poetry of
the most famous singers will resound loudly through the ages
if read by intelligent descendants."

Wait, O Muse! You have already strayed from the path.
Better to shorten such ravings sooner, for you have inopport-
unely flown into moralization. There is enough work remaining for you yet. Tell me, what next did the messenger do? I
am afraid lest he say something foolish and be subjected to
the wrath of Zeus. You are entirely indiscreet, but he is a
real scamp.

Hermes did not wish now to delay further, and after shaking his wings flew straight to Ceres. Cutting all the moisture
of the air with his wings, he finally came upon her. This
goddess also was not passing her days in idleness, but occupied herself pretty much with her home. After rising with the
sun, she worked on the threshing floor with a pine thresher,
beneath which sheaves of wheat sighed. When he caught sight
of her, the messenger directed his steps in her direction and
then made known the cause of his mission. Bowing, he then
took leave of her and flew straight from her to the police.
Turning himself into a crow, he alighted on the roof, not
knowing how to penetrate it, for there was a multitude of
guards around and if he got into a fight with them, they could

[35] The entire passage that follows is an attack on the poet
Petrov.

easily have defeated him with a club and put him away like some mischievous child.

Just as an eagle faint with hunger flies all around roasting meat lying on the coals of Mordvinian fires, so flew Hermes trembling all over with excitement and thinking that if he did not take the coachman away as booty then Zeus would surely torture him like a devil.[36] He said, "I would rather fall into the hands of the police than have to suffer at the hands of Zeus. And to tell the truth, lest either happen, I shall get you, my dear coachman." He did not continue these empty words longer. He began to howl like a ball shot from a cannon. He lowered himself and shook his wings three times. Then he assumed his earlier guise. He put his wings beneath his nose like a black moustache, changed his clothes into a corporal's collar and his staff into the likeness of a long sword. And so our Hermes, full of courage, boldly entered the police station as a messenger, a corporal, and a thief all in the same person.

End of the First Canto

Canto the Second

Thus Hermes now resembled a corporal, capable of deceiving anyone anywhere. Not only a gypsy or a crafty Greek, but even a Frenchman would never have been able to cheat him. He was so clever and enterprising, the Jews themselves could not have done better.

When the evening light dimmed and desert and sea were covered with darkness, ruffians ceased noising about the streets and twinkling stars began shining in the sky. Our messenger then opened the prison doors and entered, not as a thief, but as a soldier. Although the hinges on the doors began creaking, the guards were snoring, their mouths agape. Nevertheless, so as not to awaken them, Hermes began proceeding quietly down the staircase to the jail, or rather to sneak in, if one may say that in Russian. Unfortunately, the steps on the staircase were narrow, and this nimble god stumbled, flew down, fell, and landed with a thud. To put it simply, he skidded on his behind, which put a finish to the whole Shrovetide week. And if it had not been Hermes, but really a corporal, he certainly would have hurt his back and

---

[36] A parody of part of Petrov's ode *To a Carousel*.

would have caused no little damage to his spine. A soldier
cannot get along without his coat-of-arms or insignia, to put
it simply; no less would he be able to get along with broken
ribs. But as a deity Hermes did not feel any pain. He slid
harmlessly into the prison depths where boredom, extending
its terrible power, had heralded an attack on all the prisoners.
Exhaustion and tears could be seen on all sides, and all the
prisoners were in stocks and irons. The residents were also
clearly deprived of all necessities. They had only water to
drink and bread to eat. No purple couches stood there. On
the walls hung mats and matting; tattered rags were their
usual dress. And the only smell there was a foul stench.
Throughout this awful and dull establishment, no steward
was anywhere to be seen. The inmates neither slept peacefully
nor ate sweetly. They all just seemed to be staring into empty
space. Deprived of their freedom they vainly lost themselves
in groaning, but only the frightful vaults echoed their groans.
Their tears, their words reached no one. This sight was
dreadful even to Hermes. He then espied a collection of all
sorts of drunks, but they all resembled one another. Nevertheless, even the darkness of the night could not conceal the
coachman's ruddy features. The blood excited by hops fer-
mented inside him and came to the surface just as bright as a
cranberry.

It was by these signs that Hermes recognized Elisei. He
went up to him quietly on his tiptoes. He approached him
lying unconscious and saw alongside him a young woman who
also had a strong liking for drink. Knowing that she was to
be without drink for seven weeks, that very day she had
satisfied her hunger and had anticipated Lent in advance. She
was without any defense at the time, for her robe, or to say
it more explicitly, her thin jacket,[37] was completely undone
on her.

Fulfilling the will of him who sent him, Hermes then tried
to drag the coachman away from there. He pushed and
shoved the sleeping fellow on all sides. But even his blows
failed to rouse the drunk. Elisei was sleeping as heroes in days
of yore slept. There was no other way to rouse them from
their slumber than to pass a cudgel along their sides.

---

[37] *Telogreia*, in Russian; a jacket or "comforter," usually sleeveless, worn by women in Old Russia.

O you renowned creators of *Venetian, Peter of the Golden Keys, Bova*, and *Iaroslan*, your warriors always slept so soundly that not even a fist could wake them up. So strong were they that they could even throw beyond a cloud an iron club more than fifty poods in weight. Now I believe that you never lied about them, since such a man was found here whom Hermes could not force to rise. He shoved him, pinched him, beat him, but he still could not wake him up.

When Hermes found that he was not able to rouse Elisei, he seized on the idea of exchanging his clothes with those of the young woman. So he took the clothes of both of them, dressed the young woman in the coachman's coat and the coachman in the woman's outfit. Hermes was satisfied and pleased with this scheme, since with all his beating before he had not been able to awaken Elisei. In this new dress Elisei no longer looked like himself, and all traces of Hermes's theft were concealed.

The coachman had no moustache, the coachman had no beard, and in a word, it was impossible to regard this as fakery, for Elisei looked like a young girl. Then Hermes revealed all his talent: he bound Elisei's head with a kerchief and put the snoring fellow on his lap. This time the door was no longer necessary. Hermes, like a diety now, did as he pleased. In a minute he flew to a window, soared up, and sped away. Neither fetters nor locks held him back. And is it possible to restrain such thieves before whom guards and locks are nothing? After all, the Hellenic gods are not our peasants!

Where the Black River joins the Fontanka and both flow as an estuary into the mouth of the Neva, at the very point on confluence of these rivers, where the Kalinkin forest grows, stood a huge house. The name of the house was derived from the forest and was therefore called the Kalinkin house. All the immoral women were put in it for their lustfulness. The rooms there contained their handicrafts: some of them turned flax into thread; others wove lace from the thread; some knitted purses and gloves. Thus did all of them keep occupied, putting their hands to good work. In a word, the place was a miniature Paris. Each girl was an angel in the flesh. That is why the house was always kept bolted.

Night was still stretching its curtain across the sky; dawn had not yet opened to Phoebus the gates of the world and he was still reposing on the arm of his beloved on a soft mattress when Hermes appeared with his load. The load was the eighteen-year-old Elisei, or perhaps he had already lived longer in the world. Hermes carried him and carefully put him in the residence of the girls who were good out of necessity and perhaps not even so bad as people thought. It is somewhat difficult to judge the conscience from the outside. One would be free, for example, to condemn minor officials for being all very greedy for money. They really all should not be accused of the same thing, since all of them do not tax you in money. Some of them take oats and sugar for their troubles; others clothes, wine, and vegetables, furs, and all sorts of other things. Well, let us surrender these foolishnesses to oblivion and return our story to its hero.

Even the beauties themselves did not know that a coachman was in their midst, like a wolf among sheep, but he was just covered in sheep's clothing. Doves, it was not a sheep lying among you, but a ram! When the rosy dawn came up, the directress of the girls woke them up, announcing that it was time for them to leave their beds. She then distributed the work among them. Now was not the time for the beauties' games. From hand to hand passed clews, hanks, and bobbins. Each one took her own handwork, and the labor suddenly descended upon them like a storm. Because of the noise going on, Elisei awoke, but how he found himself among these girls, even though you tortured him, he himself would not have known. Is it not a dream, he thought, that is appearing now before my eyes? And suddenly thought cleared his eyes and he looked like a madman in every direction. Wherever he looked he saw wonders; wherever he looked he saw terror and said to himself in his hangover: "What sly devil brought me here? Or was it that I was not intoxicated with vodka, but with bane, which is why I am having such terrible dreams now? Of course this must be the work of Satan." So did Elisei, coming out of his drunk, meditate about the matter, and while he himself was guilty he reproached the devil.

But finally he himself was able to see this frightful dream clearly. Now, he thought to himself, now I understand that I am in some house, but in whose, I do not know. The beauties all around him he took to be nuns, and the directress in his mind he called Mother Superior. But he did not dare enter into conversation with her. He could only direct languid

*An illustration accompanying the plan of St. Petersburg pub-
lished by the Russian Imperial Academy of Sciences in 1753.
It shows the Fontanka River and, at bottom center, the
Kalinkin Bridge—that part of the city in which some of the
action of Vasilii Maikov's mock-epic poem* Elisei *takes place.*

glances at her. Through these he communicated his fear to the Mother Superior. Then he began to think differently of his situation. This holy mother already fathomed that this girl did not have girlish features and also indicated to him by her glances that there was no little danger for him here. O wonder! Just when he thought that his end was at hand, fortune bent its knees before him and in fact pulled him onto its back. The directress became his trustworthy shield. She was a wall to him, I shall now say boldly, because Cupid himself took a hand in the matter. Unexpectedly, he pierced her heart with his arrow and kindled in her a raging fire. She now wanted to know about everything that had befallen Elisei, and desired to tell him all about herself in private. She took his hand in hers and led him into her own little room. Then, when she was all alone with him, she said: "In this world I have learned sufficiently how to distinguish the real things from the false, and so you should not keep silent before me. Tell me the truth: Who are you and where do you come from?" Now Elisei no longer continued to conceal his true identity.

"O Mother," he cried out, "although I am beardless, mind, I am a resident of Iamskaia. For five years now I have been fulfilling the responsibility of coachman; for five years now I have been driving horses with a knout. I have ridden on fast ones; I have ridden on tired ones; I have ridden on meek ones; I have ridden on bold ones. In short, the Isabella-colored, the bay, the dun, the chestnut, the light-red with whitish mane and tail, and the raven-black—for me it's the same ride on all of them, just so long as I've my knout, just so long as they're all bridled.

"I lived in Petersburg without my own carriage house. I came there to live from Zimogor'e, from whence I had been driven to stand station because I couldn't hire another coachman in my place. . . . But now let me tell you about the most dreadful and bloody battle we had with the Valdaians. Forgive these tears flowing from my eyes. They are my way of proclaiming to you the grief I feel now when I recollect my misfortune: I lost my mother, my brother, and my wife.

"We had already sowed a whole field in barley, and after these labors we and all the cattle were resting. The sown grain had already grown half an inch, and the time had come for us to cut the hay. Our meadow, as all know, bordered on that of the Valdaians. No one could tell them apart except a surveyor. The strongest hand was the one that took the grass from them. So they were always a source of trouble between us. In fact, they were the whole cause of our dreadful battle!

"The day had already come, and we went into the meadow. We took along milk, eggs, and curds and loaded ourselves up with kvas,[38] beets, pancakes, coarse bread, drinks, and groat cakes. Hardly had we appeared with this paraphernalia, when we caught sight of our misfortune ahead of us. The proud Valdaians were standing there with arms. We shuddered, and then all of us ran away like rabbits. We ran and looked for similar weapons: poles, stakes, staffs, splinters, and clubs. We tried to outdo one another in taking sticks; we tried to outdo one another in preparing for the fight.

"The chief of our Iamskaia district, foreseeing terrible consequences, mounted his horse and gathered the lot of us together. Once he had assembled us, he took a pen, then started soiling paper with it. Although he was not a Frenchman or a Greek either, but a Russian, he was a government official and was dressed in a brown uniform. God keep a scrivener from becoming a military commander! After taking out his pen, he began to write down the names, when our backs were already feeling pain from the descent of a hail of stones upon us. Is it possible that Pallas was by this scribbler's side? He was writing names while the Valdaians were beating us. Old women in the huts were lamenting to heaven. Small children, all the girls, women, and chickens hid themselves beneath stoves and crawled into kennels. Seeing that there was to be no end to his writing, we ceased paying heed to the scrivener.

"Like whirlwinds we descended from all sides and pressing forward in a mass, hastened to battle! They could hold us back no more than wattle water, and the only salvation for the Valdaians was flight. However, they stood stubbornly against us and nimbly wielded their wooden arms against us. We were unable to tear apart the order of their ranks. From both sides flew stones and mud—the military contrivances of men in rage. We spattered and struck each other mercilessly. But our men stood their ground like a strong wall. Forgive me for mentioning names now that should not be introduced here except that without them we would not have

[38] A popular Russian beverage made of bread and malt.

carried off the victory. Even if our scrivener had been wiser
still, he would not have broken that wall with his own head
which we scarcely tore apart with pickets.

"We had already been striking each other painfully with
stones when our Stëpka, a dreadfully mischievous fellow,
insignificant in all respects, but a strong little peasant, was
the first to tear into the battle in a fury. He broke into a thick
crowd of Valdaians and began beating on all sides with his
club. A shout rose up among them, but Stëpka was carrying
on with them like a butcher. Then his nephew, taking up a
club, darted, became frightened, and turned his back on the
enemy, whereupon a frisky Valdaian hopped upon it and was
on top of our hero. In the very midst of the bloody fray he
jumped upon our hero's shoulders and there boasted to the
entire crowd that he had begun with a battle but had ended
with leapfrog. Such a joke ended poorly for him, however, for
the Valdaian had not yet succeeded in thanking us for the
ride when Stëpka's nephew grabbed him by the sash and so
hurled this hero on the ground that he broke his nose and
made it so flat that from this time on he always puts a patch
on it. Just then we all noticed in the distance a rider all
covered with dust. It was the proud leader of the Valdaians
himself. This beast was a manager similar to our own. Raging
against us, a fire burning inside him, he was galloping on his
horse in the direction of our hero. Everyone thought that they
would end the general battle by a terrible duel between the
two of them. All looked, all stood rooted to the spot, and fear
seized the lot of us. The heroes already had drawn close to
each other on their horses. But suddenly their thoughts
changed completely. They did not fight, after all, but only
exchanged curses, leaving us alone to finish the fight. Their
horses took them back to their homes.

"In the meantime, if you wish to know it, the sun shone
so that it was time for us to eat. And if the damned battle had
not taken place, I might have already downed perhaps two or
three bites by then. But in the circumstances in which our
lives were at the time, neither cabbage soup nor gruel entered
my mind.

"When the horses had carried away the commanders, we
then conducted a real war. All order disappeared among us,
and at the same time there was suddenly no difference any
more between the bigger and the smaller. We were all mixed
up and we all became equal. The pants and breeches burst

on many there. Dust rose in a column and hovered overhead like a cloud. Screeching, clattering, noise, and shouting resounded on all sides. I saw all kinds of beatings there. One dealt his adversary a blow with a club; another threw down his enemy, after tripping him, and held a log raised above his back. But suddenly having been knocked down by a club, he himself lay on the ground and was peppering his conqueror with curses. Others were seizing each other by the temples. They were already pressing each other, ruffling each other, and tearing each other to shreds. Even if a shaven Tatar had jumped in among us, I think he too would have received a good pummeling. O you beards! You schismatic attire! Here you suffered the greatest tyranny of all: no sooner does someone give someone else a poke in the belly than they go at each other's beards and in a while not a tuft is left. And so we fought long with the Valdaians, not letting up the exchange of blows in order to determine who would carry away the victory. But finally we yielded to their agility and unwillingly turned our backs on our rivals. We ran through the dale—O dale, lamentable dale! We saw all the women with their hems between their teeth. They were all running about and making different kinds of movements. But it is not nice for me to tell you about this. I shall just say that we saw many of their bodies. Suddenly my brother swooped down to our aid like a hawk. He mixed up the battle like home-brewed beer in a vat. Don't accuse me of lying for what I'll tell you about my brother: holding a heavy club in his hands, he bore terror with it to all our enemies. Wherever he passed with it, there a street opened up, and wherever he turned about, there stood a square. Close to an hour had he been vanquishing the Valdaians, and each of them was running away from him, when suddenly a rival appeared against him. Suddenly my brother's exploit was completely stopped here. This Valdaian suddenly hung upon his neck and bit off my brother's right ear. And thus my brother, beloved Iliukha, who had come to the battle with both his ears, left with just one of them. He dragged himself along like a stuck pig, eaten away, broken up and, worse, disgraced. Think of what a loss has befallen me! He lost an ear, but I lost a brother! From then on I no longer recognize him as a brother. Don't think that I have made this speech for nothing. When he still had both his ears he was moved by the words of unfortunate people. But now this door is completely locked and he hears only one thing, when someone says, 'Here!' But the little word 'Give!' he no longer understands and with his left ear no longer accepts anyone's requests. You'll find treasure in an empty well quicker than I need a brother like that.

"After the loss of such a zealot we were bereft of all means of victory. The Valdaians took true supremacy over us. They struck us down, beat us, pressed in on us, and drove all of us from the field. We should have completely succumbed that day had not Stëpka then saved us from misfortune. Like lightning he suddenly rushed to us from behind and stopped us who were already in full flight. 'Stop, fellows,' he began to cry, 'stop! Collect yourselves together and form a new array.' Everything changed, O happiest of hours! At Stëpka's voice crowds of people began to gather. They gathered, ran, thrust down their adversaries, and snatched from them the victory that had been in their hands. They rushed together, collided with one another, straightened out their disorder, and a fight hotter than before was begun again. We were already driving the enemy to their own village. We were taking their sticks and cudgels from them, and this of course would have been the end of the battle if a monk had not ridden out to their help. This new Valaam was urging on his beast and was beating it with a stick for its laziness. But for all his beating of the little horse it didn't move a step ahead. Somehow he reached the top of a hill. There he tried to frighten us. From out of his holy mouth he began to loose curses upon us. But neither these nor wooden arms restrained us. We flew at our enemies and did with them as we pleased. When he saw our stubbornness, this worthy man descended from his horse and showed the agility of his legs. This was greater than when he rode out to us. He showed us his backside and ran home.

"The veil of dark night had already appeared. Nobody had the strength left to fight anymore, and so we all left the battle, having defeated the Valdaians. And I returned home alive but hungry."

End of the Second Canto

Canto the Third

"Everything had already grown quiet and night had extended its veil across all the forest nearest us. It covered all the earth and us together with it. There came the hour of tranquillity desired by everyone. We rested, the Valdaians rested; on the battlefield only hares wandered and shepherds were playing their small horns. At home only I and the cocks who were shouting their song to an audience of hens were not asleep. And the hens were answering the cocks the way hens do. As soon as I went into the house, I found my wife without braids and my mother suffering an attack of diarrhea from fear. She had remained in the hut, beside herself, and kept gaping like a jackdaw from the stove to the chimney, enumerating all the saints she could remember so that they should protect us in battle and return me and Iliukha home in one piece. But it did not happen as she wished. They bit off the ear of one of her sons, and a fate worse than this befell her. No sooner had I entered the house than I got terribly frightened seeing my mother all wrapped up. When she saw me she cried, 'Forgive me, forgive me, my child, I am leaving this world.' While she was saying this, tears were flowing from her eyes. Then in came my brother bloodied from war. Our mother's death and the wailing of our wives moved our hearts to grief. We strengthened ourselves, but oh! We too began howling like women. The soul had already left my mother's old body, and a body without a soul isn't worth a penny even though my mother was still not a very old lady. I was crying, my brother was crying, but he already had one ear less and it was difficult to determine whether his grief was for the old woman or the loss of one of his ears. Our loss seemed irreparable to us, and besides a dead old woman in the house was unpleasant. The next morning we paid her our last respects. We ordered her taken out of the house as soon as possible. She was covered over completely with a shroud in a pine wood coffin and surrendered to the earth's womb with singing. That is how my final grief came to an end. Later I was sent to the station here, about which I already told you before. But how I come to see myself now dressed in the clothes of a girl I myself don't know, and how I was brought to this house here, into the midst of pretty girls, for Christ's sake, I just don't know. . . ."

Here the directress interrupted him and ordered him as follows: "If you want to be gay and happy here, my boy, then you should not be talkative. Silence is dearer than anything else on earth. You shall have one couch with me, or to put it simply, one bed in which you will spend your nights with me.

But so that we can keep this to ourselves without any blundering, take a little needle here, sit yourself down, and begin sewing blouses."

He answered her: "O Mother! I'll tell you straight out that when it comes to sewing I'm no master. I can only unstitch, but if you have enough of this kind of work just give it to me and don't worry. I'll take care of everything without dallying. I'll unstitch at least a dozen blouses in a wink!" She saw then that the fellow was clever. She stayed a while longer with him alone, then left him in her little room. She went out and locked Elisei in alone, not letting a single girl in the house know anything about it. And so he remained now in this most pleasant prison.

Zeus, in the meantime, had slept off his drunkenness and was drinking only tea with Juno when the messenger entered the godly chambers and announced that all the gods were already sitting in assembly. Then Zeus, in order not to lose any time in managing things, put his crown on his head and his royal robe over his shoulders, and taking the great Juno by the hand put a similar crown on her head. He had already entered the hall where the gods were assembled when they all rose from their places as soon as they saw him and this way showed their esteem of Zeus. When they had seated themselves again, Ceres was ordered to speak. She approached Zeus respectfully and began her plea before him thus:

"O great god! Zeus, giver of all blessings, my mentor, my father, and wise teacher! You know that for the most important necessities I taught the earth-dwellers to sow grain. I was successful in this, I saw their progress when they plowed wheat without any obstacles. But Bacchus carried away a victory over me when he taught them how to make spirits out of grain. All mortals have now become addicted to drunkenness, and only brawling has resulted from it. Almost all the earth has grown over with sloe. The peasants run away from their trade into the cities and find themselves in such great confusion that almost all of them peddle strawberries like old hags while each of them could have been plowing the earth. Now you judge this for yourself, great god!" All the gods began now to argue among themselves, but Zeus ordered them immediately to be silent. He next commanded Bacchus to answer the charges brought against him without delay if he had anything of which he could find Ceres guilty.

Bacchus then began to speak in his own defense: "O, gods! Is this my retribution now, that I must stand here together with Ceres in this assembly? That I, a fine fellow, must be in court together with a hag! Or is it that you hold me responsible for idleness because I introduced spiritual pleasure to the earth? When a person lives unhappily in it, he is happy if he can just have a little wine to drink. When an unhappy man drinks down a glass he forgets all his grief with the glass. Even a warrior who has a little vodka with him goes more boldly into battle after taking a few swallows. The prisoner in chains cries tears of happiness after quaffing some wine. But why am I speaking about such trifles? Ask the religious and the secular about it. Asks clerks, ask scriveners, ask the blind, ask the seeing. I think that they will all answer you the same thing: that for mortals the best gift on earth is wine. Wine invigorates the heart, strengthens the stomach and, in a word, brings cheer to all people. All feasts would not be gay to them, all celebrations would be deprived of their amusement, if mortals did not know this gift. The only people who do not drink wine are the Turks and Tatars, and just ask them if they are not bored because of it." He ended his address with these last words, fell into silence, and had no desire later to see the light.

Zeus then said to him: "Hear the answer that I shall now give you regarding this matter." And he loosed from his lips a honey-flowing river that had no equal in floweriness:

"Listen to me, you, Bacchus, and you, Ceres. To you, Ceres, drink is repugnant; to you, Bacchus, the tax farmers are repugnant. But you judge as private deities, while I judge everything impartially and justly. I think you are surprised that a Moslem is jealous of his wives, and a Jew, Frenchman, and Greek given over easily to deceit; that a Spaniard is proud, that the Swedes are poor, and that the Russians are their neighbors; that the Dutchman is coarse, the Englishman loyal and firm, the German candid, the Indian merciful, and the Negroes possessed of wild beasts' hearts; that the Italians are all crafty and impertinent, the Pole is not the master of his own words, and that not a single Gypsy ever tells the truth. You are surprised that I have made all of them different in their customs? Believe me, my intentions were well thought out in this matter. I leveled Troy in order to raise Rome, and you want to know the end of my intentions! I shall act in

such a way that the both of you will be in agreement, and
that from this day on you will not be harmful to each other.
Sometime I shall raise Wisdom to the throne. She will create
a most useful law that will put an end to treachery in the
farming of taxes, and her reign will be satisfied with this.
The tax farmer will not be able any longer to obstruct the
plowman, the plowman will enrich himself, and all will be
happy with their lot. Now you no longer quarrel among
yourselves." With these words Zeus pacified the two of them
and restored harmony between his son and Ceres.

As Zeus was telling the gods what he had to, the sun,
meanwhile, was entering his home where his wife was preparing the bed on which he relaxed after his labors. So also was
the directress of the honest women preparing herself for the
night's lodging with Elisei. But in order to present her wares
to the young man in the best light, she rubbed herself with
some homemade wine, then with a hand skilled by various
enterprises she placed a cap atop her hairpiece. To increase
her charms, she loosed around her shoulders her curly hair,
which was the color of bitter oranges. She used as much
powder as rouge, and so as to excite her lover to pleasures
determined to dress herself up a little better. She thought of
spending the entire night in peace, but here is the misfortune
that befell her.

The commander of the local guard put on his sword and
uniform and decided to make a sudden patrol of all the
rooms in the Kalinkin house in order to inspect the girls with
his own eyes, for in this matter he trusted no one, not even
his sergeant.

He was some forty years old, or perhaps more, had served
for twenty years, and all the time in the field. A wrinkled
forehead and knitted brows betrayed an emotion of love that
had already turned cold. Although he had once studied in this
school, he had by now so exhausted himself in military
formations that he completely forgot the science of love and,
in a word, was more of a soldier than a dandy. But standing
guard over all these girls, he felt in himself, he felt . . . well,
what? What anguish the old fellow fell into! This man felt
in himself the passion of love. That he became inflamed by
itself would be nothing, but with whom was he in love? Oh,
horrors! He had become captivated with the directress herself.
Suddenly the hour of capriciousness had blown his way,

although his better judgment told him on more than a single occasion: "At twenty a man is attractive to pretty girls. At thirty perhaps he can still be useful for them. But whoever has already passed his fortieth year is nowhere called to dinner. Be sufficed with your family: eat, drink, live, show off, but from now on don't go around offering your amours to women. Your time to love has already passed!" Thus did his own judgment speak to him then, but he did not accept such sound advice. He determined to burst into the directress's room, and declared to himself: "No matter what, I'll spend the whole night with her alone. But what if she denies me the favor of coming to lie down with me in her bed? Well, I still won't be ruining myself if I tell her I love her. And if she does not wish to squabble with me, will she argue about such a trifle?" The commander deliberated with himself in this manner and anticipated his success. With such an unclean thought in his mind he came to the room in which the grandmother and her grandson were in bed. She had arrived there a half an hour before him and found Elisei asleep and snoring. With trembling hand, she shoved him gently to awaken him and then called him softly by name, touching him the while: "Wake up, Elisei, wake up, my darling!" Awaking, Elisei saw the holy mother, moved over, and made room for her on the bed.

But no sooner had he risen to the height of bliss, than the formidable commander appeared at the door and wished to enter. With a cane he pushed and opened the door wide. Elisei was just then fainting on the summit of pleasure, but he jumped from it like a madman at the commander's entry. The commander concluded the worst and began to interrogate Elisei most severely: "Where did you come from, girl, dressed so poorly? And why is it that I do not have you in my register? Tell me, darling, where are you from?" Elisei at this point did not know what to answer, although there was neither a lock nor a stamp on his mouth. Casting his eyes down, however, he remained silent while the commander raged and shouted. The directress saved herself from trouble by presenting herself courteously to this hero so that he should not get angry with her in vain. She explained to him that he saw before him a niece of hers who that very day had come on a visit, but apprehensive of the evil of malicious people, she did not dare to leave for home so late lest she fall victim to violence. And besides, what was he doing coming to her at so late an hour? With such tricks she sought to draw him off the track. But the commander was not taken in by her deceitful words; he was sure what she told him was nothing but lies. He searched through all the girl's pockets to see if she was guilty of anything, but he did not even find a tick and there was thus no evidence of any theft. Nevertheless, he ordered her taken away under guard.

Can the mind fathom this? In a single day Elisei again fell into prison. And this time he would not have been able to escape punishment if Bacchus had not felt well disposed toward him. Bacchus took the matter up with Zeus; Zeus appointed Hermes again with the commission of freeing him from his bonds.

Hermes at once flew down to him as though borne by the wind. This time, however, Hermes was dressed as a fop. High headpiece, touched-up temples—he had already removed the corporal's moustache he had worn earlier, and was also no longer dressed in a collett. Hermes with a walking stick, my Hermes with a lorgnette through which he looked at girls, swaggering.

When he came upon the coachman, Hermes put a little hat upon him. And this little hat had a wonderful power: whatever head it was placed upon, whoever used it as a covering, disappeared and became invisible. And so, covered with this covering, Elisei proceeded a second time to the superior's room and passed the entire night with her in pleasures. In the meantime the ninth hour of the morning had arrived when the angered lover woke up and noticed the absence of the girl he had arrested the previous night. Anger and a desire for vengeance then shone in his eyes. He issued an order for her to be brought to him without delay, but the sentries did not succeed in finding her and they considered the would-be girl escaped. The sergeant ran to his chief, quaking at the thought of telling him the terrible news. Nevertheless, he finally reported her flight. The stern commander requested his sword and coat. No sooner had he run out, dressing himself on the way, than he at once shouted, "To arms!" and ordered a muster struck. "Who let the girl loose? During whose hours on duty did it happen?" He shouted and poked each man in the moustaches and snout. However, no matter how much he tortured someone, not one of his subordinates revealed who freed the girl and where she had disappeared. Although the girl till then had not left the house, they thought that some spiteful devil concealed her on himself and took her away with him. And so the entire uproar there ended in this battle: the sergeant answered for all with his back, although he himself was not in the slightest guilty for what had transpired. Perhaps his only sin was the fact that he happened to be a sergeant.

Elisei in the meantime was having a merry time and till then had not removed the cap from his head. Under this marvelous tent he was invisible to all. From time to time he left the mansion, walked about, drank and ate, spent the night with his Mother Superior, and the commander neither saw nor heard him.

But finally he grew tired of this life, although he was completely satisfied with the food and everything else. Bacchus, however, had implanted in him the desire to leave and to do the work that had been assigned him, and that was to scold the tax farmers a little. And Elisei was the master to carry this out.

During the unfortunate old woman's sleep one night, Elisei left her bed and pillow, left even his own pants and waistcoat,[39] left her in sleep, and went on his way.

But hardly did the directress rise the next morning, yawn, and turn to the other side of the bed, on which her beloved Elisei had been used to reposing, when his traces had already grown cold; her lover had run away. When she grasped his pillow with her hand she found the pillow cold. Just as Theseus had left Ariadne, and Aeneas changed mistresses,[40] so did Elisei do the same thing with his old woman.

After collecting the last of her strength, after summoning all the power of her spirit, the unfortunate old woman at first

---

[39] *Kamzol*, in Russian. Actually, a sleeveless underjacket, cut like a waistcoat, worn by peasants.

[40] Theseus, in Greek legend, was the principal hero of Attica, son of Aegeus and King of Athens. His most famous exploit was the slaying of the Minotaur. Ariadne, in Greek legend, was the daughter of King Minos, who gave Theseus the thread that enabled him to find his way out of the Minotaur's lair. Theseus took Ariadne with him, but later deserted her.

Aeneas, in Greek and Roman legend, was a Trojan, son of Anchises and Venus, and the hero of Virgil's *Aeneid*.

thought that Elisei was just playing a little joke on her and
that he really had not left the room. She got out of the bed
and went roaring about all the corners like a madman, looking
for him with her hands behind chairs and beneath tables, but
no matter how she carried on she did not find Elisei. She fell
onto the bed and shouted: "Oh, my darling! Where, Elisei,
where did you disappear? And where did you learn to deceive
people so that you exceed even me in that? Where, Elisei,
where, my darling, did you go? Where did you hide yourself
and where are you staying? Or are you living with some
unworthy woman who was captivated by your tender glance?"
In the meantime the old woman had to go outside. With
trembling hand she took the washbasin and was just about
to fulfill her necessity when she caught sight of Elisei's pants
and waistcoat on the floor.

"Now," she began to shout, "do I sense how bad you are!
You increased my anxiety and woe no little; why did you
leave your pants and waistcoat here except to have me
exposed? Didn't Satan himself put you up to this! Well, if
the commander comes by here on inspection, you won't conceal such junk from his sight if he wishes to notice it. And
then what explanation will I be able to give him? Doesn't
clear evidence indict me? No matter how you think about it,
my distress is great!" When she was bemoaning this in her
grief, just see—the commander was already entering her
room. She shook all over at the sight of him and, suddenly
struck dumb, did not succeed in snatching the pants and
waistcoat. She just jumped onto the bed, and when the commander came in the pants and waistcoat leaped to his eyes.
He then approached the bed like a madman. He saw the
waistcoat on the floor in plain view and also the pants lying
there. "O heavens!" he began to shout, "there are peasants
in the house here!" He pressed her closely on the matter,
shouting: "Are they living here so honestly, my pigeon? What
kind of a uniform is that you have there? Was a commander
stationed here over you just so that you could fondle him with
words—and then at night let strange people in to spend the
night with you? I don't want such a disgrace on myself. I'll
tame you first with the whip." She shook her little tail back
and forth, went up to him, and began to pet him. My commander now withered before her; he grew quiet and settled
like grain kvas. Although he was angry enough to give her a

whipping, he and the old lady, however, finally made peace with each other. There was neither hymen nor love between them, nor was there a flame in their cold blood. But they had no great need for this since it was no longer winter, but summer. They made their peace between themselves, and the old-timers gave each other pleasure without ardor. Her love wound had already begun to heal when from a tyrant her commander became a friend. Although not many days had passed since Aeneas had taken leave of this Dido,[41] she did not moan as her predecessor had, and remembered Elisei with less grief. She no longer wanted to hear any more about him and burned his pants and waistcoat in the stove when she had it heated up to bake pastries. In this respect she was more like Dido.[42]

End of the Third Canto

Canto the Fourth

Phoebus had already passed the Gemini across the Zodiac when my Elisei ran away from the old lady. Although rare are those of such low species that they are given the chance to feast their eyes on the beauty of fair nature, since Elisei had been visiting in this miniature Paris he began thinking and judging differently. He knew already, for example, that on this earth there are love affairs, that only idiots are constant in their love. He knew how one had to play up to coquettes. He knew how one had to swear and lie to them. If he would ever have visited the great Paris, he of course would have been closer still to idiocy. But is it not silly to be in Paris itself just in order to yawn at such trifles, and just to observe the fashions of those living in it, not caring to see their laws and revenues, to discover what France is abundant in, what it is poor in, and whether it would be able to endure without other states? Like its trades, so its sciences. But dandies travel there not for the sake of boredom, and if one is to pass a pleasant time there one must make the rounds of the coffee-

---

[41] Dido, in Roman legend, was a Tyrian princess who founded Carthage, which she ruled over as queen. In Virgil's *Aeneid*, Dido greets Aeneas when he comes to Carthage after the fall of Troy. She falls in love with him, and kills herself when he leaves.
[42] Probably an allusion to Dido's killing herself by throwing herself onto a burning pyre.

houses, find out on what days entertainments are held in them, what kind of and when coats are put on, what kind of hairpieces are worn, how the temples are worn, what kind of shoes, looking-glasses, stockings, cuffs, and buckles are in style, so that upon leaving there one will know how to dress himself correctly and, lest one be judged by those like one's self, know how to explain one's shameless lust, twist about, and jabber according to the very latest fashion, the only kind that exists, in fact, in a flighty nation. Our coachman similarly sharpened his mind with such things. With the affected he began to speak in an affected manner. If a woman was dazzled by some flirt, Elisei would say, "She was hooked by him."[43] And if he himself began chasing after someone, he would babble a multitude of affected words. If they are not very appropriate here, then it is only because they are too political. No matter what anyone thought about him now, he was already a learned parrot.

The coachman had already delighted his spirit with the beauties of spring. He went to Petersburg, not along the streets, but through woods in which many mushrooms were then growing. He would have gathered at least ten boxes of them, but he did not have with him at the time even a small little basket because he ran away from the old lady of Kalin house so fast that he left behind even his own clothes. So he went along, gladdening his sight with nature. The sun was then already turning from midday and sent down to earth only mild rays. Thus it no longer badly burned the coachman. Waters as clear as clean glass, coiling between green bushes, or elsewhere running together into a single brook, flowed slumberingly along irradiated banks and reflected the trees standing above them. The rose and the narcissus also saw themselves in them. The pipes of shepherds could be heard everywhere guarding the flocks of sheep from wild animals. The pleasant nightingale was also heard there, the nightingale who, having become the prisoner of the beautiful Venus, chirped of love in many different ways. Here there was no tapping of woodpeckers' beaks and there were also no eagle-owls and hoot owls. It seemed that all nature was reposing. Only a single turtledove was sighing for her loved one, whom she had just lost that very day. When Elisei saw her he said:

[43] "Ona im zatsepilas'," in the original.

"This is the way, I think, my wife remembers me now and like a turtledove moans because of me. Although she is without braids now, she is still dear to me." Such a thought did this bird give birth to in him. He lay down on a bank beneath green boughs, wishing in this way to give rest to his wearied members. So he lay down and was soon asleep. But he started when he was alarmed by a feminine shout. Through a tangle of bushes he saw a bloodstained woman running toward him. She was a fair beauty: her unbuttoned bosom and disheveled hair foretold her distress. The coachman, however, did not have long to think about this, for he saw two men running after her and one of them was already close enough to touch her clothing. The other one was shouting: "Stop! You won't get away from us and you'll be our victim today for sure!" Stirred to anger, Elisei then stood as light as a horse and as strong as a lion. He got up and putting on the cap that made him invisible fell upon them. He flew at them just as an eagle does at a bird, and then landed such a blow on the one who was causing the trouble that he felt alternately hot and cold all over. The other one he gave such a poke in the stomach with his knee that he fell as though struck with a log. Then Elisei rained dozens of blows on him. Although he was not a doctor or even a veterinarian, nevertheless he gave them both a good bloodletting. He blackened the eyes, cheekbones, and brows of both of them. But as he was invisible to them, after all, it seemed to them, as he was pummeling them, that they were fighting among themselves. They grabbed hold of each other, pulled each other by the hair, beat each other's mugs, and poked each other's noses. Their cheeks, behinds, and temples got it good. Now they jumped apart suddenly; now they suddenly tore into each other again just like a pair of lively cocks scuffling. Thus these mischievous fellows fought each other. Their hair, coats, and belts trembled. And as for you, underclothing, I think there was slim hope even of your saving yourself. But finally it reached the point with the two of them that they would have torn I do not know what. Everything got it, and they beat each other so unmercifully that they were reeling about like a couple of drunks who were dead to the world. Then my coachman had no desire to tarry here any longer, and ran away nimbly from them with the woman! Oh, what a joy! When he caught his breath, the coachman found his wife in this woman. Today, coachman, your service has been rewarded. You saved a young woman and she proved to be your wife! Fate often saves innocence from distress and the good-doer takes supremacy over evil.

Thus the coachman finally found his wife. After taking off the cap that made him invisible, he kissed her. Then all her grief turned into happiness. Has not my husband, she thought, come to me from heaven? But he told her everything that had happened to him, and ordered her to do likewise. What power brought her here on this occasion and who were these thieves she was dragging after her?

She began to cry, sighed, and then said: "As soon as you left me to go to Petersburg, that is when the height of misfortune befell me. Your brother could not keep me in his home, and I was forced to run to you here. And by the time I dragged myself as far as Petersburg, my purse had completely worn out. I came to Iamskaia, but you were no longer in Iamskaia. Everyone thought that you had perished, my darling, and that I had remained a wretched widow. A brickyard became my shelter. I lived there with the workwomen of a German. And perhaps I might even have been happy there had his wife not been so peevish and, worst of all, jealous of him. But the master was like a needle to thread with me. Once in the evening when I had already lain down to sleep, he rose quietly from his wife's bed, came up to me, and began to kiss me in a lordly way. The wife fell asleep, and before you could shake a hand the bed was empty of the husband. The two of us were lying together when the wife got out of her bed and found the two of us together in the next hut. Just think, my husband, what was there for her to get jealous about just because her husband came to kiss me? But he did not suffer in the least for having tasted food from another plate. When his wife came in upon us he began to fondle her, and she flew into a rage and started pulling me around like a madman. She blackened my eyes and threw me out of the house in the middle of the night. I left, and misfortune followed after me. I was very much afraid of falling into the hands of the police. However, this woe did not escape me; I fell into the hands of the police and spent the night in jail. But then suddenly I was freed by a most wonderful occurrence. I do not know who it was who changed my clothes and put a coat on me. And so in the morning, after giving my back a good tanning with a stick, they let me out of their clutches—"

At this point Elisei interrupted her: "Oh, my little wife! I myself was in the police station that very night. You were let out dressed in the coat I had been wearing until then so that I might be able to get away dressed as a woman. But who it was that dressed me in your dress I have no idea, because I was very drunk. Later on I found myself in the Kalin house where I fasted out all of Lent."

At this, his wife again said to him: "When I was freed from the prison, I did not know where to take myself dressed in a man's clothing so I went off and spent the whole night in a public bath. Later I went to live in a secretary's house, to whom I am still thankful: the clerk's purse got fuller each day, and because of this my life went along happily. But suddenly misfortune descended on us when a decree was released about bribes that forbade officials to ruin people with them and that promised transgressors a very strict punishment. Then when he no longer found any means for profit, he went into retirement, satisfied with what he had from before. He left Petersburg with his booty because he did not trust himself very much. And today, after getting up almost with the dawn, I ran up against these two scoundrels. They fell right across my path, took one look at me, and then began making up to me. They wanted to show me a place to stay, but there is nothing more now I have to tell you. You saw for yourself what their evil intentions were toward me. I would not have been able to get away from them if you had not come along to save me. And for that I am grateful to you and the heavens."

Had Elisei not been a worldly sort of fellow, there would have been a lot of work here for the club with which he would have given his spouse a scolding. But since he was already familiar with all the transgressions of the world, he gave her a verbal rebuke and did not offend her with anything else. After they had explained things to each other and returned to harmony faster than anyone would have expected, he ordered her to go at once with her passport to Petersburg along the straightest road. He also ordered her to put up in the Iamskaia section so that he would be able to find her there in time. Then taking his leave of her, he remained in the small forest, where he thought of assuaging the envy and anxiety that had made him terribly upset because his wife's heart had not remained very faithful to him. Although he himself never forgave her, it was, however, the German he had on his mind all the time.

While my Elisei was thinking about the German, Bacchus sent Silenus down to him at just that time so that he could relieve Elisei's anxiety. He led him, therefore, straight to the home of the tax farmer who was the most annoying to him. Elisei was now thirsty for drinking and brawling. Silenus took him by the hand and led him straight to the home of a rich merchant who was the distributor of vodka for a certain district. Silenus led him to his house and then left him behind there, after telling him to do as he wanted, and he himself flew to his drunken child. My Elisei stood and thought about a spree and then began estimating the vodka in the merchant's cellar. The merchant was three girths wide and tall of stature. His whole life he ate horseradish, radishes, and garlic, and if he bought ruffs for a kopeck he thought that he was eating the clothes off his wife's back. The whole year with him was Lent. He was not miserly, only when it came to lending money out on interest. Exercising himself in this profitable hunting, he would stand for whole nights through praying for God not to hold him a sinner because of it, and in church he seemed more religious than anyone else. But all such scoundrels and hypocrites are sooner of the Christian faith than any other.

Cease roaring, woods and forests. Dear reader, bend your ears to me. Hearing the voice of my gay lyre, draw a little closer to Parnassus and listen to what I shall recite you now in song. By now I myself must look like the coachman. I would plainly be lying to you if I told you so shamelessly about the coachman that his whole rear was showing. His entire back was covered to the very edges, and only his seat was on the outside. But this part of him was already accustomed to the cold. When the coachman was garbed this way, he was able to see everyone, although he himself was invisible. So, half naked he went into the merchant's chambers just like a poet into a theatre, without any admission whatsoever. He went in and saw nobody at home, not only no servants, but not even the master himself. However, as soon as he saw a bottle on a window, he went up to it and grabbed it in his embrace. Here the bottle was just like a mouse, and he like

a cat. He grasped it and, thrusting the neck into his mouth,
began sucking it like a wench. Without delay he finished off
the vodka that was inside it. This was the coachman's first
success. But he did not come to the tax farmer's just to take
profit from such a trifle. He wandered all over the place and
was himself surprised at coming across nobody in any of the
rooms. "I didn't come here," he said, "just to steal this little
bottle for myself. I can drink up the entire cellar in this
house." He said this and flew out of the rooms like a hawk,
but still found no liquid bodies around the house. But when
he went out to the back courtyard and sniffed there, he caught
the smell of a steaming bath. The tax farmer and his wife
were steaming themselves in it at the time. Elisei went straight
over to it. But now he saw other movements in the bath. He
espied two naked bodies pouring water on themselves there.
It was the tax farmer himself and his young wife. (I do not
know why this desire possessed them, but I forgot: it was
Saturday then, and with merchants this is the big day of the
week.) Then the coachman entered the butcher's guild: taking
a ladle of water he threw it onto a stone. It so happened that
the coachman tortured both of them. The pleasant steam of
the bath soon became most frightful, and the heat was
unbearable to them. This annoyed the merchant no little.
He thought that the Evil One himself was tormenting him
for his many sins collecting taxes. The merchant and his wife
had already quit the higher levels of the steam bath and from
their lofty places had descended to the lower. But what? They
found here the same kind of heat! Over their entire universe
the climate became the same. Eden was there before, but now
Hell had come into it. It was impossible for the merchant
and wife to struggle with an invisible power. Both of them
had to get their things on outside the bath. The husband,
however, forgot his coat and the wife her hair ribbons. He
just threw some pants on himself and she a blouse on herself,
and they both ran cautiously across the yard. The wife became
Alcestis and her husband Hercules.[44] To add to their woe,
they had a watchdog at home who, not recognizing his masters, suddenly hurled himself on them howling like the hellish

---

[44] Alcestis, in Greek legend, was the wife of Admetus, King of
Thessaly. She offered her own life to save her husband's, but
was rescued from hell by Hercules.

Cerberus.[45] He jumped right on top of the merchant from behind, lodged himself in the side of this new Hercules and tore out a piece of his side as from a lump of dough. If Hercules was bitten, at least Alcestis managed to save herself. At the shouts of the merchant and his wife, a crowd began to collect. Oh, what a sad sight for the eyes! Oh, strange turn of fate! The people beheld here a new Hercules. The domestic rascal was dragging him around the yard, whereas the ancient Hercules had purified the hellish Cerberus with a club and, grabbing hold of him by the ears, carried him away from Hell. Somehow, nevertheless, they managed to free the hero, and conducting him into the house set him down on a bench. He was groaning, or, to put it more clearly, he was screaming, and in between his cries said the following: "Today, wife, you lured me on. Was it not Satan himself who put you up to tease your old man with a bath? Oh, no! Not he, but just you yourself are the guilty one here." So the old man scolded his young wife. Although it was he who was guilty, nevertheless it was his wife whom he reproached. No wonder she might look for another man!

But let us leave this couple now and have a look at what our coachman was doing with himself. Having driven the master and mistress out of the bath, the coachman gave himself a wash there and emerged from it dressed in the coat belonging to the merchant. So stood my Elisei now, completely dressed except for the fact that, wearing his cap, he could not be seen by anyone. The merchant was a big man, but Elisei was just of medium height. So he stood in the coat like a priest in a cassock in a churchyard. Unseen by anyone, he went out into the courtyard and cast his avaricious gaze in all corners. His only intention at the time was to try to find a way of getting himself into the wine cellar. This day, however, he had no luck in finding it, so he strode into the merchant's house as though he himself were the master of it. In the meantime, night had already extended its cover and smudged the whole azure sky as though with soot from a furnace. Clouds added to the darkness and gloom. Dressed in the merchant's coat, Elisei crawled into the house like a lobster and found a hiding place for himself beneath the merchant's

---

[45] In Greek and Roman mythology, the three-headed dog who guarded the gates of Hell.

bed. The merchant at the time had just lain down with his wife to sleep. Placing the schismatic crosses on his fat forehead, he read, "Shall this bed truly be a grave unto me?" His wife then read the same thing along with him, for she ardently wished her husband just that. But no sooner did the merchant lie down with his wife in the bed than a frightful storm began blowing on all sides. The storm became stationary above their very house and filled the whole house with its lightning and thunder. Terror hung above its roof in the darkness. Rain and hail and bolts of lightning flew downward. Such a change brings fear to the living. Did not Zeus after all descend to Danae on bolts of lightning? Did he not descend to her in a shower of gold? Did she not give birth to a new Perseus?

Not Zeus, but the coachman himself got up from underneath the bed and went to spend the night with the merchant's young wife. When the master was aroused by a crash of thunder, he got out of bed and lit a candle. Then with prayers he went to conduct the cloud out of his house. But the thunder paid no heed to such an icon worshiper who collected lives with falsehood and ruined his neighbors' holdings with his "farming." The mistress, in the meantime, also did not continue her rest. She stretched out in the bed and began yawning. Elisei took advantage of this propitious moment. He got up and beheld the merchant's wife in the bed. Playfulness and mocking laughter were in her eyes. Below her neck he saw two marble hillocks on which he saw also two rose shrubs. Pleasant face and crimson mouth excited all the coachman's blood to joy and urged him to scramble up onto the bed to her. Not thinking further, he dashed straight for her and lay down on the bed together with the young woman. She did not see him, but only felt his presence. Then her blood began growing alternately hot and cold. At the same time she was smoldering and trembling, and was lying in invisible embraces. Not knowing herself what it was that was happening to her, she was in this respect very much like the Danae of whom I spoke earlier.

While this was transpiring, the fearful storm had passed and restored to the night its earlier pleasantness. The merchant then returned to his wife. Several times he called her by name. "Sleep, my darling, sleep, my dear! All the clouds have gone away and there is no reason for you to be afraid any longer." His wife answered with a stammer, and the old husband then noticed her movements. He quietly poked her on the side with his hand. As soon as he felt his touch, Elisei leaped from the bed. Pretending that she was just then falling asleep, the woman turned over on the other side, facing her husband. The merchant now asked his beloved wife: "You must have seen Satan in a dream, otherwise why was your body trembling from fear?" Then it behooved her to tell the whole truth: "My darling husband! I dreamed while I was sleeping that something heavy was lying on top of me." The superstitious merchant immediately concluded that it must have been a household spirit[46] who was separating him from her. He grumbled to her: "Tomorrow I'll have an old woman brought to the house who knows how to deal with Satan. Now, don't you be afraid any longer, dear, and come and sleep with me." When he heard this, the coachman, himself a superstitious man, did not want to see himself become an example of how a devil is driven out of a house, and so he got up and left the rooms in an angry mood because an old devil was the cause of his being separated from the mistress of the house (Satan himself, of course, was his tutor in such matters), and because the merchant wanted to send for an old woman the next day and the old hag would play such a game: she would summon there the devils and all hell, who would drive him from the rooms. "It would be better for me to take myself to the cellar," he told himself; "I'll go there and lock myself up inside. Let her drive me out of a place where I have enough vodka and wine."

End of the Fourth Canto

Canto the Fifth

O Muse! Take pity upon me now. Leave your most lofty realm, if only for an hour. Slip on a mantilla, put on shoes, get up and come to my aid. It is not a Spasskii student who is asking you for this, but a singer of Parnassus who needs you, one who always dwelt with you in harmony and who always served your sisters zealously.

Hark! I hear a voice from her high throne: "I sent down Scarron to you a long time ago. Therefore, do not flatter yourself with the hope of my help. I am singing with Kheras-

[46] *Domovoi*, in Russian.

kov of the Chesmé battle.[47] Taking a lyre tuned by me, he is now proclaiming to the world this most famous victory. Now am I acting with his pen alone. From beneath his hands a powerful thunder emerges. But if you too are ignited with the same fire and desire to sing to the world of Russian arms, then I shall come down to your assistance and I shall speak of the deeds of all heroes." O Muse! Instill a true flame in me. It will pass through me to endless generations. Come and strengthen my will; then shall I intone a new song on my lyre.

And now I shall again take my little fiddle in hand and heed closely the voice of the singer Scarron. He is already drawing my thought after him; his style is now glowing here again.

No sooner did Elisei sneak into the cellar than he buried himself alive in this grave. Although it was bolted with a Pavlovskii lock, he managed to break it from its clamps with a fist. With a bold hand he opened the grating, went down into this abyss, and saw there casks lined up everywhere against the walls. He also saw glasses and bottles, and big barrels of spirits by the dozens. He delighted himself with the sight of such things and flew at them like a falcon above a flock of timid birds. He beheld swans and jackdaws and tomtits. He then raced to the first bottle nearest him and grasped it to his embrace. Within the wink of an eye, he popped out the plug and downed this little birdie in three swallows. Then he approached the biggest barrel there, uncorked it, and put his mouth to the middle slot, from which the liquid flowed into his throat. Elisei, my boy, get hold of yourself; collect your senses, get up. The barrel is not small, after all; you will blow yourself up with it. But he kept on sucking and seemed not to hear my words. Later on he used to say, if he was not fibbing, that it was just as though Bacchus himself were helping him along with his whole retinue, and were laboring together with him in this work. It was, he said further, just as though Silenus himself were uncorking the bottles and were himself swallowing the wine from them. It was just as though the Bacchi were dead drunk, as though the wet nurses and

---

[47] A reference to Mikhail Kheraskov's epic poem *The Battle of Chesmé* (Chesmesskii boi, 1770). The Battle of Chesmé was fought on July 6, 1770, during Catherine's first war with the Turks (1768–1774). The Russian fleet scored an impressive victory over the Turkish.

governesses were drawing the wine. Then suddenly such a roar tore through the entire cellar that all the glasses and bottles were upended. All the hoops quivered; the wine began pouring out of the casks, and not a single drop remained in any of them after a while. Soon this magnificent labor was at an end and they all left the cellar, leaving behind them a pond of wine. The tax farmer, not perceiving the roar, was resting himself in his burglarized house. But as soon as he emerged from his bed, he called for a worker as one whistles for a dog, and sent him to fetch the old woman whom he wished to employ in order to drive the devils from his house. Such was the nonsense that came into his mind!

The old woman was coming now, leaning on a pair of crutches and carrying with her various kinds of beans, roots, and herbs, and many magic condiments. There were lightning shafts, shriveled spiders, devils' claws and the embers from Epiphany eve rites, of which she had no small quantity in her bag. And the wisdom of this Medea consisted of such things.

No sooner had the old woman crossed the threshold of the house than she put down on a bench the concoction in which were all her magic artifacts, her beans, and other such nonsense.

My tax farmer had already run into her on his way out of the house, and said to the hag respectfully: "Help me if you please, Grannie! This very week devils have taken possession of my entire house. Yesterday one of them drove me out of my bath. Another brought my poor wife the most frightful dream. This happened just last night. Help me, for no strength has remained in me!" No sooner had he said this, however, than the housekeeper ran up crying bitter tears and shaking all over from fear. He reported to him the woe that had befallen the wine cellar. In a mad rage, the merchant asked for a priest so that he should not die in sin and burn forever in the fire of Gehenna. O base soul! To what are you proceeding? Is this the price with which you are trying to buy heaven? When orphans humiliated by you proclaim that you should be in hell, does such a confession suffice you? Hell will be your home, and your retribution torture. First you must sincerely repay those whom you injured and afterward fly straight to paradise on those wings that bear honest people there, and those injured by you will plead for you.

But finally this mortal dread left him. In the hands of the old woman the merchant collected his senses and begged her to reveal to him wherefrom the awful sinew of these misfortunes flowed. The old woman said to him then in answer: "O my child! Where are there no evil people on this earth? I know that evildoers have wreaked vengeance on you in this way and sent it down on you along the wind. I shall show all this to you in deed. I shall work my beans, and remedy the situation. Devils no longer will continue coming into your home. I shall drive them out or I shall beat them all to the death. Three days ago a versifier asked me to bake him a roll that would break his desire for poetry; and I completed this work successfully. No sooner did I let this hornlet into his stomach than he also swallowed together with the hornlet his desire to write poetry. Now he no longer breathes with this foolishness, although he still writes prose, but not in a foppish style. Oh, if other versifiers like him ate such rolls more often they would certainly also lose their desire to compose verses and would not be offending the tender hearing of other people. Another one asked me to help him become a rhymester, and he ate a root by my grace. From that time on, he made the acquaintance of heaven and hell, and writes a multitude of silly verses. However, to him they seem good. It costs me nothing to do these things. When some loss occurs in a house or an old man thinks about wooing a young girl, my labor has never remained fruitless. Merchants and clerks come to me from all over, some so that people will be anxious to buy their goods, others so that a decree will be released permitting them to take bribes. I willingly work my beans for all of them and I never tell a falsehood to any of them. To a doctor last night I prophesied that the world soon would consider him a horse doctor. This prophecy quickly came to pass. Today in the city people everywhere were saying that from his healing there was a great loss of life, and so from Hippocrates he became an executioner. And if someone is a drunk, I can take this passion from him as easily as waving a hand!"

The merchant now forgot all his illness, and interrupted the old woman's speech with his own: "Mercy, Grannie, don't do this. If you cure people's fondness for drink, this will result in injury to my income and it will not be convenient for me to collect my taxes. The best thing that you could do for me would be to make everyone drunkards. In that way you would bring me the greatest income." The grannie then said to him: "I understand that, but I am unable to work evil, my child." Then the tax farmer answered her: "So listen, my dear. Your harmful advice is of no advantage to me. When you turn drunkards away from drink, you stir up the whole rabble against me this way. The more alcohol that flows, the better it is for me. So you see your aid is no longer necessary to me. I don't believe a windbag like you. Take your beans and get out of my house fast, before I give it to you with a whip."

The tax farmer said this in anger, and the old woman flew out of the house like a swallow. She wanted to send down on him a host of devils that would fly to him like jackdaws and eat up and drink up all his provisions. All because the merchant deigned to warm the old woman's ears. Then they began to quarrel among themselves like two base souls!

When the coachman had emptied this house of wine, he went off and devastated other cellars. Zeus then announced to the other gods: "You see how the coachman is ruining the merchants; if I do not give them the benefit of my assistance now, so will I in this way deliver the weak unto the hands of the strong. Tell me, what am I to do with him?" Here the whole assembly roared like the ocean, and the sound lasted among them for more than an hour. Afterward, they all expressed different opinions. Although they all deliberated differently, however, they were all unanimous in censuring Elisei for it. Then the father of all the gods took the floor: "In your opinion, I see, we ought to burn him. But I do not agree that he should be punished so severely. Since there are so many such rascals on earth, if I were to deprive them all of their lives now, I would have to devastate the entire world. If, like you, I were of so many discordant thoughts, I would destroy a host of unworthy creatures who are just a burden to the world. The first I would throw down into hell would be the adulators, then all the hardhearted ones, and all the ignoble ones, the unjust judges, thieves, perfidious friends. Afterward, those who crawl to Parnassus without being asked would also not escape my edict. Just think what I would subject the world to when I threw these creatures down into the abyss of hell! Listen to me: let us give up all thought of vengeance. To each one I shall give time to make amends. The coachman is not so guilty as he seems to you.

So now he is going to make peace with me a different way. In two days at the Ruka there will take place a fist fight in which this new hero of ours will contend. He will defeat terribly many fighters there; for brotherly love he will flatten all their noses. I have imposed on him the following limitation: I want him to take the place of several men. You will see what he will be worthy of. Before he was a plain coachman, but now he will be a good warrior."

Zeus made this pronouncement to the gods in all seriousness and then ordered all of them to return to their own homes. If all mortals would have so deliberated and chosen their professions according to their aptitudes, then perhaps the least worthy physician would have ceased treating people and become the best executioner. The judge, who has absolutely no understanding of the cases presented before him and only occupies his place behind the cloth, would have been better off as a blacksmith. There are people who by mistake even take lead for silver. Sometimes a prudent man is a poor duelist, a respectable little clerk the most wretched rhymester. Thus, if each person would have fallen onto his proper level, then the world would not have tumbled into ignorance long ago.

The day of the great fight finally arrived. The roar of bears could be heard, and at this roar a host of boors assembled. People from all over streamed to the Ruka. There were many peasants, officials, and landowners. Some were coming here just to quarrel among themselves. Others, just to amuse themselves with the bearbaiting. O comfort! To yawn from boredom as the dogs tear some innocent beast to pieces or to jeer at similar fools as they play at being knights beating themselves with their fists. Discord has already reigned there for a long time, and malice distributes wine among all the fighters. Ignorance wields its authority over everyone there. And wisdom does not dare make an appearance in such places.

Two walls stood ready for the struggle, and the renowned warriors, drunk with wine, who were presenting this entertainment, stretched themselves out and straightened their hands. One took off his cap and sash; a second clenched his fist at a neighbor; another one, stuffing his shirt into his belt, was figuring out how to swing at him and how, for the sake of brotherly love, to let flow from his opponent's nose his superfluous blood or how to hang a good black eye on someone's mug, by which he would be able to amuse all the onlookers.

In the meantime, Zeus opened a window in the zenith and so spoke to all the immortals: "Now, my gods, all this will become known to you. Gods and goddesses may look out from here as once you looked with me from these places on the terrible battles between the Greeks and Trojans. But then you often slandered me and helped both nations by stealth. Now, however, if someone of you dares to give aid, this person will not in any way escape my wrath. The helpmate will run around for a whole year like a starving dog and will not find refuge in baths or in prisons. Even though he hid inside a tavern, even there I would have him poked in the sides until a fixed time passed. No matter how much you want, you won't push yourselves into this stirrup." Then they all lowered their eyes and waited for this storm to pass them. They all sat humbly around Zeus and stared at the little window just like screech owls.

Then the hour of the fearful battle came. At first a child's voice was heard among them, and the air resounded with their dissonant voices. But here this was just like music. A storm cloud, after dimming the clearest horizon, after burdening the quiet sea with its weight, blows with a fearful storm against the water; the tranquillity ceases, the sea is stirred up, and then thunder strikes from the dark clouds. The noise from the fists was like this, and from the dust thick clouds rose up into the air. Heavy blows resounded across mugs, a bloody river flowed from noses, blows rained down on backs and sides, and from these blows different kinds of sounds emerged. Millions of slaps sounded on all sides. One gave his opponent a good blow below the stomach and afterward was himself stretched out like cattle. Another fist went for a clean swing and aimed straight for his opponent's nose. But he missed the mark and opened up a free path for the other's fists, and the latter strolled along his cheeks as through a bazaar. Another gave someone a pair of black eyes, while still another, grabbing hold of his opponent by the throat, was choking him. The face of one was flattened like a pancake, but he went to the tavern and after drinking a little wine returned to the fight with his former boldness and tore through the wall better than before.

Thus brainless peasants fought one another. Merchants

were ranged on one side, and coachmen on the other. As soon as a hero came out from the merchant side and found no opponent for himself among all the others, he was just like a lion who after breaking the lock on his cage roars and, casting a hungry glance, races at a herd of timid cattle pasturing nearby amid the soft grass of a cool valley where a poor little shepherd, seeing him and throwing his staff from trembling hands, is able to save his life only by flight and has to leave his flock to the beast of prey as booty.

So this new Ajax,[48] or rather Diomedes,[49] a heroic appearance on his brow, burst in and shared the blows of fists. The coachmen ran like fainthearted Tatars when a Russian sword shone in their fields—so should all the coachmen then have taken flight. . . . But this verse is somewhat florid and not very appropriate here. Should I not just say that they should have run? But this terrible hero flew upon them like a vulture and harassed those fleeing with his fists.

All were thrown into confusion like dust before the sight of an ominous cloud. One fell headlong, another crawled along like a lobster, a third bellowed like a wounded bear, and a fourth howled like an ox struck down. O terrible, terrible fight! Fight of no advantage to anyone. Neither the strengths of horses nor the elbows of men could restrain the heroes' swiftness. . . . Everything wants to imitate lofty words. Calm yourself, my fiddle, since you are droning just nonsense. Strings of lofty words are so pleasant to you that you now need more moderate speech, but lest it be neither turgid nor tender follow the path of Scarron, for that way will you sooner reach the crown that the god of Parnassus gives to singers.

The merchants' hero beat the coachmen's heroes and numbered their passports on all their behinds. The coachmen's

---

[48] Two Ajaxes appear in Greek legend: a) Ajax Telamonian, or Great, the son of Telamon of Salamis and Periboea, next to Achilles the bravest Greek hero at Troy. Upon the death of Achilles he claimed his armor but lost out to Odysseus, who had the support of Athena. b) Oilean Ajax, or Lesser, the son of Oileus and Eriopis, another Greek warrior at the siege of Troy, who abducted Cassandra from the sanctuary at Athens but drowned after a shipwreck on his way home.

[49] Diomedes, in Greek legend the son of Tydeus and Deïpyle and later a king in Argos. He also distinguished himself at Troy.

shirts and pants trembled there. All thought that the merchants' hero was carrying a bolt of lightning in his hands and that he would make an end of the fighters. But suddenly the battle deprived itself of this awful sight when a hero arrived protected against all harm, hidden from all the eyes of the onlookers. It was Elisei beneath his cap. Unseen by anyone, he changed the entire course of the battle. In a single hour he saddened and drove away the merchants. Their strong wall trembled because of him, and he placed on them his bloody banners. From his fists all split in different directions. Not hundreds, but thousands reeled before him! In the wink of an eye the victory returned to the coachmen, and Elisei had already caught up with that warrior who had fought among the coachmen like a devil. Elisei had already begun to punish him with his fists and showered a multitude of blows at his eyes by which he smashed and blinded him. He fell like an oak tree chopped down by an ax and lay smashed and maimed by Elisei. Three times did he try to raise himself from the sand and three times did he fall down on top of it and finally lay on it hardly breathing, and there he inscribed the victory of Elisei. Or simply, he drew it in the sand with his behind. But he could not find in himself the strength to get up. Such actions moved all to pity. His comrades at once rushed over to him, bore the half-dead warrior off to the tavern, and there brought him a grivna's worth of wine, with which they emboldened his weakened spirit and so returned his breathing to him.

The merchant regained his strength, left the tavern, and entered the battle for the second time, now against the coachman. Elisei then thrust himself upon him and, landing a good twenty blows, gave him a stronger push than before so that he fell on the sand flat on his behind. Moreover, the coachman had given him such a solid thumping that the outline of his whole seat was stamped in the sand, and all who enter the tavern say that to this day this sign is still visible there. After overwhelming him, the coachman began to harass all those running away, increasing the number of the beaten and maimed. He drove all the merchant scoundrels into a dense thicket, and in a word was as brave as Achilles.

But can anyone argue with enraged fate? I do not know who accidentally knocked the cap from him, but he stood with bare head like a lobster. He wanted to run from the battlefield into the tavern, but his own men seized him as he was running, took him to his own department, and placed him in chains. Thus the truth of Zeus's words came true. They shaved all of Elisei's head to his ears. What kind of a sign was this, what were they getting him ready for, if not to send him straight into the army? Alas, this was the truth! A verdict was reached: "As a fugitive, and perhaps even a thief of no worldly value whatsoever, Elisei should be sent into military service and there taken into the ranks."

End of the Fifth and Last Canto

8. *Dushen'ka: An Ancient Tale in Free Verse*

IPPOLIT F. BOGDANOVICH

Bogdanovich's place in the history of Russian literature emphatically rests on his major work, the mock-epic *Dushen'ka*. The first song, or canto, of the poem, which bore the title *The Adventures of Dushen'ka* (Dushen'kiny pokhozhdeniia), was published in 1778. When the complete work appeared five years later, in 1783, it was called simply *Dushen'ka*, and was subtitled "an ancient tale in free verse" (*drevniaia povest' v vol'nykh stikhakh*).

The most impressive piece of Russian eighteenth-century "light" poetry, *Dushen'ka* is a humorous travesty of the ancient myth of the love of Amor (Cupid) and Psyche modeled on La Fontaine's *Les Amours de Psyché et de Cupidon* (a Russian translation of which, by F. Dmitriev-Mamonov, was published in 1769) and based ultimately on an episode in *The Golden Ass* of Lucius Apuleius (c. 135– c. 182), a Russian translation of which was published shortly after *The Adventures of Dushen'ka* came out in 1778.

Little more than a delightfully diverting interlude, the story of Amor and Psyche occurs in Books IV, V, and VI of Apuleius's *The Golden Ass*. The beauty of the myth continued to inspire artists through the ages, each of whom chose to approach it in a different way. In the spirit of the myth-debunking rationalism of the eighteenth century, La Fontaine greatly enlarged the plot of the episode in *The Golden Ass* and chose to treat the legend in a frivolous manner, accenting its erotic element and giving it rather much the flavor of the salon. His approach was not entirely consistent, however. Certain episodes in *Les Amours de Psyché et de Cupidon* are by contrast moving, even exalted—anything but frivolous.

Bogdanovich, on the other hand, chose to invest his own version of the Amor-Psyche myth with the lightness and humor of the mock-epic genre. The occasional seriousness of the La Fontaine work disappears completely, and what is left is vivacious retelling of the tale in a comic vein. This can be

180

clearly seen in those places where Dushen'ka attempts to commit suicide or when she sets out to fulfill the demands of Venus. The title itself—a Russian diminutive form of Psyche—at once sets the tone of the entire poem.

Two features of *Dushen'ka* merit closer attention. The first is its form. In his own mock-epic poem *Elisei*, Maikov (like most other practitioners of the mock-epic genre in Europe) was content to operate within the traditional epic frame. For an eighteenth-century Russian poet this presupposed use of the six-foot iambic (alexandrine) line. Bogdanovich more daringly completely discarded this pattern, drawing his inspiration from the tradition of the Sumarokovian and post-Sumarokovian fable. A most appealing feature of the original composition—and one regrettably totally lost in a prose translation—is the use of iambic lines of varying length and rhyme.

The distinct folk flavor given *Dushen'ka* by its verse structure is reinforced by Bogdanovich's introduction of figures and motifs from the Russian oral tradition: the many-headed Serpent Gorynych (Zmei Gorynych of Russian fairy tales); the sorcerer Kashchei the Immortal; the "living" and "dead" water Venus sends Dushen'ka to search for, also in the tradition of the fairy tale; the peasant dress, or *sarafan*, Dushen'ka garbs herself in at one point, and so on. Other small details of Russian reality give a distinct Russian coloration to the work.

The light, humorous spirit of *Dushen'ka*, its unusual and appealing form, and its simple, naïve, curious, somewhat vain but lively and appealing heroine made the poem an immediate success. By 1832 the work had already undergone ten editions, which was a very high number for the period. *Dushen'ka* thus remained popular well into the nineteenth century and in fact proved influential not only on such poets as Batiushkov and Baratynskii, who greatly admired Bogdanovich's skill, but also on Pushkin. Tracing the genetic ties between Pushkin's *Ruslan and Liudmila* and his fairy tales and Bogdanovich's *Dushen'ka* is no difficult task—despite Pushkin's admonition that Bogdanovich should not be overrated. When he came to writing his immortal classic, *Eugene Onegin*, a work intimately bound up with the mock-epic and "light" poetic traditions of the eighteenth century, Pushkin was to recall Bogdanovich in affectionate terms:

The Gallic touch, no use recanting,
To me will always be enchanting
As youthful sins when youth is gone,
As Bogdanovich's verse. . . .

(*Eugene Onegin,* tr. Walter Arndt, New York, 1963, III, 29)

The present translation is based on the text in I. F. Bogdanovich, *Stikhotvoreniia i poemy*, Biblioteka Poèta, ed.
I. Z. Serman, Leningrad, 1957.

Preface from the Author

When I began to write *Dushen'ka* my sole motivation was
personal amusement in idle hours. But later the universal
favorable opinion of my countrymen concerning the style of
my amusements persuaded me to permit this composition to
be printed, as much corrected as possible. Later I had the
time to correct it still further, encouraged to this task by the
printed and written praise accorded my work. Accepting such
praise with the necessary gratitude, I am not so much over-
whelmed by pride that I could not sense my inadequacy in the
face of the comments of an unknown writer whom it pleased
to declare in courteous verses that the composition *Dushen'ka*
was a creation of Psyche herself. My forefathers, who faithfully served their ruler and Fatherland with an ordinary but
good name in the nobility, left me no example of how to
raise myself above ordinary human perishability. Not being
of the ranks of established authors, I feel how much I am
obligated to many people for the charity they will substitute
for the many errors to be met in my works.

Verses to the Virtue of Chloe

Pulchritude and virtue quarreled,
And this quarrel long ensued;
Often was the world a witness
Of their rivalry and feud.
Chloe! You yourself embody

Two things in one entity:
You lure not nor bring by capture
To your sweet captivity.
He who wants to be a witness
Of hearts' vincibility––
He who Chloe's beauties views
Finally himself will see,
Virtue has its special sweetness.

BOOK ONE

Not the anger of Achilles and not the siege of Troy, where in the roar of eternal conflicts heroes ended their days, but of Dushen'ka I sing. You, O Dushen'ka, do I summon for aid to embellish my song that I compose in simplicity and freedom. Not the loud sound of the lyre—but the reed will you hear! Come down to me, come down from the places agreeable to you. Instill your fire in me and embolden my mind to touch upon the happiness of blissful habitations where you eternally pass the sweet days free of cares, where pleasure alone reigns without tedium. Along the chilled ice-bound shores of the Slavena,[1] where Phoebus[2] envelops himself in fog and hides from the eyes of others, show me the springs of the wonderful Hippocrene.[3] Covered with snowy hillocks, Parnassus here thawed out more than once at the sight of you. Tender zephyrs abide with you; boring satyrs, censures and criticisms, and sadnesses and woes flee from the places where you are.[4] Without you amusements bring only labor; pleasures wither; cupids cry, orphaned.

O Homer, singer of the gods! Father of verses divided by caesurae, even, graceful, and suitable for singing.[5] Forgive me if I do not trouble myself over the form of my lines and do not here compose measured songs in orderly fashion. I

[1] A common name for the Neva River.

[2] In late Greek mythology Apollo in his aspect of sun god.

[3] A fountain on Mount Helicon sacred to the Muses; a symbol of poetic inspiration.

[4] These and the following personified figures represent a common feature of the eighteenth-century light poetry.

[5] Bogdanovich refers to the obligatory break, or caesura, in the verse of the Homeric poems.

shall chisel their features in a free way, without even feet, for I am not following a prescribed model here. Some lines will be of small measure, others of large, and I shall often place at the ends blank rhymes that have no legal status in verse.[6] And if I get tired of this, forgetting my dread of ink and pens, forgetting the threat of satirists and critics, I shall begin easily and courageously to write without rhymes or simply in prose. Cherishing my freedom, I sing not for praise but so that Chloe[7] should laugh pleasantly in hours of refreshment, merriment, and peace.

In ancient times Apuleius and later La Fontaine, to the eternal memory of their names, sang of Psyche in both prose and verse, in languages different from ours. In this tale they showed the delight of a keen mind. The Graces, it seems, guided their pens, or the Graces themselves even did the writing. But if it is impossible to imitate their style, I shall strive, following their lead, albeit in simple lines, to present carefully a shade similar to theirs and sometimes to introduce into the tale an amusing verse.

In ancient Greece, in the time of Jupiter, when the race of sovereigns multiplied itself so that there was a separate ruler in each small city and, if he wished, was a god and had an altar, among many kings one was distinguished by the size of his army, by his mind, his looks, his curls, by the abundance of wheat, of cattle, and of inhabitants in his realm. There were neighbors there who were evil and greedy, like wolves and bears. Lycaon, of whom Ovid wrote a history, is renowned.[8] It is well known how he among the Greek kings was actually turned into a wolf for predatory deeds and evil talk. But he of whom I wish to relate now was not a beast

---

[6] Bogdanovich herewith declares his intention to depart from the fixed rules of classicist poetics by mixing lines of different length and introducing verses without rhymes.

[7] Chloe here simply refers to the feminine readers of *Dushen'ka*.

[8] Lycaon, a king of Arcadia. The son of Pelasgus, first King of Arcadia. According to Greek mythology Zeus once visited earth in the guise of a mortal and came to the house of Lycaon, doubtless to test him. Lycaon cut up and cooked a child (possibly his son Nyctimus) and offered it to Zeus. To punish him, Zeus destroyed his house and changed Lycaon into a savage wolf. Ovid included the legend in his *Metamorphoses*.

by his image or manner. He was of good to the world and was loved by the gods. He assigned awards fittingly, passed verdicts fittingly, and if he found beasts' souls in those who were under his jurisdiction he pinned donkeys' ears on them, or put coarse bristle and talons on their feet, or gave them howling mouths or pairs of horns. The archives of many deeds have long ago been destroyed by caustic antiquity, which devoured true fact. But later times revere the image of his laws even to our own day. As is known, he ordered the envious to labor so that the happiness of others should tire their gazes and they would be unable to enjoy peace; he commanded the miserly to sit beside gold, to gaze upon gold, and become tempted by gold, but not be sated by it; he forbade the arrogant to come together with people, and bequeathed the same arrogance to their heirs, which has remained visible even to this day. He ordered everyone never to believe anything said by the liar and flatterer. Everywhere he commanded slanderers and the carriers of falsehoods to sovereigns to bear the most disgusting faces that could be expressive of their slandering. Such was to be seen not long ago in Moscow, during a masquerade, when during the Shrovetide parade the people derided shameful deeds.[9] In brief, he ordered that all malicious cranks should wear fur hats with appropriate inscriptions according to which people could recognize them faster and flee from them. This regulation was sound in its judgment, and was not harsh. It pleased the people who could no longer honor the ancient evil practice of throwing people into the water, several a year, as though they were some species of fish.

Ovid, hereditary writer of mendacious ages,[10] who often bared the truth, Ovid, in very lie a true friend of the Muses, described in detail how frequent punishments had been among the Greeks until then. The metamorphosis of the Cerastae

[9] The masquerade referred to was held in Moscow during the coronation of Catherine II, January 30–February 2, 1763. The masquerade was given the name "Minerva in Triumph" (*Torzhest-vuiushchaia Minerva*).

[10] Bogdanovich means here that the Roman poet Ovid used myths of earlier times, of Greek, Latin, and Eastern sources for his *Metamorphoses*. Because the tales are legendary, they are the products of "mendacious" ages.

into cows; the whole race of the Cercopes, for evil and deceit, into a pack of monkeys; adulators, for the baseness of their souls, into frogs; the inconstant—into whirligigs; the talkative—into magpies; the cruel-hearted—into lumps of marble. Tantalus, Sisyphus, and Ixion, for their greedy evil, were condemned to eternal exile to Pluto. And many others would have considered it benevolence and grace shown them had the king just punished all the bad creatures in the world with shame by putting horrible masks on them. Such a new rule held all in fear without punishing people further. The good king out of kindness also invited friends to his royal domicile to partake of his hospitality.

O Homer, if you could but awake now! Guarding the honor of your heroes who, forgetting their vengeance, loved to drink and eat often, you would be terrified upon hearing my poem that I, a weak singer, finally dared to liken himself to you, father of verse! Is it possible to capture in worthy style the magnificence of the banquets of Greek royal courts of which you wrote so elegantly? I can only say that the king liked to parade himself, to praise and to rebuke others, to eat, drink, and then, later, to sleep. And for such hospitality, and more, for his good humor, envoys came to him from all the neighboring states. He was especially distinguished among rulers because of the fact that he had three lovely daughters. But when the sun in all its beauty illuminates the universe, it plunges the moon and stars into darkness. So was the youngest of the sisters more lustrous than the others, and obscured, as the sun the moon and stars, the merits of the older girls. The beauty of the rose and the whiteness of the lily and, in a word, Nature never revealed anything on earth the equal of her.

It would be useless and impudent to search for appropriate words to describe what shone so superbly in a multitude of ages. I shall say briefly: the king's youngest daughter, for whom many were they who sighed both day and night, was called Psyche by the Greeks. In other languages, in the translation of the word, she was known as Soul, according to the interpretation of scholars. Later, in the ancient tales of Russian masters she was given the name of Dushen'ka. And they write that when it came time to give her a name the most fitting new word was sought, and with no small travail. From then on, Dushen'ka's place of glory among us was confirmed when her name was placed by the people among the prettiest words in the lexicon, and love gave its approval.

But praise frequently appears more dangerous among people than slander. Contemptuous boasting does not like it when the loquacious goddess Glory trumpets the plain truth out loud everywhere. Someone else's honor, someone else's rights torment the spirit of the envious. Such, Dushen'ka, was your undoing, when the whole Cytherean world[11] and all its environs personally deified you and all ran to you in order to increase your magnificence. You did not know the grief of your rival! An assemblage of merriments, laughters, and games abandoned the charms of Venus and fled in a crowd from Cythera. Running all about her court the goddess saw neither sacrifices nor burning incense pots wherever she cast her glance. The priests were then shepherding flocks, and many Cytherean temples were grown over by grass and forest. The gardens of the goddess were orphaned, and her house presented a disgraceful appearance. Only rarely did the zephyrs whistle, and when they did it seemed to her that they whistled in shame. The inconstant cupids, flying from temple to temple, could not accustom themselves to the doleful emptiness of Nature there. They all wished to fly away and so all took wing, ascended after Dushen'ka on a new path, and sought a free voluptuousness for themselves where the zephyrs began blowing, where the heavenly courses flowed. A small number of those who remained, chafing under the yoke of the chariot of their bored queen, carried despondency everywhere.

Not long afterward, according to the most reliable reports, the goddess of beauty at last discovered with an anger that knew no bounds the reason for the tedium and desolation about her. Although Dushen'ka had no thought of angering Venus and had the necessary faith in the virtues of the goddess and always was decorous in her conduct, she soon fell victim to all the calumniators. Moreover, evil-speaking spirits, sowing wicked rumors about her, gave a twisted meaning to all her deeds. And those who anticipated or begged for favors of the goddess reported, in order to please her, that Dushen'ka, out of spite and just to vex her, had appropriated a number

[11] Venus (Aphrodite) was said to have arisen from the foam of the sea near the island of Cythera.

of her Cytherean servants. To whomever it was an advantage then could lie freely about Dushen'ka. But so as to wreak vengeance on her in deed, Venus, having collected all the lies and fables, ordered sixteen post zephyrs attached as quickly as possible to her traveling chariot. She then set out to call on Amor as quickly as they could fly. The reader himself can easily imagine how she pleaded with him one way or another, having come to beseech him about Dushen'ka and to inform on her:

"Amor, Amor! Intervene for the sake of my honor and glory. Show your justice, show your wisdom. You know Dushen'ka, or you may have heard of her: a simple mortal, defaming the gods, holds your immortal mother for nothing. She has already dared to order about our servants and to lord it over me in my own regions. Can I endure and see with equanimity that Dushen'ka alone is everywhere and every way heeded! Chasing after her, all our admirers, friends, cupids, and zephyrs flee from us; soon the planets themselves will be obedient to Dushen'ka. Jupiter himself sighs for her day and night, and it is rumored that he is planning to take her for wife, an impudent Greek girl, just a king's daughter, and has already forgotten Juno's fidelity and favors! What kind of god will you be and where will your throne be when a second Cupidon is born to them who will take away from you your bow and arrows and insolently subjugate territories now subordinate to us? You know how bold Jupiter's sons are: they freely go about the heavens and work all sorts of miracles on earth. And can you suffer that Dushen'ka by herself, without your help, incites in all a passion that you alone had the power to ignite? For a long time now she has been laughing at you, and uses my misfortune for her own triumph. For the sake of your own honor, for the honor of Venus, show examples of your severity: make Dushen'ka forever unloved, and so emaciated and so ugly that every person would be estranged from her, or give her as a husband the worst that could be found—so that she would find in her husband a tyrant and would torture herself loving someone cruel, so that her beauty would fade because of this, and so that I may remain in peace again."

Amor then wanted to interrupt this imploring speech. Although he knew that it was the custom of the goddesses always to slander their rivals, he still had to pacify his enraged mother and promise her afterward to scare Dushen'ka in due order for her insolence. After hearing these words, the cupids were terrified, Merriment gasped and Laughter trembled. Venus alone was pleased at having falsely brought anger against Dushen'ka. Tossing her gaze pleasantly at all with a smile, she directed her course back to her own island, and to enjoy her triumph to the fullest presented herself now in the glory of a true deity. The aerial chariot borne by her winged flock was abandoned and returned later with refreshing leisure. But the goddess, after donning her ancient ceremonial dress and seating herself in a shell, as they paint it in pictures, glided across the waters on two large dolphins.[12]

Extending his imperious look, Amor stirred all Neptune's court. Perceiving Venus, the frisky waves swam after her, filled with delight. The watery nation of tritons came out to greet her from the abyss of the waters. One dived all around her and pacified the impudent waves; another, whirling in the depths, gathered pearls on the bottom of the sea and dragged all the treasures from the ocean to place at her feet. One, struggling with monsters, forbade them to touch the places where Venus was traveling. Another, seating himself swiftly in the coach box, loudly quarreled with those he met, and ordered them to stand aside. He proudly held the lines, steered his path away from rocks, and crushed the impudent monsters. One, with trident, rode ahead of her atop a whale, driving all far away from the path. He cast stern looks on all sides, and so that all might know of his coming he blasted mightily on a coral horn. Another, from far distant lands, having succeeded in swimming up to the goddess, bore before her a fragment of a crystal mountain instead of a mirror. This sight restored pleasure and joy to her brow. "Oh, if this sight," he declared, "remained forever in the crystal!" But Triton's wish was in vain. This vision was to disappear, like a dream. Only the stone would remain, and in the heart only a fatal flame with which he would smolder hopelessly. Another, joining the retinue of the goddess, acted as a shield for her against the sun, and cooled the burning ray by sending upward a watery stream.

Meanwhile sirens, sweet singers, sang verses in her praise

[12] A reference to the famous painting by the Italian Renaissance artist Botticelli.

and mingled fact with fable trying to extol her. Some danced before her; others, in her service, anticipating her every labor, cooled the goddess with a large fan. Still others, borne along on the crests, panted heavily after their rapid post and from the beloved meadows of Flora brought her a wreath of flowers. Thetis herself had sent them for small and great favors and wished for herself only that her husband would stay at home. In most favorable weather, storms did not dare come to bother her, and only the zephyrs were free to fondle Venus.

Then, miraculously, the runaways, the zephyrs who were so impudent before, now flew back like a seed of wheat in the winnowing. One puffed her hair up; then, uncovering her charming bosom, stopped blowing for a time, vexingly let her hair down and tangling himself up in it, flew off. Another, sighing and groaning tenderly in an unknown language, whispered love into her ear. One, trying hopelessly to remove the covering of other charms, twisted about in the folds of her raiment, but fell amid the waters, deprived of his strength. Another blew on her mouth and eyes and kissed them furtively. Chasing after her, the waves pushed each other enviously so that tearing faster away from the circle they might fall meekly at her feet. And all zealously desired to conduct Venus to Cythera.

In a short time news, which Zephyr hastened to bring her, reached the goddess that Dushen'ka's woes passed all belief, that Dushen'ka had already been abandoned by all, and that all her former admirers, as if to scorn her, avoided every meeting with her. And even when they appeared at her father's court, they no longer declared their love for Dushen'ka. They no longer approached her, but only bowed low from the distance. Such a strange turn of fortunes saddened the Greek people. They had experienced floods, plagues, conflagrations, poor harvests, wars, and internal upheavals, but this event was something new for all of them. The interpreters of dreams and inquirers of the gods engaged in various quarrels about its meaning. One saw it as a good omen, another promised imminent disasters. One, making nonsense of the whole thing, said neither one thing nor another. But all unanimously affirmed that such wonders had not been seen in Greece from the beginning of time. Then the simple people came to wail to Venus in grief: "Why are the fates angry at the people? Why have the princess's admirers run away from her?" —It was known that her superb beauty had caused this turn of events by hostile miracles.

Venus finally decided the fate of all. She revealed to the Greeks the true reason why the king's daughter had lost her former esteem, why she had incited against herself a higher vengeance. With fearful and stern look she ordered the king's family to prepare themselves for new misfortunes, foretelling woes and terrible punishments for them in the days ahead until such time as they delivered Dushen'ka into her hands.

But the king and all his family loved Dushen'ka beyond all measure and did not pass a pleasant day without her—could they then deliver her to the vengeance of Venus? And all with one voice boldly rejected the goddess's demand, saying that it was a thing they could not imagine. Some held her altar up to laughter; others began to cry bitter tears. Some, without hearing the matter to the end, hastened to agree whenever the king uttered a word. Others, to console Dushen'ka, told her that this particular fault was laudable and glorious for her, when, to the humiliation of the goddesses, they deified her and that Venus's hatred of her and desire for vengeance against her only increased her honor. Although these words were flattering they would have been pleasanter to the princess had they been spoken by a lover. From pride she hid her grief from all eyes, but secretly was often dejected, called herself unlucky, and often, in sorrowful tears, cried out to Amor: "Amor, Amor, happy god! Why are you so harsh and stern to me? Has it been so long that I have been sought after? Has it been so long that I have been fondled? I spent my hours in triumphs; I could captivate lovers and love whenever I wished. Why has misfortune now become my lot? Of what use are my charms now? The poorest shepherdess in the fields has her shepherd. I alone am not anyone's sweetheart, although I am neither bad nor ugly! Is it shameful to me alone to love? But if the heavens have decreed so obstinate a fate for me, then it would be better for me to go into the forests, leave all people behind, and live out the rest of my tearful life as a hermitess!"

While Dushen'ka was preparing to go away, concealing her grief from all her relatives, they were no less crushed by her misfortune and everywhere sought fiancés for her. But wherever they looked the young men were afraid to anger

Venus and the gods, who, evidently, had decreed the contrary.
Nobody wanted to marry Dushen'ka, or nobody dared to.
Finally, her family resolved to seek advice and to consult the
Oracle about future events. The Oracle gave his answer in
orderly verses and the priests-prophets, for greater sense,
added their own lines to them. But the addition made the
answer no less confused. Word for word it went like this:

"The husband for Dushen'ka designated by the fates is a
monster who stings all, disturbs the tranquillity of entire
regions and frequently destroys them. He often rends hearts,
feeding on tears, and wears a quiver of dreadful arrows on
his back. He shoots, wounds, burns, imposes fetters—on
earth if he wishes, or, if he wishes, in heaven. Even the Styx
does not bar any paths to him. The fates and all the gods, so
determining, give a true sign by which he may be sought: let
the princess be taken to the very summit of an unknown
mountain thirty lands away where no one has ever gone until
now and there be left to her destiny, for happiness or for
sorrow, for life or for death."

Such an answer brought fear and sadness to the whole
court. All were filled with doubt and dread. "O true gods! Is
it possible that you have become so stern? Is there any reason
why Dushen'ka should be given forever to a monster to whom
nobody knows the way?" All the relatives so agreed tearfully,
and those of them who were familiar with all the folk tales
imagined to themselves processions of evil monsters and the
horror of a cruel death either in their paws or in their fangs.
From their nurses long ago they learned about the existence
of such serpents and spirits who open their mouths wide and
who have seven heads and seven horns and seven or even
more tails. The relatives were terrified by such horrors.

Later, without saying anything further, they began to howl
in a multitude of different voices. They promised to conduct
the princess to the place the Oracle spoke of, and in advance
said goodbye to her forever. Only, they did not know where
the mountain could be to which Dushen'ka had to be taken.
The Oracle did not say, or if he did, then it was too little.
Where was it to be found? Was it far from the court? What
time were they supposed to arrive there, and what was the
name of the mountain? Sinai or Lebanon, Tabor or Caucasus?
And those who revered Dushen'ka's high intelligence, trying
to guess, thought that she had to go, of course, to Mount

Parnassus. They had heard that certain of the Muses had ties with her, that Dushen'ka learned from them to sing songs and to understand the mysteries of the beauties of Parnassus. But those who read history supposed the opposite: that from olden days the Muses passed their entire life in virginity and no human being ever went there, that it would be impossible to find a husband for Dushen'ka there and that frequently there was a frost from the North there and the people who lived by the Castalian waters often froze, even though the paths there were holy.

Others, having selected the hottest climates, wanted to take Dushen'ka to Africa, where they knew that monsters were held in great esteem. Besides, following the Oracle's counsel, they wanted to take her specifically to Atlas once they learned that this mountain, which reaches up to the heavens, was famed from ancient times for the number of miracles associated with it. And they thought that by this sign this was precisely what the Oracle had said in his answer. Then the bolder of the bereaving kin proposed, out of a desire to protect her blossoming days, that serpents might easily devour Dushen'ka there and that the Oracle should not at all be heeded. Without further deliberation they all unanimously exclaimed then that the Oracle himself did not know Dushen'ka's fate and that the Oracle was just raving in delirium.

At last in council the princess's family, and especially her father, the king, judged it better, contrary to the authority of the gods, to suffer persecutions and all sorts of misfortunes than to take Dushen'ka as sacrifice without knowing where. But Dushen'ka herself was magnanimous and wanted to be obedient to the Oracle. Or perhaps, if I am not deceiving myself, she was just tired of living with her relatives without a spouse, and finally determined to look for one on her own, whoever and wherever he might be.

So that her sacrifice would be evident to her family, she said to them resolutely: "I must save you by my own unhappiness. Let the higher will have its way with me; and if I die, then such was my fate."

While Dushen'ka was announcing her decision to her father, the king and all his council began crying anew and in their sorrow were unable to utter a single word, for only streams of tears were coursing down their cheeks. But grief itself, in most sorrowful lament, could be seen above all on the face of the queen. In front of all she burst into a rage of grief and contorted her face in horror. Losing her senses, she rolled on the floor as though deprived of her legs; or in her misery, losing all sense of measure, she began cursing Venus in every way she could; or taking her beloved child strongly in her embrace she shouted out loud before all the people and swore by her entire race that as long as she lived she would never again pay heed to the Oracle's words and that not for any miracle would she let her daughter go from her. Although she shouted this at the top of her lungs, nonetheless, despite her vows, Amor, the fates and gods, the Oracle and priests, the family, king, and daughter ordered provisions readied for the road.

In those days the Oracle was held in such great esteem in Greece that every person endeavored to fulfill his words and himself sought the prophesied woes so that what was possible only to foretell would unfailingly come to pass.

The princess was ready to leave the city, and her attire for the road was arranged. But where was she to go? This was a secret to all of them. Finally the princess herself resolved the uncertainty in the same way that she decided all matters— by her own judgment. To all her family she said only that they should outfit her handsomely for the road and that they should seat her in a chariot, leaving the horses to themselves without a coachman or reins: "Fate," she said, "will do the driving. Fate will show the true course to the dwelling place of joy or sorrow where I must be left." After these words of hers, preparations for the journey did not take long.

The chariot was ready; the king's daughter was ready, and with her the queen, who was unable to restrain herself and insisted on seeing Dushen'ka off. The horses started off without waiting for a command. They carried her without reins; they carried her from the court; they carried her from the city and, finally, from the furthermost towns. For this journey, whether short or long, the king had arranged a funeral procession. Sixteen men carried candles all about in broad daylight, just as at night; sixteen men, to the accompaniment of sad music, very slowly intoned a doleful song; sixteen men, a little behind the others, carried the crystal bed in which Dushen'ka liked to sleep; sixteen men, having placed them on cushions, carried the princess's tambours and bobbins, which her mother, the queen, herself had made, her traveling toilet, combs and pins, and all the other things that went with it. Later in the procession marched a regiment of bearded priests bearing before them the Oracle's pronouncement. Each one of the priests gave his own interpretation to the utterance, and each one wished besides to reach peace as quickly as he could. Behind them came the Senate and every high rank. After that rode the sad chariot in which the queen sat with her daughter. At her feet stood a silver pitcher. This was a mourning urn the ancient Greeks used to give as a gift when they were parting with someone forever. The king walked beside the chariot with his neighbors, begging the gods for all their blessings, and surrendering the management of royal affairs to the fates, sighed freely along the way at each step. Beholding the king, a crowd gathered close to the chariot and each person went together with the princess on the journey as far as he could. Some sobbed, others wailed loudly not knowing where they were carrying both daughter and mother. Some thought that from the looks of things they were taking Dushen'ka to bury her alive. Others strewed wreaths and flowers before her along the way. Some were singing hymns decorously praising the beauties that they were beholding for the first time in their lives. Others called the princess a deity, and returning to their homes announced that they had witnessed a miracle. The priests vainly shouted that in so honoring the princess they were offending Venus and, as was the custom, they tried to lead the people away from this misfortune with a push or whatever way they could. But all, despite the priests' authority, having forgotten the harm that Venus could do them and all the possibility of woes, insisted on following Dushen'ka in crowds sincerely and touchingly.

After several weeks, they had already passed the thirty lands but did not see even a single hillock, and those who grew more tired protested with each curse that they had no idea where they were going. Finally, after traveling far and wide, no sooner had they come up to a mountain than the horses suddenly stopped and refused to proceed any further no matter how much they were beaten. Here they found all the signs of the fates. The priests unanimously confirmed the signs and all announced that Dushen'ka had to be left on the very top of the mountain, according to the words of the Oracle, under the vault of the sky. All entrusted her to the gods-protectors and led her to the summit along the stones and gravel, where there was no sign of a road, hardly lifting their tired feet, across rocks, hillocks, and deep chasms, where there was neither forest nor grass, and where hungry lions roared. And even though the priests admonished the people to courage in these places, at each step of the way they met a new dread: terrible caverns, steep climbs above and abysses below, without form and without measure. Some thought they saw termagants there, others flying dromedaries, dragons, and cerberuses that with their different roars deafened their hearing and dampened their spirits.

Such was the path along which the princess was hastening, along which the groaning retinue behind her was crowding. Only the queen stayed behind, unable to climb more than half the mountain. Crying bitter tears she parted with Dushen'ka forever. In all the hardship of the ascent the princess's bed smashed in the hands of those carrying it, and many, out of fear and much belabored, threw off their caps, which dragons quickly devoured. Others tore their clothes on bushes and, looking naked, could hardly conceal their shame from the eyes of others. Finally there remained only a few pins and several of the Oracle's verses for reference. But is it possible to describe in writing the king and his court when they all appeared at last with the princess on the summit of the mountain? The reader can imagine it in his own mind. I shall say only that all bade her farewell, and afterward the king, doubled over by sorrow, had to be torn from his daughter's hands by force. Then the light of day, looking upon the sorrow of these separations, seemed to shorten its usual course in the world and hastened to plunge into the waters. And night, seeing the king's daughter alone, covered her with a black veil and with the languishing beam of faintly shining stars revealed in the darkness the whole horror of those places. The king then quickly undertook his departure from there, not knowing what the end would be to such blind beginnings.

BOOK TWO

But where can I find the lines to express the fear that all nature manifested upon seeing Dushen'ka left alone in this expanse of darkness without father, without mother, without family and, in a word, entirely without people, among the dragons and beasts? Now everything the king's daughter had heard from her nurses and everything she had read in marvelous tales presented itself to her confused mind. Spirits and magical apparitions with which she had once been frightened revealed signs of various deaths to her there and increased the gloom of this dark night. But no sooner had Dushen'ka opened her mouth to utter a complaint without saying to whom, when suddenly a miraculous force bore her above the earth on wings of air. An invisible zephyr, her fortunate abductor, companion, and guardian at that time, beholding a beauty unheard of until then, forgot at first to inform Dushen'ka that a gracious ruler ordered her to be carried up high with due respect, and concentrating only on his own wonderment just raised her coverings in flight. Seeing, however, that Dushen'ka was barely alive from fright, he overcame his ecstasy and broke her fear by telling her with a softness appropriate to a zephyr that he was carrying her to a most blissful world—to her mate whom the Oracle had prophesied to her, and that her mate has been sighing for a long time without a spouse, that regiments of spirits had been assigned to her as servants and that he himself was ready to fall at her feet, and to this he added a number of flattering words. The cupids who now surrounded the princess unanimously confirmed these words by the smiles on their lips and the joy in their eyes.

In a short while the zephyr bore her to a region of the heavens unknown to her. He set her down amid a court and at once disappeared. What a host of wonders now appeared to Dushen'ka!

Through a grove of myrtle and palm trees splendid halls presented themselves to her sight. They shone amid a countless number of fires, and the paths everywhere were strewn with roses. But the roses assumed a pale appearance before her and caressed her legs with tender feeling. Porphyry gates, in front and on the sides, sapphire columns, a balcony of ruby, golden cupolas and emerald walls must seem wondrous to a simple mortal, but to the gods alone these things are not difficult. Such was the path—reader take note—that opened up before Dushen'ka when in the form of a goddess flying upward from darkest wilderness she unexpectedly came to some beautiful paradise.

Placing her hope in the gods, trying to bolster her spirits with their signs, hardly had she taken a step when forty nymphs all dressed alike ran out to greet her. They had been watching for her arrival. The oldest of them, bowing very low to her and speaking in most respectful tones, delivered the required welcoming speech in the name of her friends. A great chorus of forest sprites then sang twice as soon as they heard her words of praise, and an entire assembly of cupids flew to serve her. At each honor bestowed on her the princess answered graciously, now by a sign, now by words. The zephyrs, pushing each other with their heads in the crush, wanted to lead her or carry her to the palace, but Dushen'ka ordered them to be at peace, and went herself, surrounded by all kinds of servants, and laughter and merriment flying all about her. The reader has seen such activity in a beehive when the young generation, abandoning the old bees, spins around, sports about, babbles, and flies away, but after the queen, whom it esteems, it humbles itself and flies to its new destiny.

Amid these fine honors the princess did not know if her promised mate, the ruler of these blissful places whom the zephyr had partly portended before in confusing words without saying directly, was a spirit or simply a human being. Upon entering the house she wished to see her mate and questioned the servants about him many times. But the whole throng that accompanied her or flew about her could not tell her about him in more detail, and Dushen'ka remained in ignorance about him. In the meantime she passed the steps of a porch and was ushered into a most spacious hall from which on all sides, through many doors, there opened before her a handsome vista of lanes, groves, and fields; farther on, high balconies revealed the kingdom of Flora and Pomona, cascades and ponds and marvelous gardens. From there the forty nymphs led her to rooms that only gods can create, and there they brought Dushen'ka to a bath prepared for her so that she might refresh herself from her journey. The cupids brought her the purest dew, which they gathered everywhere, instead of water. The zephyrs warmed the air with their breathing, blew up bubbles from various perfumes, and prepared the fragrant soaps with which Eastern potentates wash themselves and which have a known stimulative power.

The princess permitted the removal of the coverings of her charms only after seeing the new clothes prepared for her choice, but not without the embarrassment, argument, and stress usual at such a time. Regiments of all kinds of servants, after first bowing, could not leave there without sighing and even behind the doors, although their service to the princess was finished, willingly kissed her footsteps in their leisure. Only the zephyrs, having entry everywhere, the predatory zephyrs, because they were small in stature, found tiny cracks in the windows and doors and stole in among the nymphs and splashed about the water where Dushen'ka was bathing. She appeared to them—or rather touched them—in all her beauty. But Dushen'ka had no inkling of it.

Zephyrs! You whom I consider most fortunate, you beheld the beauty of the princess. Zephyrs! You must instruct me how I am to tell the readers, or perhaps you yourselves will tell them in detail the shapes and lines and all the charms of the princess, which are awkward for me to present with the pen. For then you beheld neither a vision nor dreams. . . . But now you are silent. . . . I understand your silence. To picture the divine gifts both you and I need a special gift of the gods; I shall not dare to describe her charms here.

Upon finally leaving the bath, the princess cast her glances with pleasure at the clothes and outfits and a certain crown that had been selected for her. Then they dressed her, as a royal personage, in the richest robes. It is not hard to understand that at her disposal there poured forth handfuls of precious stones and pearls, and an unknown power, at a word from Dushen'ka, brought her all sorts of rare delights. Dushen'ka would no sooner mention something than the desired object suddenly appeared before her eyes. Captivated by her beautiful raiment, she wanted to admire herself in a mirror—at her very glance mirrors sprang up everywhere and stood in a great row along the walls before her so that her beauty might in this way be multiplied. After looking at herself from the front, back, and over the shoulder, from head to foot, the princess could easily judge of her future husband that he was obviously not very poor. In the meantime, for her pleasure a table appeared prepared in a special room. Decorations for the table, and viands, drinks, and sweets of all kinds appeared there in plenty and even to excess. No less than what could serve for the dining only of the gods in a most splendid residence stood before her now in row after row. One dish, upon her tasting of it, made her forget about her sorrow; another imparted to her beauty and strength. The cupids, running all about to show their diligence, tried to share the obligations of host. One held the rank of cupbearer, another carried the plates and dishes; one set the table, and each poked his nose in everywhere. And he considered it the highest honor from whose hands their domestic goddess deigned to lift half a glass of nectar. And many gaping faces stood before her, although the cupids, in truth considered not at all greedy, took greater pleasure then in the sight of the princess than in wine.

While the princess was so feasting, high above her from the summits, in the sorrowless halls, resounded the sweet sound of musical instruments and songs of praise to her which only the god of poetry could create. At first the heavenly singers celebrated in song the beauty of their new queen. The reader himself knows how much she enjoyed such praise. Nevertheless Dushen'ka was unable to decide whether or not she preferred the pleasantness of the voices, the dignity of the violin, the harmony of the harps, or the flute—they all held an equal place in art and all were permeated with the same spirit so that Dushen'ka would discover her own place in paradise by touch, taste, sight, and hearing. If one can regard as truth everything that is said, the Greeks have a saying that for this magnificent chorus it was as though Orpheus and Amphion were purposely sought and that, losing his heart to Dushen'ka, Apollo by choice himself played and directed the orchestra. Afterward the chorus of singers, slowly, in a certain pleasant tempo, sang verses with uplifted voices, verses so slow, so distinct to the ear, so pleasantly charming in their composition that Dushen'ka was easily able to follow the words, was easily able to memorize them, and soon learned them by heart and later repeated them throughout the entire court. Later the immodest zephyrs carried these verses to the four corners of the earth, and eventually they even reached us:

> In love participate all hearts;
> The gods themselves bow to its arts.
> You, Dushen'ka, will know love too,
> And happiness will come to you.

This song was sung three times before Dushen'ka, and for many years thereafter was it sung to the princess. Finally, one of the nymphs appeared to announce that it was already time for Dushen'ka to retire to bed. The princess blushed at the word "bed" and, as a bride, was frightened, but she did not wish to argue. Dushen'ka was undressed and taken to a room, and there, as necessary for rest from her journey, she was placed in a bed on a certain pedestal after which all the servants bowed and then took leave of her. Suddenly, it is not known from where, her husband appeared to her, unseen. And if people ask how did he appear unseen, it is not difficult to answer: he appeared in the dark, and although she could feel him in her embrace she still could not see him. He was like a spirit or a sorcerer, but he did not reveal himself.

Nobody has dared to part the veils of nightly deeds. I do not know what they said to each other nor what the circumstances were at the time. This secret has remained with them forever. But on the following morning the cupids noticed that the nymphs were softly giggling among themselves, and the guest, being somewhat shy by nature, appeared among them with veiled eyes.

Marriage could be pleasant to the princess, but the secrecy seemed inexplicable to her. One could say that Dushen'ka did and did not have a husband. He came to her at night and left at dawn. He was nameless, ageless, statureless, featureless, and instead of a required answer, he concealed his identity and responded to Dushen'ka's questions by begging and admonishing her that there was no need for her to fear anything and that she should not wish to see her husband until a certain time had come.

And Dushen'ka did not know with what monster or god she was passing her nights.

Such a marriage was unheard of. The princess, thinking about it one way or another, sought the solution to the mystery in the Oracle. Long ago the Oracle had described her husband to her as a frightful horror. Her husband seemed to agree with the Oracle's description, for he never showed himself to her. When she felt her husband's body and listened to her husband's words, however, Dushen'ka thought the contrary, that he could not be frightful to behold. Nevertheless, the Oracle had so spoken and the gods themselves had declared that her husband bore terror wherever he went. And if it was so that he had horns or beast's legs, or claws on his hands, or a foul shape, then it was better for Dushen'ka—

for as long as she lived—not to see and not to know such a
freak who terrified all Nature.

While Dushen'ka was wrestling with this problem in bed,
dawn came to drive away the veil of night, and day took on
a light appearance. But even the light could not cheer the
confused princess, who could not put the night that had
passed out of her thoughts. Then, without waiting for night,
an obliging dream again closed her lovely eyes in the morning.
Her husband, flying all about her face, then appeared to her
in all his beauty—comely, tender, tall, fair, and cheeks glowing brighter than crimson. He looked like a young Apollo or,
one can say, a handsome Cupid, about eighteen years old or
so, that is, close to twenty, and in all his beauty and glory.
The princess, beguiled by this dream in her sleep, yearned
to see her husband in daylight, and grasped the shadow and
shouted: Stop! The apparition had led her into ecstasy, but
the apparition was leaving her as though it were drifting far
away. She called after it, pursued it, and caught the fugitive;
but this movement finally interrupted her false dream, and
Dushen'ka, waking up, discovered in her hands, not the
fugitive, but just her sleeping robe.

It is known that her husband, hiding there, wanted to
eavesdrop on her love delirium, but fate obstinately opposed
the meeting. The princess saw only the traces of her husband,
and she could observe only that he really had visited her, that
he had left her love in his absence and that she was now
burning with this love. "But who is he? Who?"—she asked
again, and again wanted to sleep and dream of him. And
again sleep, circling about her quietly, calmed her thought
with pleasant dream for the second time just as it had for the
first. I do not know if this dream lasted long, but Dushen'ka
did not awake from sleep until noon had passed and it was
already one o'clock in the afternoon.

Then all the servant girls came in an assemblage to dress
the princess again and they brought with them forty garments
and all that went with them. For that day she designated the
simplest dress of all, for Dushen'ka was hastening to view
the rarities of these marvelous halls. Following in the princess's train, I shall hasten to present this mansion and shall
describe in detail everything that could bring her delight there.

At first Dushen'ka went through all the chambers and,
running all about, did not pass by a single room or corner

where she would not have spent an hour. Thence to the belvedere, thence to the balcony, thence to the veranda, thence down and outside, so that she could see the mansion from all sides. The crowd of girls was unable to keep up with her. Only the zephyrs were able to follow her and everywhere protected her, as was fitting, lest she fall in her running. She thrice looked over the entire mansion inside and out. Meanwhile, the zephyrs and cupids pointed out the architecture to her and all the wonders of Nature that Dushen'ka, looking all about her, suddenly wanted to see and did not know what to look at first. One thing quarreled with another to captivate her gaze, and Dushen'ka would have gone everyplace she could had she not become weary from her running.

When she was resting from these labors she looked at statues by the most famous masters. There were likenesses of inimitable beauties whose names, in prose and verse, in various tales both short and long, have reigned immortally among all peoples in all ages. Callisto, Daphne, Armene, Niobe, Helen, the Graces, Angelica, Phryne, and a multitude of other goddesses and mortal women appeared live before her eyes standing along the walls there in all their wondrous beauty. But right in the middle, in front of them on a high pedestal, stood the image of the princess herself, and surpassed all the others in beauty. Looking at her own image, she fell to wondering, and remained that way, beside herself with joy! Then another statue might have been seen in her such as the world had never before beheld.

Of course, Dushen'ka would have remained longer looking at this image of herself with which she was so taken had the servants who were attending her not indicated elsewhere other images of her beauty and glory for the new delight of her eyes. They portrayed her to her waist, to her feet, or her whole figure, or to her very heels; they were of gold, of silver, of bronze, or of iron; there were heads and busts and medallions; and still elsewhere mosaics or marble or agate presented new views of equal pricelessness.

In other places Apelles, or the god of painting, who directed his brush with his own hand, portrayed Dushen'ka with all her beauty—which the mind till then could not imagine. Did she wish to see herself in pictures? Here fauns bring her Pomona's horn and plait wreaths for her and pluck flowers in valleys and play songs for her and jump in circles all about her. There, with a fearful buckler on her chest, dressed as Pallas, she strikes terror from astride a steed, and more with her beautiful look than with her lance wounds hearts with a sweet plague. And there before her stands Saturn, toothless, bald, and gray with new wrinkles on his old face; and, trying to forget that he is an ancient grandfather, he straightens his decrepit figure, desires to be younger, curls the locks of hair still remaining to him and, in order to see Dushen'ka, puts on a pair of glasses. And there again she is seen like a queen, surrounded by cupids, in an aerial chariot. To the glory and beauty of Dushen'ka the cupids shoot hearts in flight. They fly in a great throng and all carry quivers of arrows on their backs, and all, taking pride in her beautiful eyes, fly with war to the entire world, their bows raised. And there fierce Mars, the destroyer of the laws of peace, assumes a gentle mien upon perceiving Dushen'ka. No longer does he stain fields with blood, and at last, having forgotten his rules of war, humbled at her feet, he burns with love for her. And there she appears now amid merriments that precede her everywhere and, with the inventions of games, everywhere bring a radiant smile to her face. And elsewhere the Graces surround the princess, adorn her with different kinds of flowers, and a zephyr, flying quietly about her, draws this picture in order to embellish the world with it. But in jealousy of licentious glances, tempering the minds of the lovers of liberties or as if shunning seditious critics, he conceals in the painting the greater part of her charms. And many of them, miraculously of course, then suddenly painted themselves before Dushen'ka.

Everywhere in the halls there the princess's eyes were met by magnificent objects dedicated to her glory. Portraits of her appeared everywhere along the walls, in simple attire and elegant and in different masquerade costumes. Dushen'ka, you are lovely in all raiments: whether you are dressed up like some queen or whether you are seated by some hut in the simple garb of a shepherdess. In all, you are a wonder of the world, in all you appear a beautiful divinity, and only you are prettier than your portrait. Posterity knows that this wondrous house, where the residents zealously deified you, this temple of your beauty was erected by the cupids, that the cupids embellished it, that the cupids showed your image everywhere, and that, finally, it was the cupids who fitted to the face in each picture different costumes capable of enticing your delightful glances.

Is such attire pleasing and are these new dresses of need to you? You shall see that they are ready, that your admiring glance already has been noticed and from your aerial retinue a zephyr has come to announce to you that all the new dresses have been sewn—when will you order them to be brought to you?

I should like to describe in detail the other wonders of these marvelous rooms, where everything filled the eye and was unlike anything else; but I meet Dushen'ka everywhere with my mind, I grow enchanted and quickly forget about the rooms. Was not each house and each country transformed into a paradise by her presence? Did not paradise assume its existence and beginning with her? And if I have said little about these rooms, the readers will certainly forgive me because of it. I must follow Dushen'ka into the garden, whither she now draws the thoughts and gaze of all.

In these happy places the earth was warmed by the constant heat of summer, and the year round bountifully brought forth harvest without any spells of inclement weather. The throng of servants then flew to greet the princess, and everyone sought to keep busy with something while in her presence; to show her the way, to tell her stories, or simply to amuse her. The entire court understood that Dushen'ka liked to run about and go for walks, and in the groves or gardens, as soon as she appeared, Nature refreshed itself with her presence: the trees bowed their branches to her as though they recognized their own inclination, and with quiet rustle beneath the shade proclaimed to one another the beauties of their princess. And the grass and flowers, sprawling newly on this day that was delightful for them, doubled their aromatic fragrance in the gardens. But the jasmine shone more than the others, and wherever the princess went it grew out to greet her. She was very fond of the fragrance of jasmine and gathered these flowers for herself for a bouquet. This fortunate bouquet, pressed to her bosom, as though animated bent to cling to her. Choruses of birds nestled close, hearing the rustle of the trees, and set out after the cupids on the familiar path in order to have a closer glimpse of Dushen'ka. Some of them hovered all about her while others flew before her, and many chirped among themselves in wonderment. There were not to be seen there any ill-omened birds of night or any sullen faces. The quarrelsome Satyrs did not dare to intrude, and only the quietest of zephyrs wafted there. Fountains exerted themselves to rise higher in order to have a better look at the beauty of the princess that the surrounding throng screened from them. And if Dushen'ka walked near to them, they strove to fall down from on high to her feet. Naiads, splashing about the waters, impatiently awaited her arrival at their fortunate shores. Others climbed up on cascades to look at her path, their heads raised and, once they caught sight of Dushen'ka, they threw themselves headlong at her. In this general festival of Nature even the stone figures above the currents everywhere opened their mouths wide in astonishment and from their insides released a flood of water. This sight presented to her all kinds of creatures in countless representations: crawling, leaping, feathered, four-legged; and all the creatures and wonders of Nature then appeared in this happy dominion for Dushen'ka's service or for her amusement, or for the glory of her triumph.

She went next to covered lanes that led to a thick and dark forest. At the entrance to it, in the shade of overhanging branches, new artistic inventions presented themselves: goddesses, gods, fairies, mighty warriors, and famous kings of history or legend appeared in their true images there, with descriptions of who they were and whenceforth they came. In a word, this was a history of the ages. Then the obliging cupids sought to recount various tales for her enjoyment. And there amid the wonders of Nature Dushen'ka found in these scenes her own people, her father and her mother. And in this uninhabited wilderness the whole world appeared to her with great accuracy, as though on a map. Although Dushen'ka enjoyed walking through the woods by herself, and later went every day to these shaded places either alone or accompanied by her retinue, on this first day she did not venture into the thick groves either because of the oncoming night or because, not seeing a road into the forest, she feared all the wonders there, or because her feet were simply tired from all the walking she had done.

I shall not pause to present before the reader's eyes her pleasant dreams on the nights that followed. He can easily imagine them for himself. But the days there became the cause of her separation, for despite all their pleasures the days still had their tedium. It is rumored that Dushen'ka then began to take a great interest in dress. Especially on the days when she prepared to go into the garden she attired herself in new garments with all the fuss of a dandy. Rumor often has an element of truth in it in this world: it was certainly becoming for Dushen'ka to take walks and sometimes drive away boredom with frivolity.

On one of these days, going far into the deep forest, the princess came across a brook that began to flow anew, as though upon her summons. But in the flow of the crystal waters the beauty of the shores was concealed in distant groves, and a seductive glance led later to mountains from which clear streams, breaking through the resistance of the earth, offered her nourishing juices. Then a grotto opened up, settled among the waters in a new manner. It led thence to a cave where the rays of the sun shone only at the entrance and where bubbling fountains just as at night revealed in darkest freedom a hidden view or a mystery of nature. History informs us, and the folk know it, that upon entering this path, which was unknown to her, Dushen'ka did not dare go farther because of the dark beginning of the enterprise. But then miraculously, without saying anything, her husband invisibly grasped her under the shoulders and in the very darkness on a certain high place of green turf, by the currents of the waters of streams, sat down with her together and spoke much, in prose and verse, as we do among ourselves. Nobody knows what the princess answered him: we know only that she later wore out the small path to this place. From that time on, the princess spent hours both day and night together with her husband, and loved the dark grotto more than all other pleasures. When she was overtaken by the darkness of the night, she returned together with her husband to their own room. Then the aerial chariot carried them in a thick cloud beneath the dark tent of the sky, and each day the princess of these places, pacified by a sweet dream, set out on the same course as before from the house to the grotto, from the grotto to the house.

But reason demands hours of freedom; it is boring to spend a whole day making love, and the princess was just following the laws of nature in this respect. She would then devise various amusements: gay dances of cupids and nymphs, blind man's buff, and hurdles, with all kinds of games that have remained with us to this very day. Finally, the cupids tried to compose, according to Dushen'ka's taste, comedies, ballets, concerts, operas, amusing operettas, and everything a clever mind can create in happy and carefree days for the pleasure of the tender feelings. In Greece Menander, in France Molière, Quinault, Destouches, Regnard, Rousseau, and Voltaire himself, in Russia, finally, the like foe of vices, the writer of our own times, esteemed Sumarokov, all tried to imitate the theatre of Dushen'ka, and only in later ages could they depict the various deeds of nature the cupids presented there for the very first time. So that the merriments should continue there without any hindrances, the sad sight of deaths, sorrows, and betrayal was unknown in paradise, where only laughter reigned and where, amid pleasures, the dagger of woeful Melpomene was put aside. But with the growth of more mature years the princess longed to see the world that she knew before, and often, abandoning children's amusements, she wanted to know better the different customs of peoples—who they were, how they lived, and if they were of some use to the world. She could have easily found this knowledge in her library. The great number of books in it, both large and small, at first turned her away from reading. But soon Dushen'ka discovered that the mind is capable of learning anything. She found out how to distinguish sensible thought from jokes, how to judge and be observant. In true histories she found a sufficient number of false additions; in the writers of philosophic systems she found, with each concoction, no lack of idiotic arrogance, although frequently their pretense ended in nothing. By chance, in this great collection of books she happened to come across one tragedy by which the writer endeavored to move all his readers to tears and where the beloved, in most sorrowful array, not knowing what to say often shouted: Oh![13] But with what and how did fear intrude upon her woes? After saying "I love you," she ran out of a room and left the hero alone to sigh.

The princess also took poems to read, but as she read them, as though in punishment for sins, she came to know for the first time in her life complete and utter boredom, and throw-

[13] A reference to the tragedy *Panteia* (1769) by F. Kozel'skii. In the monologues of the titular character the exclamation "Oh!" is repeated frequently.

ing them under a table, she bruised her hand in the process. The rumor later circulated that the author of these unhappy verses, on a decree of Apollo, was driven forever from Helicon and that Dushen'ka, fearing like boredom, or for the the sake of saving her hands, refrained from reading poetry for a whole week, although she liked it and herself sometimes composed it. In the time of this exile of poetry, when neither songs nor odes were read to her, the princess wished to look over translations of the most famous masters. But frequently she did not understand them, and for that reason ordered the cupids to translate them anew in careful style so that she could read them without difficulty.[14] Finally, the zephyrs brought the princess different sorts of papers, which from very old times appeared impudently[15] among the useful ones[16] and by their sheer weight of numbers threatened gravely to burden the Helicon. The princess, when she learned the law, did not transgress the liberties of the paper-wasters, but she did not read their creations.

The princess had already spent three years here, and would have remained longer if this brilliant paradise had been able to satisfy all her desires. But a curious mind, no matter how strong the will, often appears a weakness in the female species. Once she had become familiar with the agreeable mind and ways of her husband, the princess wanted to know still more about him. In all her meetings with him, on days and nights, and on flights on clouds, she besought him sorrowfully to show himself to her so that she might see him. But her husband always assured the princess that he concealed himself for the most important reasons, and he gave her to understand that it was impossible for him to break his oath and that he had sworn on the Styx to the gods about this. The princess ridiculed the Styx and often tried to detain her husband at home in the morning and often, exerting herself greatly, tried pulling him out of the cave into the light, but then he flew out of her hands like the wind and went away, nobody knows where. At other times such tender arguments would have

[14] A reference to the Empress Catherine's committee on the translation of foreign books that met from 1768 to 1783.

[15] Doubtless a reference to the satirical journals of 1769–1774. The "impudent" ones were those of Novikov and Èmin.

[16] By "useful" papers Bogdanovich means simply Catherine's *All Sorts and Sundries*.

given rise to joy instead of further quarrel. But Dushen'ka's husband was frequently pensive and cheerless, and often repeated sullen conversations by which he sought to show her the vanity of the world and praise. Afterward, he admonished Dushen'ka in tears to preserve their agreement lest she be betrayed even by those closest to her. He told her further that envy could bring her many woes and if the summit of supreme gods so judged he could not save her from cruel evils. Having instilled such awful fears in Dushen'ka, her husband hardly flew away from the house when a certain zephyr dispatched for just this purpose brought her wisps of news from all over. She learned that her two sisters had come to look for her on that terrible mountain from which she was once borne by a most fortunate zephyr to the superterrestial realm; that there beneath the mountain they were scared by devils from a multitude of caves and that he could bring to the princess letters and greetings from her sisters, which were more reliable than all the news. Zephyr! Zephyr! If you had but known the insidious flattery of these wicked sisters, then you certainly would have concealed such news from Dushen'ka! Why could not some swift spirit have met him who possessed more information about this and who could have told the zephyr, in the face of such betrayal from her kin, not to talk so much? But it was the will of the heavens that the zephyr, without meeting anyone, hunting in the air all manner of talk on earth, should bring what he heard with the wind to the princess. And so it was that malicious gods arranged for her later to bring her sisters to her.

Since Dushen'ka was accustomed to loving her family ties and to preserving the required love for her sisters, she completely forgot all her husband's admonitions to her. She then ordered the zephyr immediately to bring her sisters before her to paradise as fast as he could. Seeing no sign whatsoever of their perfidy, she wished to show them her fine dresses and brocades and precious stones and her bed and house and all her belongings and to share with them the excess of her riches. Wealth cheers little when nobody knows about it, and one tastes pleasure only when one shares it with others.

Not long afterward, the princesses came to her, and both of them greeted Dushen'ka in happiness. They shook her hands, embraced her tightly, and showed how happy they were by the smiles on their faces. But envy released all its poison

in their hearts when they beheld before their eyes, as though
it were a sin of nature, that their younger sister was alive
because of her beauty, was holding sway in a most beautiful
paradise, and that zephyrs and cupids were serving her. Moreover, the princess told them boastingly that she was married
to a divinity and that her spouse was dearer than Apollo and
more handsome than Cupid; that he chose her to be his wife
from among all mortal beauties; that he surrendered unto her
power the whole of his winged people, and that he placed
paradise at her disposal. Did such a boast have any falsehood
in it? The reader knows—when we love someone we trumpet
the truth about with some embellishment. "But where is your
husband, tell us? . . ." Not knowing what to say and how to
handle herself, the princess, blushing, said to her sisters by
way of answer, "He is not at home." But when Dushen'ka
later tried to amuse them, they could easily imagine then that
Dushen'ka's husband had a paradise in the sky, and a throne,
and many servants, and beauty, and happiness without sorrow,
and that he had elevated Dushen'ka to the heavenly circle for
life. And envying their sister, they easily imagined what they
did not know and did not see, and whispered between themselves with bitter lamentation: "Why did the fates give her
such a husband? We on earth barely found ourselves husbands, and these are as old as grandfathers and not at all
suitable for us as partners." And seething with envy, the
princesses began mercilessly defaming Dushen'ka and kept
repeating afterward that she was not in the least pretty.

Malicious envy, everywhere judging harshly, has many eyes
and sees hidden things through their veils. Although the
princess hid her secret from her sisters and kept up her
pretense for one day, two and three, saying that she was
waiting for her husband to appear in person, her sisters, however, presented the cause of his absence in the darkest possible
light. What will perfidious malice not think of? According to
their words, he was fearful and bad-tempered, and Dushen'ka
truly was living with a monster. Dushen'ka then forgot the
counsels of modesty. Whether it was the sisters' fault, or
destiny or fate or her own flaw of character, she sighed and
revealed to her sisters that in her marriage she loved only a
shadow. She revealed to them, moreover, how and where the
shadow came on schedule, and described all the incidents in
detail. But the only thing she could not say was who her hus-

band was and what kind of creature he was: a sorcerer or a serpent or a god or a spirit. With smiling faces, her perfidious sisters then exchanged glances, and this sly glance doubled the poison of flattery that was covered over by a superficial guise of friendship. Now with pity, now with anger or shame and a certain dread they tried to suggest to their sister that they feared everything in these frightful places, that the house there was one of evil, that it was of course inhabited by serpents or evildoing magicians who first created a paradise and all possible pleasures and then seduced people to this marvelous land just to poison them. To this they added that in the morning they had seen from the balcony of the house the likeness of a dragon in the air above the grotto the princess had told them about and that a terrible serpent with horns was flying there and that this serpent was breathing fire from his nostrils and that finally he inclined from the mountains to the garden, stooped, and crawled into the cave in the grove before their very eyes. After that, the princesses introduced into the conversation dishonor and ignominy on future generations, telling Dushen'ka that she would bear absurd freaks or monsters with whom it would be impossible to live and who would terrify the world.

It was difficult to convince Dushen'ka of much, but the truth is she herself did not know what to make of her mysterious marriage. Her married life always seemed strange to her. If her husband was really not a serpent or a cruel sorcerer, why was it necessary for him to hide from people? Dushen'ka later thought, upon reflection, that some terrible force in the house had charmed her; that her husband, as a serpent, as a most predatory thief, did not dare show himself to anyone by the light of day; that he was beyond faith or law and was worse than a dragon.

In this most sorrowful hour the princess forgot all about the pleasures of paradise; the voice of pleasant songs fell silent, and Merriment and Laughter grew despondent. The words and glances of her wicked sisters increased the poison of gloomy boredom. The cupids suddenly began to tremble and, weeping, flew far away from these halls that were so dear to them. The princess was then left alone to continue talking to her sisters in freedom, and nobody could watch over her words with the necessary fates. "Can I live in the world?" said the princess. "My husband has become hateful to me and my life has become hateful to me." Unhappy Dushen'ka! You thought you were in paradise and you regarded your lot higher than everyone else's. But, parting with your family and outside the circle of the earth, whom do you have as a husband? Only a magical phantom who makes your marriage the most disgraceful and frightens all with a secret treachery. And what sort of progeny will you have? Monsters, vipers or some kinds of serpents. "But if such a lot has been prescribed me by the fates, I would quickly plunge a sword into my unhappy bosom. Dear sisters! I am parting with you forever now. Please tell all my relatives, as I tell you now, what you learned from me and what you saw with your own eyes; that I was deceived here, that I am ashamed to go on living here. . . . Tell them—that I have died!" The sisters, as though they were already expecting punishment for their evil, then advised the princess that the untimely end of her beautiful days would not save the world from sudden rapacity, and later, perhaps, the creator of such cruel evils would devour or strangle all her kin, and that, arming herself against her own life, she should before her death, as an honest woman, kill the sorcerer at an appropriate daylight hour. But for Dushen'ka this crime was dangerous, ugly, and frightful. She shunned villainous deaths, and pity always held sway in her. And perhaps love, which she was ashamed of, was still concealed in her breast. Listening to the murderous counsel of her sisters, the princess suggested in hesitant and sluggish words that there was no sword in the house, nor were there any lethal weapons either, and anyway, how could she kill what was only an empty shadow at night that disappeared in the day? And where would she get for this task a lantern with fire or an icon lamp? On these sorrowful days the zephyrs extinguished all fires in the evenings. The sisters resolutely and boldly answered Dushen'ka that they would immediately bring her a most trustworthy blade, and together they also promised to bring an icon lamp. Whether the readiness of these services was pleasant to her could be observed from her sorrowful words. Confused, Dushen'ka then without further thoughts wanted only to find out what kind of husband she had, and directing her glances toward the garden, several times asked her sisters, who were on their way there, not to forget to bring her the icon lamp.

The order was already given the zephyrs to conduct these

sisters to the earthly sphere, and a pair of boreases was harnessed for the journey. Flying from world to world they mixed ether with air and with storm, rain, and hail appeared before a certain house. This was the Kashcheev arsenal where from oldest times was kept the magical sword, or dagger, with which Hercules fought. With one strong blow this sword had chopped off nine of the Hydra's heads. This sword was kept under guard there, and in fairy tales was known as Samosek. It was kept behind strong walls, but whether it was now bought, or simply taken or stolen from there, writers have not informed us. We know only that it just shone in flight; that the two princesses, taking the aerial paths from earth, bore this sword together with an icon lamp to the very halls of Amor, quickly took their leave of Dushen'ka and were swiftly on their way home again. Oh, if the king's daughter only knew how harmful this sword and this icon lamp were to her! Could the cupids help her with advice? She fled their presence and glances and had in her thoughts only the night that lay ahead.

The light of day already inclined to the forest; night extended its black veil above the house, and together with the darkness the princess's husband came to her, to the room in which the miserable villainy was concealed. And if the tales do not lie, the lovely Dushen'ka used the intelligence, speed, shrewdness, and pretense that are peculiar to wives who, when they have affairs to tend to at night, somehow give peace to their husbands faster. But whether her wiles succeeded at the time or whether her husband himself inclined to sleep with the gnawing of sorrow, he spoke little, sighed, yawned, and dozed off. The princess then carefully got up as quietly as she could and went down along a path of gold, barely touching it with her heels, to a certain room where many barriers concealed the sword and the light of the lamp from people's eyes. Then, with the lamp in her hand she returned, trembling all over with fear, and with a sad expression on her face hid the sword beneath her sleeping gown. She went and lingered on the way, but suddenly hastened her steps afraid of her own shadow and fearing to find a serpent there. Finally, she entered the room of her husband. But who presented himself to her there? Whom did she find in the bed? It was . . . Well, who? . . . It was Amor himself. This god, the ruler of all Nature, to whom all the cupids were submissive. In a deep sleep, almost naked, he was stretched out in the bed covered over with a very thin shroud that hung down over the sides of the bed and only part of which was on his body. His face to one side, his hands spread out—it seemed that in his sleep he was searching everywhere for Dushen'ka. The color of roses was on his cheeks, lilies were strewn about his head, and three rows of white curls clustered all around his very white neck. The form and tenderness of all his limbs exposed in all their beauty, or those which were concealed from view, could have humbled even Adonis, with whom Venus herself had fallen in love and pursued to wild deserts through rain and mud after laying aside the majesty of a goddess. Such a god did Amor reveal himself, or such a god did he resemble: handsome, light and fair-haired, pretty, comely, adept at love, but unencumbered in his thoughts. With these brief outlines the readers themselves may imagine how the god of joys and king of all beauties looked.

Seeing a beautiful deity instead of the viper she feared, Dushen'ka regarded this vision as sorcery or a dream or an apparition, and was dumbstruck for a long time. And seeing finally what everyone could see, that her husband was the handsomest of gods, she was just on the verge of throwing away the lamp and dagger, and forgetting the very thing that had been on her mind, was just about to rush to embrace him as though for the very first time. But love's impetuosity was now stayed by the satisfaction of greedy eyes. So Dushen'ka, without saying anything, without moving, considered this night lovelier than all other nights. More than once did she blame herself in her wonderment, as she looked on all sides at whatever she could see, for not having come to him a long time ago with a lamp, for not having seen his beauty earlier, for being in ignorance about this god and insolently regarding him as a serpent. Then the king's daughter, letting her gaze roam at will on this lovely night, approached him and brought the lamp closer. But by an unexpected misfortune, although her movement was timid and unaudacious, as she held the flame above his body with trembling hand, she carelessly leaned the lamp over a thigh and a little of the melted wax flowed out, burning Amor's thigh and causing him to awaken. Feeling a sharp pain he suddenly started, shouted, woke up and, forgetting his pain, turned with terror from the light. He caught sight of Dushen'ka; he also caught sight of the sword that had then slipped from under her shoulders to her feet; he caught sight of all the guilt or signs of guilt of his evil-thinking wife. She vainly tried to tell him about all her unhappinesses from the very beginning, but the words halted in her mouth and the light and the sword appeared evidence of her guilt. And Dushen'ka then fell into a faint.

BOOK THREE

Dushen'ka used to be the spirit of joy. Dushen'ka used to be a great lady. In days gone by, as soon as a teardrop flashed in her eyes, or Dushen'ka sighed about something, or made a wry face, or merely cast a glance, regiments of servants would immediately appear on all sides to do her bidding, bearing waters and spirits from the four corners of the earth. And Aesculapius[17] himself, even though he lived far away, would be immediately sought to take her pulse, look at her, or simply give advice, and he would exhaust all his learning in her behalf. When rumors began to circulate through the court that Dushen'ka had violated a law of paradise and that Amor had left her because of a sin, all her attending spirits abandoned her. The zephyrs, however, were not in the ranks of unfaithful servants. Of her entire court retinue, these old gallants alone remained with Dushen'ka and flew above her in the distance. But all know that zephyrs were winds and therefore light, just like our fops. When they beheld beauties that previously had blossomed, and then beheld them when they had faded, lifeless, the zephyrs could not be faithful for a long time in their attachment. Abandoning the princess, they too soon flew away.

Although, it seemed, the lovelies of the court who had served her also grieved for her then, each of them herself was beautiful and had her own affairs to look after and her own vanities. They strove, sought, flirted, and hoped that perhaps the creator of the loveliest paradise, that perhaps this god of joys and pleasures, having abandoned Dushen'ka because of her foolishness and sin, might finally cast his glance at his very own court and perhaps might select a wife from among them. And each one, praising her mistress, herself wanted to be mistress in paradise.

[17] In Roman mythology the god of medicine and healing.

The cupids were the most well disposed of all to the princess. They had always loved her, and when they beheld evil misfortune come upon her they sincerely wanted to be of help to her, but out of humble respect for supreme authority they did not dare approach her at the time. Or perhaps they too, foreseeing her misfortunes and griefs, judged that it would be better for her to die in this sorrow, and did not help her out of pity for her. They saw, alas, at that very hour the command inscribed for the zephyrs on the wind. . . . And so the cupids parted with Dushen'ka, burst out sobbing, and escorted her only with their glances now. The zephyrs carried the princess back to earth from the high regions to the place from which they had taken her and there left her half dead, as though a sacrifice to the cruel lions and the vipers.

Die, Princess, die! Your sweet age has already flown away with passing day! And if death cannot save you from griefs, this world where until now you were the equal of a deity from now on to your sorrow will be filled with evil, and wherever you go it will present you with misfortune after misfortune. Amor left you to your suffering; your paradise, your pleasures, your amusements, your games, your laughter have passed with time, have passed, just like a dream. Who once tasted joy and then was deprived of it and knows full well its value and loss and more, who loving was separated from his beloved and sees no happiness before him any longer, easily feels, without further word, that Dushen'ka would have been better off dying in her grief. But wrathful fate was so severe toward her at the time that no matter how much she called on the Fearful Sisters for help, and no matter how much she sought death, destiny had decreed that Dushen'ka should live and that she should suffer in life.

After several hours, just as a rosy beam of Aurora, cleansed in the waters, was peeking out at the mountains and Phoebus became friendly with her in the blue heavens, or so to say in simple terms: when day appeared after night, Dushen'ka woke up, opened her bright eyes, opened them . . . and almost fainted again at seeing where and in what state she then was. Instead of the divine, lovely habitations where a host of laughters, games, merriments, and all manner of servants competed with one another to attract her thought and glance and to serve her without waiting to be commanded, instead of all the wonders arranged in paradise, she saw that under the vault of the heavens she was surrounded by wilderness, mountains and forests, caves of vipers and beasts' lairs where once the priests and the gods themselves and her very own father and mother, the queen, left her to seek her own destiny, to seek her mate, without her knowing in which direction to turn first.

By the light of the morning dawn she saw, in this terrible wilderness, on the very summit of this mountain, where according to tales now everywhere known neither beasts roamed nor birds flew and where, it seemed, only terrors resided—she saw herself without her heavenly coverings, lying in the plain and simple dress, without any decorations or fringes along the edges, in which her parents had attired her when they led her to the summit of the mountain to her misfortune.

Although already accustomed to woes, to fear and unhappiness, Dushen'ka could have expected consolation there from the gods-protectors with their ubiquitous power, and, believing in all kinds of miracles, could easily have reassured herself of their aid and so moderated her grief a little this way—but until then Dushen'ka had been the wife of Amor in paradise, and Dushen'ka, like a fool, had forfeited a love higher than all pleasures, the love of the tenderest lover and friend, or rather of a deity in the guise of a husband.

Changing her misdemeanor into a terrible sin, she burned with a hotter love for him and wanted a hundredfold to right matters, to beg forgiveness of her husband, of the gods, of one and all, but in the wilderness where she was then she possessed no means to do so. In this awful wilderness nobody—neither human being nor god—could see her tears or hear her words. At that moment Amor appeared above her unseen, pining away his sorrow in the gloom of dark clouds. And if a ray of hope penetrated to him, he was afraid to comfort Dushen'ka with this hope. He was secretly in love with her, observed her actions furtively, entrusted her to the care of other gods and, forgiving her rashness and impatience, attributed the blame to her sisters only. We know that according to the intrigues of Venus he should then have surrendered the princess to the fates and that to save her life in so cruel a lot from the wicked dominion with which Venus's wrath then threatened her, he should have contrived everywhere against his own inclination, he should have pretended contrary to his own desires that he no longer loved the princess. Not daring to offer her his favors himself, he gave the strictest order to the echo of this region that the echo should receive everything the princess said and repeat her words loudly for a hundred times.

"Amor, Amor!" she shouted. . . . And it is possible that her words would have continued had not the loud roar of a storm amid the clouds at just that time cut short her sorrowful voice for a while. At the wail of his despairing spouse that penetrated the mountains and the forests of this sad region, which the echo there, amplifying greatly, carried to the very heavens, Amor, feeling a certain horror well up inside him, forgot the terrible pain in his thigh and everything that had happened to him the day before. Moreover, he almost frogot the laws of the supreme authority, and almost hurled himself without further ado from the high clouds to the feet of his beloved with the desire henceforth forever to abandon the splendor of the heavens and to live with her in some wilderness, even in a thick forest. But recalling in the excitement of his desires the unfortunate limit of such vain hopes and the ruin of Dushen'ka ordained for her later, on harshest sentence, the gentle god calmed his passion, sighed, came to a halt, and in his glory descended to Dushen'ka from the heights. He appeared before her eyes, he appeared . . . and revealed himself as he was, as a god. But in order to please Venus and the fates, he looked at her sternly and as though he were abandoning her forever, while he recited to her contemptuously, in an irate voice, the terrible judgment decreed against her by the gods:

"From now on," he said to her, "you have a mistress over you. From now on you will be the slave of Venus. From now on I shall be unable to share your pleasures with you . . . but I hold your wicked sisters more guilty than you." "Amor, Amor!" the princess again cried out. . . . But as she was uttering these words he concealed himself in the clouds, paying no heed to the fact that she was begging forgiveness! He concealed himself and then set out on the heavenly path and appeared no more. The garrulous echoes of distant places, perhaps trained by Venus, overheard the talk in the nearby cave there, saw the rendezvous and departure of the god, and afterward spread the report throughout the world, for fact or fable, for truth or fancy, that, feeling a frightful burning,

Amor limped on his wounded leg; and that this god, as he set out on the return trip to the heavens, himself singed the princess with his beam and brought down a large number of trees with its heat. Be that as it may, the force of tender love or some other dominating power aroused an agonizing longing in her. She forgot all her husband's sternness and remembered only whom she loved and what she had lost because of her insolence. What then was she to expect from the heavens? In despair, shedding streams of bitter tears, filling the surrounding valleys and forests with her wails, the princess cried: "Forgive me, Amor, forgive me!" And at just that terrible hour, seeing a bottomless ravine beneath the mountain, she determined to throw herself from the summit of the mountain into the abyss below. She went, began to cry, a handkerchief at her eyes, sighed, groaned . . . and threw herself over the side!

Whether Amor left the zephyrs without any instructions, whether he ordered them to watch out for Dushen'ka on all the mountains, the reader can see for himself from what transpired. At that time, just at the moment when Dushen'ka hurled herself over the side of the mountain, zealous Skoromakh, the zephyr who had served her on her aerial journeys, when he saw the princess in such obvious danger, awaited no special order. He put aside everything in the high heavens, shook his wings, fluttered them three times and, protecting Dushen'ka as she was flying down with the edges of his aerial robe from every impertinence of the crowd collected on all sides at the bottom, he caught her, delivered her from the bottomless abyss, and quietly laid her down on the soft grass of the fragrant valley. With soft breathing he dissolved the air there, forbade the insolent north winds to blow above her, and did not leave her for a long time, forgetting his beloved Flora. He grieved that he finished his journey so soon and that he could not serve as a support to Dushen'ka longer.

When she saw herself there on the grass, brought there by fates unknown to her, a jasmine shrub in her hair with other different flowers all about, she first thought that she was dreaming the whole thing! And in doubt and wonderment she pinched herself and for a long time could not believe that after she threw herself over the mountain she was still in the world alive. Then dozing off, losing consciousness, she passed into a deep sleep. But historians have forgotten to record if she dreamed about what had happened to her, whether it was good or bad, about her husband on the mountain summit or about sleeping in his bed or about his dreadful angered mother. They have given us to know only that the god Amor ordered the sleep-giving Morpheus to fly over her and to prolong her peace with sleep. Then he sent the zephyr home again.

Now all know that sleep and all Nature itself were governed at the time by statutes of Amor. Amor, who perceived her misery and labor, Amor the worker of miracles, could easily cause Dushen'ka to doze off and rest in sleep. And perhaps, hating the world, she was attracted to the emptiness of this wilderness like a prisoner who sometimes, wearied by tortures and griefs, tries to approach death through sleep. Well, however it was, several hours later the enamored Amor, awake in the heavens and protecting his unfortunate spouse, decided to shorten the service of Morpheus. Dushen'ka awoke, raised a languid glance . . . but, remembering her disgrace, turned her eyes from the world, watered the flowers and grass again with her tears, and called plaintively to the stones and forests: "I will not live any longer! Come, O Death! Come to me!"—she shouted. But Death, however the princess wished to precipitate it, refused to be of service to her. A snub-nosed scarecrow with a bald head, at whose sight every creature trembles, then appeared to her, bearing a long scythe, but only to cut the grass or weeds where Dushen'ka's little steps might tread. When she saw at last that Death ran away from her, she sought ways to end her life now by force. "I'll cut my throat!" she shouted, but she did not have a dagger with her nor any sharp instrument that would have been suitable for cutting off her unhappy life. The reader knows without any further information that Dushen'ka had previously lost all her pins when she was flying down from the mountain, whether by a miracle or simple chance. In this emergency, without thinking any more, she looked for stones in the field, for she wanted somehow to plunge a sharp stone into her breast. Then an end to her unhappy lot appeared: she found a sharp stone. But Dushen'ka led herself, not to death, but to miracles. No sooner did she take a stone in her hands than the stone turned into bread, and instead of mortal torture appeared to her a store of provisions, which she consumed. When Death no longer wished to listen to her, although the world was hateful to her, she still had to eat a slice of bread in order to regain her strength. Then, beholding the forest, the bottomless abysses, the sky and the grass, and again beholding the forest, she thought of another way to end her life; namely, to strangle herself. In olden times such a death was honest and respected. Even to this day the Turks consider it a blissful death when someone is strangled for a crime instead of being slaughtered. Often the viziers and military leaders and even the sultans themselves end their lives in strangle collars for their own treacheries or the treacheries of others. Although strangulation is not considered honorable in other places, and only knaves are sentenced to such a death, the person looking to end his life is prepared to die any way, and Dushen'ka's death was neither an act of shame nor a mere gesture. She would have preferred ending her life with poison, but this whole country where death was prohibited seemed a heavenly garden, seemed created just for benefit and pleasure. And it was fruitless to look for any evil plants there. For like reason any poisonous snake was driven from there. And so it was no wonder that Dushen'ka wanted to strangle herself to death. But where, and with what, and how? According to many tales, a true sign remained: not far from where she was grew an oakwood, and there were tall, thick, and rough oak trees there. Dushen'ka had on at the time a wide shawl that hung from her white shoulders along her sides. In a little while, bearing her beauty to death, the unhappy Dushen'ka appeared in the forest; in a little while, about to end her cruel sorrows and bemoaning her fate, she appeared at the oak tree. After selecting the strongest branch, she took her last step and attached her shawl to the branch. Dushen'ka then placed her little head in the noose. But miracle of miracles! The whole valley and forest trembled! The thick oak branch on which she had strung herself up, out of respect for her lovely head, bent like a twig grown out in vernal days and placed Dushen'ka on the grass safe and sound. And then all the other branches, drawn down by her, or of their own volition, sounded gaily above her and, uniting their ends, plaited various wreaths for her. Only a single insolent branch caught onto her dress and raised up Dushen'ka's covering. Then the whole valley and the forest beheld another miracle of miracles! And the mountains exclaimed as loudly as possible that Dushen'ka was truly lovelier than all. And then Amor himself, looking from the clouds with keen gaze, verified this without words. While Dushen'ka remained among the living, while Nature beautified itself with her presence, another convenient type of death appeared to her by means of which she thought of ending her life. Since she was unable to hang herself from the oak tree, she determined to drown herself. It so happened that a river was not far away. From the steep shore where the river bottom hid itself from view beneath the water, the princess again pursued her death. But fate decreed otherwise: she rode on a pike and, traveling along the surface of this very dangerous road, wet only her train and feet. For her protection a convoy was added: other pikes, trained by the gods or simply without training, having gathered in formation, guarded the princess from further mishaps and splashing all about sent her on her way. Some say that the pikes were really naiads, a squadron of whom appeared to Dushen'ka with a bow. I do not know if this is true or not, but there is no doubt that some of these naiads, or fish, whose race has long ago perished together with the river, until then had served in paradise under a happy law. In their ancient formation they now hurried after Dushen'ka to acknowledge their mistress out of duty, forgetting that from the time the god of beautiful paradise turned the life of paradise into nothing he had dismissed, as if in punishment, all those who had been serving there.

Poor Dushen'ka, no matter how hard she tried to drown herself in the river current, she was carried safely back by a pike and got from one shore to the other. In these torments she vainly cursed life and again vainly summoned death. At her call the aquatic assembly cried in chorus that in her misery Dushen'ka was trying to end her life in the waters uselessly and vainly and that the gods should prolong her lovely years and that henceforth the waters would not receive her unto death.

Finally, one kind of death remained that Dushen'ka had not yet tried. She nourished the hope now that perhaps she might end her life by fire. In the distance smoke could then be seen curling skyward, and a new road to death appeared. Dushen'ka went in the direction of the smoke, and then by seen or unseen chance came to a riverbank, and there on the grass found a fire burning that a fisherman had prepared for his night's lodging. The owner of the wood, an old fisherman, was off fishing at the time in his boat. The

princess could easily end the burden of life, could easily burn
herself in the wide open field, in the spaciousness and open.
Nobody could have extracted her from there if the heavens
had not removed her from this hour of death and created new
miracles about her. Saying her final words to all, no sooner
did she throw herself onto the flaming wood than suddenly an
invisible force extinguished the fire beneath her. Immediately
the smoke disappeared and the flame and heat went out and
there remained just the necessary warm air for the princess
to dry off her little feet, which she had gotten wet not long
before in the river. When she saw herself safe on top of the
firewood, she shouted loudly: Oh! . . . Her voice resounded
on the waves. The quiet waters shook, various species of fish
splashed up, the fisherman's boat spun about three times, and
all that happened just because of Dushen'ka's word. I do not
know whether at her sudden shout the old man headed back
to shore in his boat of his own will or whether he was carried
by a miracle along the surface of the water back to shore; but
I do know that afterward this ancient grandfather, when he
looked at the proximity of his hut, forgot the infirmity of his
late years, released the fishing nets from his hands, jumped
from his boat to the firewood, and fell at the feet of the
princess, although he had no idea that a miracle had happened
to her, or who she was, or why she had come here, by what
road, and from where.

"O forefather of earthly races, or son certainly of forefathers!" the princess called to the old man. "You remember
the existence of all ages and all the changes that have taken
place in the world. Tell me, as the world has been since the
beginning, has a misfortune like mine ever befallen anyone?
I cut myself and put my head in a noose and drowned myself
and threw myself onto a fire, but to my bitter lot I came
through the fire, I came through the water, and after leading
all Nature to horror with all aspects of deaths, I am alive
despite my wishes; immortality is my torment and vainly do
I summon death to myself. Extend your hand to help me.
End my life, this world is hateful to me!"—"But who are you?"
asked the old man. "I am Dushen'ka. . . . I love Amor. . . ."
Then she began to cry like a fool. Without her saying anything
else, the old man also began to cry together with her, and all
Nature sobbed with her. Later, the grandfather said to her
that there was no death for her in the world, since she

was longing so much for it, and that she still did not know what new woes awaited her; that the anger of the wrathful goddess toward her penetrated even the wilderness; that, as an example and terror to all, in all places under the sun, all her faults were already exposed and that announcements about them had been put up at all crossroads and on all gates. Then the old man murmured in his tears that the gods permitted this malice; and, blaming harsh fate, he led the princess to a post where the nearby roads came together. The princess was able to read for herself there the announcement that had been put up in large letters. And what she found in this announcement I shall relate in strict accuracy:

"Because Dushen'ka has angered Venus, and Amor shamefully praised Dushen'ka to Venus; because this same Dushen'ka belittles rouge and darkens before her the virtue of powder and everywhere offends all beauty; because this same Dushen'ka, possessing a comely figure, charming eyes, and pleasant smile, does not revere the goddess of beauty and holds her in light regard; because she wounds hearts with her glances, dresses herself up as a goddess and wears a train of three spans—because of these things and others, Venus informs one and all of her anger at Dushen'ka in the required form, and promises every courtesy to him who presents Dushen'ka at a fixed time before Venus's eyes. But whosoever helps her in opposition to the force of these lines or conceals her anywhere or shows her any way of concealing herself, this person will not succeed in cleansing his guilt even with his own blood for the rest of his life."

Dushen'ka clasped her hands as she read such fearful words. "O Gods! You see," the stones and trees wailed, "why is Dushen'ka alive, why has she been blessed with beauty, and how is she guilty before you if she has been born so?" The whole world was then reading the warrant about her; the whole world likewise grieved for her. Some scolded the wicked goddess, while others wanted to tear down the announcements. Some sly old Cytherean codgers repeated the commands about Dushen'ka in the mornings out of obligation but promptly forgot about them afterward, and anyone who was able would willingly have concealed Dushen'ka. But be that as it may, whether fearing the sly old codgers or fearing the commands, led by the old man or by her own mind, the princess finally considered it best to ask help of the highest-

ranking goddesses. She would have felt happier asking the
gods for help, but from the time when she fell in love with
Amor she had no thought of finding anyone among the gods
who was not impudent or cowardly or proud or a stupid nag.
And perhaps at that time she found in the highest gods no
small number of simpletons.

At first Dushen'ka went to ask Juno, who had then left the
heavens and was running after her husband over mountains
and through forests. She might have given support to the
unfortunate Dushen'ka, but she had her own sorrow at the
time. Although Jupiter loved Juno according to the law, he
still loved others, and could not remain faithful to her. He
trailed around the whole world and was as coarse and as wild
as a wild boar or a bull, and often soaked himself for days
on end in the rain, and later the rumor reached Juno's ears
that he appeared as a real bull to Europa and then descended
as real rain to Danae, having forgotten the dignity and rank
of the father of the gods. For a multitude of such reasons, and
perhaps because, as Juno saw, Dushen'ka herself could have
driven Jupiter out of his mind, the heavenly goddess of the
throne said to her: "Go, ask Amor about the matter, or go
ask others; I have enough trouble of my own."

The princess, according to popular belief, went with a petition to Ceres. Wheat was being gathered in the fields at the
time, and the goddess of the harvest was appearing at all her
altars. Generosity, charity, and mercy then flowed to all from
her. But only priests were permitted access to Ceres in person,
and whoever went with a petition or a question to the goddess
could not be given an audience without a sacrifice and tribute.
But Dushen'ka at the time was poorer than all and she had
neither her father's money nor her rings. When she came to
hate life, as everyone knows, she made a fool of herself and
made presents of everything she had to good people along the
way. All that was left her was a shepherd's *sarafan* that had
been given to her by the wise fisherman in order to hide her
from all woes in this new attire, even though it was by deceit.
The beauty, which all proclaimed, remained to her, but goddesses do not love the beauty of others, and the priests,
following their lead, as is known, change the excellent gift
of beauty into nothing. The priests then dismissed her from
there without any answer until a future year.

In this sorrow, Dushen'ka, who was accustomed to asking

all for their help, thought of inclining Minerva to pity. On the Helicon the goddess of wisdom was then having a most learned counsel with her Muses about the certain dreadful pitch of comets that were wandering close to earth. Often frightening the timid world by their long tails, they prophesied woe wherever they visited, and threatened to upset the path of Apollo to the world.

At everything the princess then presented to her, the goddess Minerva responded without the slightest pity that the world had existed for ages without Dushen'ka, that she was not a very important person in society, and since, moreover, she frightened everyone like a comet with its tail, it was not fitting for her then to gaze at Dushen'ka. Dushen'ka did not dare appear personally before Diana, for this goddess had never known love. With a retinue of chaste maidens who aspired to freedom, to innocent liberty, carrying a quiver and bow, she set out swiftly on her course, reveling in the skill of her hands, and pursued animals in distant wildernesses. Until then nobody disturbed her pleasures; she still had not seen Endymion, and with the severity of the law prescribed to her she would have deprived Dushen'ka of all favors and rights.

Where to go? To Minerva again or to Ceres? Crying, Dushen'ka went to Venus herself. She knew from her wanderings that not far from a road, in a very lovely valley, stood a well-known temple with the following inscription above the gates: "To the most beautiful goddess." The mother of all pleasures, throwing off the burden of worldly vanities, often liked to rest in these places. Hither from many countries people came at all times in throngs to sigh.

Some came there in order to glorify the goddess, others to acknowledge her favors. Some came to ask them or simply to stroll about the temple. In such a confluence of people the unfortunate Dushen'ka, choosing the quietest hour and concealing herself in every way possible from all strange eyes, came here in search of entry with all the trepidation of a slave. In her grief she comforted herself with the sole hope that, although deprived of her freedom, she might perhaps see Amor in these places together with Venus. She forgot her fear of the harsh decree issued against her and gave herself over to the delights of various flattering thoughts with which a passionate mind is usually enraptured. With such thoughts Dushen'ka approached the temple and there, plunged in reverie, almost fell into a pit where all the refuse from sacrifices was gathered in a heap beyond the courtyard. However, all the places there seemed like a garden, and a fragrant dew rolled out, of myrtle, of lemon, of all the trees, and the temple gave off sweet-scented fumes on all sides.

From folktales everyone knows that silk meadows, life-giving water, and land flowing with milk and honey always belonged to the goddess of beauty and were in a valley surrounded by roads. From ancient times the god of war issued a very severe decree for the pleasure of this goddess, that the sound of the trumpet of war should never disturb the silence in this valley. All know that there even the wildest beasts went up to the doors of sheep, and the sheep, abandoning their fear, walked together with them through the meadows and with the freest ease fed on the milk and honey forever in life, health, and beauty. No living creature was ever killed there; blood was never shed by force; the voice of the grieving was never heard there, and all nature lived in harmony.

In the midst of these meadows, waters, and shores stood the temple of the goddess surrounded by a large number of columns. There were two ways to enter the temple from any side: one for the gods and one for the people. The threshold, gates, temple, and altars, and each part of them, each figure, and in general all the architecture, both inside and outside, portrayed a view of playful Amor or a view of the amusements and festivities of the fair deity who reigned there. The miraculous birth of Venus from foam and everything that had ever happened to her were pictured in all their magnificence in paintings and on tapestries with which the walls on the inside of the temple were covered. To the interiors of the various altars all kinds of gifts were brought from all the sciences, arts, crafts, and trades, and from famous and plain people, all of whom sought to be included in the ranks of the most worthy. One, wishing to acquire glory by his love for a certain Muse and to incline his beloved with a gift, hung up a golden flute in a nook. Another, choosing Pallas as his beloved, by right or not by right, and hoping to receive a wreath of laurels as reward, attached a silver trumpet to a column. Still another, seeking the love of the very uninclined Alcmene, splashed the walls of the temple with color, with a painter's brush. But the gifts that were brought to the temple could be efficacious, not according to their expense or accord-

ing to the ranks of the people who brought them. And often
a simple shepherd who brought only a sincere soul as gift to
the goddess was shown preference over the most illustrious
personage.

On the middle altar, under a most precious canopy, there
stood at all times the goddess's image with its special rank, in
all its beauty and in full glory, just as when she appeared in
earlier days on a certain mountain to chastise Paris and
settled a quarrel between goddesses by her beauty. This image,
it seemed, was hewn from marble by a divine hand and later
was taken as a model for art. The rumor circled the earth that
Praxiteles[18] took his model from here and, following it, closely
presented Venus for the first time in all her beauty. Anyone
going to the temple could not help bending, or did not dare
not to bend, his knees before this beautiful image, and every
person, to the best of his ability, sang hymns to the goddess,
each one in his zeal drowning out the other by his shouting.
Above the temple curled a swarm of cupids, laughters, games,
and zephyrs who flew here at all times from all possible
worlds.

In their aerial formation those who had served Dushen'ka
in paradise were also at the temple. Now in their ignorance
they again flew above the head of their former mistress,
gamboling and babbling. But under a long bridal veil, under
a long *sarafan*, Dushen'ka was then an illusion to all. She
entered the temple together with a throng of people and stood
to one side at the very first gates.

From timidity she took no special notice of these places
or, remembering her former blissful life when she herself was
a goddess in paradise and herself ordered about whole regiments of all kinds of servants and herself heard songs and
praises from all, she ultimately did not regard the temple
as any rarity—the reader may decide this according to his
own will. But no sooner did she show her face in the temple
than in the space of a minute all eyes were directed at her.
The temple was excited; all hymns ceased; the offerings of
sacrifices were interrupted, and on all sides could be heard
only reports and questions. I did not relate earlier that on this
particular day all the people awaited Venus on the strength of

[18] An Athenian sculptor of the fourth century B.C. One of his
best-known works is a statue of Venus (Aphrodite).

the rumor that she would stop there on her way from Paphos to Cytherea. Seeing Dushen'ka, everyone in chorus whispered the news in each other's ears: "Venus is here secretly! . . . She is shunning all honors! . . . Venus is behind the column! . . . Venus is beneath the shawl! . . . Venus is in a *sarafan*! . . . She came here on foot! . . . She stole quietly into the temple! . . . Certainly, with a shepherd! . . ." Everyone then began kneeling before Dushen'ka. Bearing a great number of smoking incense pots, the priests lifted up their hands officiously and begged Dushen'ka to accept the people's gifts and to look upon all their needs with grace. At this agitation of the people talk suddenly arose at the entrance to the temple that the real goddess of these places, dragging crowds of servants after her to the entrance and holding the apple of Paris in her right hand, had just arrived at the temple from Paphos in all her glory, in a brilliant chariot. Just as this was being said, Venus suddenly entered the temple.

But who can describe vividly in words or in pictures, the anger of the goddess, the fear of the people, and the general astonishment in the temple, and more, Dushen'ka, in her innocent triumph in the presence of the very deity of the temple? Then the princess explained to all who she was and the purpose for her coming to the temple. The majority of the people did not draw away from her, forgetting that Venus had already entered the temple. Seating herself on the throne and concealing her vexation as best she could, the goddess put aside all other matters that day and immediately issued a decree that Dushen'ka be presented in the inner court. "Goddess of all beauties! Do not be angry at me," the princess said to her, bending her knees. "I did not scheme to entice your son. It was fate, fate that sent me into his power. It is not I who am seeking people, but the people who in their blindness always marvel at the slightest beauty. I myself sought to humble myself at your feet; I myself want to be your slave, and the only favor I ask of you for the future is that I be permitted to gaze upon your face forever." "I know your scheme!" Venus said to her, and finishing her speech then and there determined to travel to Paphos with the princess. Then with a smile she ordered her to be looked after on the journey. Dushen'ka was placed in a special chariot, and a flock of magpies was harnessed for the journey, and for companionship for her, as though her mate, four furies disgorged by hell sat alongside her: Perfidy, Hatred, Calumny, and Slander. Let us leave the conversation of these contrived Furies and let us say, finally, to what labors Dushen'ka was condemned in Paphos by Venus and who was her leader in the services decreed. From many deeds and words impressed on our minds the vengeance of gods irritated in anger is well known. Often the stronger, having taken power in heaven, overcame, slandered, and sullied the weak and trampled with their feet everything that fell before them. In happier days, of course, there is no equal to the vengeance which, to the terror of all, was worked against Dushen'ka by Venus! She schemed to increase her own beauty and to bring Dushen'ka, as much as possible, to a state of ugliness so that all people afterward would turn away from Dushen'ka and would be thereafter enchanted only by Venus.

I do not know if it was on the first day or rather on the first night that, satisfied with her sacrifice, the goddess out of vengeance sent Dushen'ka to bring the water of the living and the dead within three hours. Everyone knows the story of these waters. Who drinks from the first receives health; but who drinks from the second loses health. However, nobody ever returned alive from this quest. In order to carry out this task the princess strapped two pitchers beneath her shoulders and without further ado went to search for such water at all costs. But whither? And who would direct her along the way? Amor, who was keeping watch on all her activities every hour, immediately ordered his winged servants to raise the princess and bear her to the source from which all waters flow, render lifeless, heal, and aid. The zephyr who clung here out of his own inclination whispered in the princess's ear that the waters were surrounded by a large fat serpent, rolled all up like a hoop, who permitted nobody to go near the waters unless someone amused him with drink. Then the zephyr provided her with a large flask of swill that he ordered her to dump into the serpent's throat once she had approached him boldly and spoken to him. When the serpent opened his jaws for the swill and moved his head and tail apart at the same time, Dushen'ka would find the way clear to fetch the living water and the dead. No sooner had the zephyr told her this than the princess completed her journey and appeared at the waters. Bowing to the serpent, she made a sweet speech to him that later entered the folk tradition:

O Zmei Gorynich Chudo-Iuda!
At all times are you satisfied—
The elephant you dwarfed in size,
The camel darkened by your beauty.
Of all things are you master here;
With golden scales you glitter brightly,
Your jaws you open free of fear,
And with your claws can crush all tightly.
I beg you end my sorrows now,
And let me go where waters flow.

Praise and titles charm all ears, and even the evil spirits
are moved by them. Upon hearing such praise from a female
person, Gorynich bent to the sweetness of the drink, opened
wide his jaws, and separated his head and tail as he set about
devouring the swill. The rivers and ponds and their different
streams of various waters opened up to Dushen'ka. The zephyr
who was attending her of course did not leave Dushen'ka until
this moment had passed. Then having freely drunk of the
water of life, she forgot all the hardships of her journey and
at once became healthier. Writers proclaim that, returning
with the water, Dushen'ka blossomed in matchless beauty,
like a rose, and shone before Venus like the sun. And although
it was the goddess's scheme to arrange for Dushen'ka to drink
the bad water, whether simply by accident or by a miracle,
perhaps, the pitcher with the bad water broke along the way
and the scheme of the goddess came to naught.

From such miracles the goddess perceived that Dushen'ka
was receiving help from the heavens, or, to put it more
accurately, from Amor himself. But since she herself knew
that Nature abounds in the destruction of peoples, she sent
Dushen'ka out on another mission in the hope that she would
thereby end her life or, if she lived through it, that she would
so live without any beauty.

In the gardens where the Hesperides dwelt, the reader
knows there once grew golden apples, or simply gold-looking
apples, and that this wonderful garden was protected by
dragons. Furthermore, in this garden or another, near the
Atlas Mountains, there lived a Princess Perekrasa. Although
all her deeds are not known to posterity, everyone has heard
at least that she was originally the goddess or queen of all
these miraculous regions. In tales she was famous in Rus, as

all know, as the Tsar-Devitsa. All the people have proof of her beauty from legend. Every day she was in the habit of eating the golden apples. It is known that from eating them she was beautiful and healthy. But because of the dangers there and the hardships of the way, nobody else was able to pluck the apples. Although there were neither dragons nor serpents there, this garden nonetheless was protected by Kashchei, who himself, as guard, did not taste the apples there and did not permit anyone else to eat them. And if someone came to taste these apples, he first had to listen to various riddles of Kashchei. When someone was unable to solve the riddles, Kashchei was in the habit of eating him without mercy. Knowing the rules of these harsh places ruled by Kashchei, or dragons, Venus sent Dushen'ka there to fetch these apples, not to live, but to die. But who would point out the road to her and help her? The zephyr—she was able at least to summon him. The zephyr rendered her a new service now: so that no cold wind should encounter her along the way, he set out on this road with her in a southerly direction. He whispered to the princess what to say to Kashchei and how to respond to all his words. Then he instructed her to place just her skirt under the apple tree, so that when the apples rolled down themselves she would be able after she left the garden to fly back with her booty and to taste the golden apples at her pleasure.

Not in a long time, not in a day—but in an hour—Dushen'ka appeared before Kashchei to receive his order. She made a curtsy, as expected and, as expected, made a speech. But she did not report to the world either this speech or what Kashchei proposed to her as riddles. We know only the later events: that Dushen'ka fulfilled her second trial, that she blossomed in a new beauty even more than before, and in voked even worse misfortunes on herself.

In order to carry out her vengeance successfully, it entered the goddess Venus's head to dispatch Dushen'ka with a letter to Proserpine, ordering her to seek the path to Hell for herself and to bring back from there a certain little pot. The princess's ardent servant of bygone years, the zephyr, now descended to earth swifter than an arrow and gave her useful advice. Go to the thick forest where there is no road, and in the forest, he told her, you will come across a little hut and in this little hut you will find an old woman and the old woman will give you a little magical staff. She will then show you a corner of the hut, then steps along which shadows descend into Hell. Then, taking only nine steps, Dushen'ka will end her journey to Pluto's regions and, safe from all dangers, Dushen'ka will immediately uncover her beautiful legs, after which she will be able to speak without fear to Pluto, Proserpine, Hell, and deliver the letter, receive the little pot, and so complete her task punctually in the prescribed order. Following this counsel, the princess entered the forest to which her eyes led her, found the underground entrance, stepped down nine times, immediately entered Hell and appeared before Pluto.

Not anticipating an envoy from Venus, the dark world grew excited. The three-headed Cerberuses of Hell let out fearful howls. But at their anxiety Dushen'ka merely showed her legs, and the hellish creatures at once grew silent. When the Cerberuses stopped their barking, frozen Hell began to thaw out. The dark ruler of the subterranean kingdom, who was dozing alongside Proserpine in the hope of new victims, was saddened by the silence all around. He raised the wrinkles around his eyebrows, flashed the brilliance of cruel eyes, cast a glance . . . began to speak, but soon stumbled and for the first time since his birth, smiled.

When she perceived the strength of the envoy's power that Dushen'ka revealed upon the delivery of the letter, and how Pluto was looking at her, the goddess of the throne of Hell ordered her to shorten the usual speech befitting such an occasion. Delivering the little pot to her personally according to the instructions of the letter, she then sent her back the way she had come without further words. The princess finally might somehow have ended this new trial happily, but her friend the zephyr evidently did not foresee any trouble in the beginning and did not warn her against opening the pot. On the way back the princess stopped many times to examine it. She resisted the temptation to open it, but later, when she was not very far from Venus's court, she scorned the goddess's warning and anger and her own fear, opened the top of the little pot, and looked into it. By evil chance, a black smoke came out of it. Because of its great thickness the zephyrs were unable to blow this smoke away, and Dushen'ka's white face and opened white bosom were then covered with blackness. She tried to wipe away the dust from herself with a kerchief, but the more she exerted herself in the wiping, the blacker she made it, as though she were trying to efface her own appearance. Afterward, she hoped to restore her former beauty somehow at least with some water, but by an unfortunate turn of fate, she only increased the blackness by washing. And although she bent her face to the currents of the clean waters and washed the blackness many times, she assured herself, looking at herself in the waters later, that she was as black as soot or, to put it simply, spoiling her beauty she was uglier than a Negro.

Looking this way, Dushen'ka was embarrassed to meet anyone and ran away as soon as she heard voices. As to her white hands, a tale circulated among the folk that she was just concealing herself from people and was only wearing a mask. Others, making fun of her, gave a strange appearance to the matter and assured everyone that the gods, to punish Dushen'ka for her sin, put a Negro's head on her white body. All the simple people, who delighted in Dushen'ka's appearance and bearing, still admired the collection of beauties in her and called her a lovely African girl. But Dushen'ka, embarrassed by her appearance, covered her neck and her face with a shawl and in her grief had no idea where to go next. Should she return to Venus to be laughed at and disgraced, or should she return to the court of her parents? But would they accept her as the real Dushen'ka on faith, despite what they saw before them? There remained to her only to hide in some cave where people would no longer be able to see her so bitter shame and bury herself there alive, the sooner to end her miserable lot.

Amor likewise felt the cruelty of these evils. He saw or knew all her woes, but why did he leave her without a guard when she was carrying back the pot of soot from hell? The reader can certainly resolve this question for himself. it so suited the fates, it so suited Venus that Dushen'ka should be black, that Dushen'ka should be ugly, and that she should hide from people in a cave. Amor was rejected on Cythera, and, being powerless in heaven, purposely permitted the woe in order thus to disarm the anger that could have led Dushen'ka to the grave.

Because of the rarity of these happenings, the whole world everywhere began talking about the family of Dushen'ka, about her lot, about her years, about all her omens. The news finally reached her treacherous sisters, whether by rumor or

whatever other way, that Dushen'ka did not live long with
her radiant husband in paradise; that for certain deeds she
was thence expelled, that afterward she wandered about without anything to do, and that she shriveled up, grew ugly, and
terribly black. To celebrate the occasion the sisters arranged
a festivity and loudly proclaimed to all that Dushen'ka was
ruined everywhere by her own sins and that her god was
punishing her because of them.

To perverse minds the existence of love is unknown and
strange. Dushen'ka's sisters, enticed by her plight and con-
tinually cursing all her deeds, did not imagine in the darkness
of their slander that although Dushen'ka was deprived of her
external beauty she could still be loved by Amor. Distracted
by the princess's misfortunes, Amor bent all his efforts to a
single goal, and that was that the wrath of the fates toward
Dushen'ka should be as much alleviated as possible, and for
the time being he forgot about her sisters' insult to her. But
later he returned their impudence to them as punishment.

To the sisters' celebration he deliberately sent a zephyr to
greet them from him, as was fitting, thank them for their
friendship and kindness, add that Amor was burning with
love for them, was impatiently desiring to see them, and was
only waiting, without further words, for them to climb the
stone mountain that appeared the highest of all to their sight
and to jump from there into the ravine below so that afterward, without wasting a minute, the zephyr would catch them
in flight, carry them off to the heavenly regions, place them
directly in paradise, and that there Amor would show them
all the necessary favors, intending to take them both together
as his wives.

Hearing such pleasant words, Dushen'ka's sisters' heads
spun from happiness. They ordered horses to be harnessed
as quickly as possible and dressed themselves up in their
richest clothes. They spared no powder or beauty marks or
rouge, splashed themselves all over with waters, daubed themselves all over with spirits, defamed Dushen'ka for her insolence and treachery, headed for the mountain, and there, from
the steep heights, hastened to hurl themselves into the rapids.
But their zephyr did not come to catch them up, but instead
blew at their rear, as is evident. And they did not fall into the
realm of paradise, but just broke their heads when they fell
from the mountain. So punishing the evil, the handsome god

meanwhile kept getting detailed news from everywhere, from all the forests and mountains, where Dushen'ka was, and learning that she was hiding amid mountains, withdrawn from all people, he gave a full report about it to the gods. He reported that Dushen'ka was already black, dried up, thin and ugly, and then he besought an already softened Venus that he finally be permitted to reveal himself openly to Dushen'ka in the cave where she was hiding. But then how did the object of his constant love appear to his eyes? The unhappy Dushen'ka, in her untold grief, did not eat, did not drink, did not see light there in her cave. The reader should know from the beginning that Dushen'ka was lying down at the time. Whether on her side or face down, whether she was sleeping or just dozing, I do not know and I do not wish to search for a testimony of faith. I know only that she was lying on her bridal veil, at the mouth of the cave, concealing her head in the cave's darkness. But the part of her that was left visible before the cave was truly a spectacle in its beauty and could then serve as a sign and proof if her loving god had any doubt about the accuracy of things. The zephyrs saw and announced to the whole world that Amor recognized Dushen'ka from afar and, approaching her, lavished kisses on her hand. But soon they lost them from sight. When Dushen'ka woke up, she looked about, groaned, hid her face in shame, and rushed into the cave, and finally there explained herself to Amor, it is not known in what words. The whole earthly globe knows only of their mutual forgiveness to each other for the annoyance and guilt they brought each other.

Later, in full freedom, Amor ordered the ancient letter that Zeus himself gave from the heavens to earth for the comfort of all ugly people to be announced to all people, and everywhere this letter was newly affirmed word for word: "The law of Time causes a lovely appearance to become ugly. The external brilliance in the eyes vanishes like smoke, but nothing ever changes the beauty of the soul. It alone always and everyone captivates." Confirming these words himself everywhere, Amor presented the letter to Venus and the gods, and together with the letter presented also Dushen'ka, whom he did not regard as ugly in her blackness. Shaking his wise head, Jupiter issued Amor a decree on the strength of the old laws that he should be captivated for the rest of his life by spiritual beauty and that Dushen'ka should be his wife forever. Then the goddess of beauty herself, out of pity or a certain vanity, as often happens, found it necessary and fitting that her daughter-in-law, having cleansed herself of sin by her suffering, should again receive her external beauty. So she washed her with the dew of heaven, and Dushen'ka again became complete, her color returned, and she was as white as she had been before. Amor and Dushen'ka then stood equal to each other, and all the gods then joined them in eternal wedlock. A daughter was born to them, as beautiful as her mother, but what name to give her in the Russian language writers have no idea. Some call this daughter Utekha (Pleasure), others—Radost' (Joy), and, finally, Zhizn' (Life). And let each wise man call her according to his own idea as he pleases. Nature is not changed by a name. The reader knows, and so do all the people, what fruit should be born unto Dushen'ka and Amor.

9. *Twelve Fables*

IVAN I. KHEMNITSER

Generally regarded as the best fable writer before Krylov, Ivan Ivanovich Khemnitser was born in the district of Astrakhan, the son of an army doctor who had emigrated to Russia from his native Saxony. When he was thirteen years old, the young Khemnitser joined the army against his father's wishes. He remained in military service for a period of some twelve years and then put in for retirement, accepting a relatively modest position as a translator of books on mineralogy and as a member of a committee convened to edit a dictionary of mining terms. His literary career began about 1770, when he became acquainted with Ivan Aleksandrovich L'vov (1751–1803), an architect, scientific writer, and poet of some talent.

In 1776 Khemnitser and L'vov set out together for over a year's travel through Germany, France, and Holland. Khemnitser's diary of the journey, which has been preserved, is still interesting reading, particularly in the light of his wide range of cultural interests.

In 1782 Khemnitser was given the position of Russian consul general in Smyrna (the present-day Turkish city of Izmir), where he died two years later after a protracted illness.

Khemnitser's first literary flight was the weak *Ode on the Victory at Giurgiu* (Oda na pobedu pri Zhurzhe, 1770), composed in the style of Lomonosov's panegyrics. This was followed by such pungent satires on corrupt judges and officials as *On Bad Judges* (Na khudykh sudei), *On the Bad Situation of the Service* (Na khudoe sostoianie sluzhby), and the *Ode to Clerks* (Oda na pod'iachikh), which for obvious reasons were not printed in the author's lifetime. Apart from these works and several epigrams, Khemnitser is remembered almost exclusively now for his fables, of which he wrote some 104.

The first edition of Khemnitser's fables included twenty-seven works and was published anonymously in 1779 under the title *The Fables and Tales of N. N.* (Basni i skazki N. N.).

A portrait of Ivan Khemnitser accompanying the first collected edition of his fables and tales in 1820.

A second edition, augmented by thirty-six new fables, appeared, also anonymously, in 1782.

After Khemnitser's death his friends L'vov and Kapnist prepared for publication a third edition of his fables, in three volumes. This bore the title *Fables and Tales of I. I. Khemnitser, in Three Parts* (Baiki i skazki I. I. Khemnitsera. V trëkh chastiakh, 1799), and included woodcuts by the artist Olenin. The L'vov-Kapnist edition of 1794 carried a number of textual emendations; these served two purposes in the main—the blunting of Khemnitser's sometimes bitingly sharp social satire and the elimination of words and phrases the editors considered offensive to good taste. The original versions of Khemnitser were restored only in the critical edition of his works published under the editorship of I. Grot in 1873.

When the first volume of Khemnitser's fables appeared in 1799 it received a quite favorable reception, and soon proved immensely popular. This popularity so increased with time that Khemnitser's reputation as a fable writer seriously rivaled that of Krylov. In fact, it was only after the middle of the nineteenth century that Khemnitser's popularity began to decline.

The subject matter of Khemnitser's fables differs little from that of the eighteenth-century Russian satire; however, in comparison with Sumarokov's fables they are much richer in social details, and reveal the author's greater preference for dialogue than for narration. In a significant departure from previous Russian fable writing, Khemnitser also usually avoids the concluding moral, which was virtually a convention of the genre. His style is light and simple and his language colloquial, although he is rarely guilty of the vulgarity we meet often in the fables of Sumarokov. As with Sumarokov, and later Krylov, Khemnitser uses iambic lines of varying length.

The translations are based in the texts in I. I. Khemnitser, *Polnoe sobranie stikhotvorenii*, Biblioteka Poèta, ed. L. È. Bobrova and V. E. Vatsuro, intro. N. L. Stepanov, Moscow-Leningrad, 1963.

The Peasant and the Cow
(Muzhik i korova)

A man who had no horse once tried
To saddle up a cow to ride.
He never thought to find out whether
Cows and saddles go together.
   In short, he took the bovine seat
   Since he was loathe to use his feet.
The cow, not knowing it should gallop, plods.
The rider, growing angry, prods;
But still, the cow maintains the only pace it knows
And merely pants beneath the blows.
The rider had no whip, so with a cudgel beat her heartily,
Convinced that it was laziness that made his mount move
    tardily;
    He thought the stick
    Would do the trick.
   The cow keeps straining,
   Her strength keeps draining,
   The sweat drips down her back:
   Her pace remains as slack.
The rider only trebles his attack.
But though you kill her you can't force
A cow to gallop like a horse.

Master and Mice
(Khoziain i myshi)

Two mice showed up together at the same household one day,
And both of them decided they would stay.
But since each dwelling place contains disparity,
The lives they led had not the slightest similarity:
   The granary became the home of one mouse;
   The other landed in an empty storehouse.
One mouse was fully satisfied,
For all her needs were gratified.

The other was impoverished, and grieved
Over the bitter fate she had received.
  It happened that the mice
  Called on each other once or twice,
But neither by honesty nor by chicanery
Could the poor one get to her neighbor's granary.
The only thing the poor mouse found in all her habitation
Was rotten lumber, which she gnawed to keep from sheer
    starvation.
Cursing her fate, and railing at the landlord too,
The poor mouse went to him at last to see what he could do
    To make more fair
    Each mouse's share.
The landlord thought awhile, then came to this decision:
He told the mouse who asked him for the redivision,
    "You both came and decided
    To settle, uninvited.
    As for the matter of equalization,
    Well, that is not a landlord's obligation.
      Besides, the storehouse and the granary,
      The two of them were built by me,
      And when you come right down to it,
      I'll use them both as I see fit.
The truth is that I really couldn't care
Which mouse lives how and where."

The Green Ass
(Zelënyi osël)

There was a certain simpleton
Who took an ass, and just for fun
Decided he would paint him green.
    He really did it, too.
    (Only, he made the legs light blue.)
He led the ass to town, where it created quite a scene:
The large and small, the young and old came running out.
And every place the two appeared the citizens would shout,
    "Why, what an ass!
    All green, just like a finch, with light blue legs besides!"
    The people raised a rumpus on all sides.

"What marvels in our age have come to pass!
    Such rarities deserve eternal glory!
    All our descendants should be told the story
    Of how such miracles abounded,
    And we were all astounded!"
To see the ass the population pours
Into the streets in countless scores.
Windows are rented out in houses when
There is no space left in the streets, and then
They even climb on rooftops, and a few
Set scaffolds up so they might get a view
    Of the green ass with light-blue feet
    As he came walking down the street.
    And as for all the ones who tried
Parading alongside,
A mob of such proportion congregated
Its size can't even be approximated.
Pushing and shoving all the way along
From both sides, back and front, more run to join the throng.
What then? The first two days the populace
In carriages, on foot, all chase after the ass.
    The sick forgot their aches and pains,
        Just thinking of this creature;
    The nursemaids made up new refrains
        For lullabies which used to feature
            The exploits of the Cat.
            (Children had heard enough of that.)
On the third day when the green ass was led along the streets
The citizens, to look at him, don't even get up from their seats.
And though at first about the ass they'd said an awful lot,
It seems that now they all entirely forgot.
    There is a kind of foolishness in our caprices:
    As soon as we see something new, we go to pieces.
    And it is all in vain to take a man who's dense
    And try to teach him sense.
Better rely on time, and not on preaching,
    For that's the only thing will make a fool desist
(Although some very stubborn ones resist):
Time knows the most effective way of teaching.

The Parrot
(Popugai)

A noble kept a parrot as a pet.
One day it managed unobserved to get
Out of an open window and to fly
Into a simple peasant's house nearby.
  As soon as it alighted,
  The bird recited
    Its store of words.
What the rabble doesn't understand it will
Consider as the work of the Devil.
    The fact that birds
  Could learn to speak
  Was something this *muzhik*
  Had never heard of in his life,
  And, terrified, he told his wife
    There was some evil witch in
    Their kitchen.
His wife began a holy prayer
Made up to fit the situation—
For of the pair,
She had the livelier imagination.
(Just as it's often held to be the case
That women are more clever than their mates.)
    She grabbed a pot, and with it
    She covered up the parrot,
Then made the sign of the cross to ensure
That it would stay secure.
"You just sit still," she stated.
And there, incarcerated,
    Just sit
    My parrot did.
Meanwhile a search was carried on
To find out where the bird had gone.
When finally those searching did arrive
  At the right spot,
They found the bird scarcely alive
  Beneath that pot.
From this what can we learn that's new?
That it is a misfortune to
    Fall into a residence
    Where no one shows intelligence.

The Horse and the Donkey
(Loshad' i osël)

By doing something for a friend
We serve our own selves in the end.
And we should always be agreed
To help a fellowman in need.

A horse with nothing on his back was walking down a road
Beside a donkey carrying a very heavy load.
The poor thing had so much piled on his back
It seemed about to crack.
"I haven't got the strength to reach my final destination.
I'll fall down dead,"
The donkey said,
And turning to the horse for some cooperation,
He begs him to take off some piece, however small.
"For you," he says, "it really won't be anything at all,
And I'd be very grateful to you."
"Well, if there's one thing I won't do
It's drag some donkey's load around,"
The horse quickly replied.
The donkey walked a little farther, then fell down and
died.
And suddenly the proud horse found
It was a vain thing to refuse
When he was able still to choose:
For he himself beneath the weight now groans:
He bears the donkey's burden—and his bones.

The Student of Metaphysics
(Metafizicheskii uchenik)

One father heard how people sent
Their children overseas to study.
(It then was held by everybody
That foreign schools were excellent;
And when the ones who'd been abroad returned,
They were esteemed as highly learned
By those who weren't.)
This man was rich and not inclined
To lag behind,

And so he took the course that fashion indicated:
He sent his son abroad to become educated.
However dull his son had been,
However much he learned in school,
When this young man came home again
He was an even bigger fool.

> He fell under the influence
> Of academical nonsense
> That he acquired in babblers' lessons
> About Inexplicable Essence.

In short, what he'd been told
Turned him into a dolt.
Before, he'd simply babbled some inanity;
Now this became pedantically expounded.
Where earlier just fools had been confounded,
Now sages couldn't fathom his insanity.
He bored his home, the town, the whole vicinity.

> Engaged in metaphysical discourse one day,
> This student got carried away

By the ancient proposition that occupied his thought:
"The Beginning of all beginnings must be sought."

> He fell into a hole while he was walking,
> And only then stopped talking.

His father, finding him, got quite upset,
And sped home fast as he could go to get
What common sense dictated:

> A rope to pull the student out.

Meanwhile the student meditated

> On what had brought about

His sudden fall into the pit.
"Why," he exclaimed, "the cause of it—
Of this there can be no mistake—
Is an earthquake.

> Interrelations
> Of the planets with this world
> Caused vibrations
> That violently hurled
> > Me into this
> > Sudden abyss."

The father now ran up and gave a shout,
"Look, I have brought some rope to pull you out.

> > Here, grab it tight.
> > You'll be alright.

And son, for Heaven's sake,
Don't let it break!"—
"No, wait, before you start to pull
Explain what a rope is, in full."
His father, paying scant attention
To such an idiotic question,
Replied, "A rope's a thing
Used for pulling
Someone out of a hole that he
Fell into accidentally."
"The rope's too simple," said the student;
"Find another instrument."
"But that takes time," answered his father,
"Why bother?
Since it is here and ready,
Just hold on steady
To the rope."
"But what is time?"
"Time is what I'm
Not going to waste on such a dope.
Till I return you can just sit,"
He said, and left him in the pit.
Now what if every other prater
Were also exiled to a crater,
Along with this man's son?
If that were done . . .
But as for holes, there are not any
Large enough to hold that many.

Privilege
(Privilegiia)

A certain lion once decided he would issue a decree
Granting some beasts the right to kill, with full impunity,
And specifying which of them could do it.
Since it was common practice of the day
Among those same beasts anyway,
He thought it best to give his sanction to it.
No sooner was the law made public than
The beasts, not even reading it again,

Got a feast under way:
Whichever one could kill and flay,
According to the letter of the law,
Went out and grabbed at everything he saw.
  How many poor souls perished here
  Was never ascertained, I fear!
Only to the vixen did the thought occur
That from this law one could infer
That those to whom the privilege pertained
Might kill and rob each other, unrestrained!
She found herself in gravest consternation
About her own—and all the beasts'—original elation.
    The vixen said, "The thing
    To do is go
    And ask the king."
    But not directly—no,
The way one asks a king a question: foxily, and weighing
Each word to emphasize what one is saying,
All cunningness and exercising great discretion
In choosing the most polished court expression:
"Do you not find yourself endangered, Royal Highness,
By granting such great power to the beasts in your dominion?"
So asked the vixen, but despite her subtlety and slyness,
The lion wouldn't give a yes-or-no opinion.
Then, when according to the lion's calculations,
The new decree for long enough had acted on its own,
The privileged beasts were all sent invitations
Summoning them before the lion's throne.
    And those who were the fattest of them all
    Never returned out of the lion's hall.
The lion told the vixen, "Now, that's what I had in mind
When I granted my strongest beasts a freedom of this kind.
Why should I struggle to accumulate
Small bits and pieces of my subjects' fat
When I can let a few beasts put on weight?
The Sultan does exactly that:
He gives his pashas the authorization
To rob and cheat the local population,
    And then he takes his fill
    By handfuls, from the till
Where the supply is more than ample.
I have resolved to follow his example."

The vixen, on the point here of objecting,
And pointing out the evil consequences,
Suddenly came to her senses
By opportunely recollecting
It was the lion she was talking to.
Now I shall give to you
An epigram on tax collectors, who
    Can easily be reckoned in among
    The pashas' ranks, of which I made brief mention. . . .
    But like the fox, I just changed my intention,
    And think it best to hold my tongue.

The Matchmaker-Lion
(Lev-svat)

A lion had a sweetheart, so I'm told
    (The beasts, you know, share man's preoccupation
    With matters of infatuation),
But then the flame of love grew cold.
Like people who are bored with the same lover
And hand their sweetheart over to another,
This lion also tried to get rid of her.
    Not wanting to appear ignoble, though,
    He chose a spotted panther for her beau.
No matter how the lion tried
To make the panther take the bride,
The chosen groom would not agree.
The lion, desperate, was nearly driven
To force him into marriage by decree;
The order, "Love," however, can't be given.
        And politics for either man or beast
        In such affairs, don't differ in the least.
It is a ticklish business for a lover
To make someone his wife,
When he himself is trying to discover
Some means of getting her out of his life.
Therefore, it wasn't odd that it transpired
He couldn't find a sweetheart for the love he once desired.
        Still, hating to delay
        Her wedding day,

He hastily picked out a lowly ass, and stated,
"Listen, you have been designated
    Husband for my former sweetheart:
    Marry her, and I for my part
Will grant you noble rank and my own friendship for the
    favor."
The ass, unlike the others, didn't hesitate or waver;
  He feels no shame at the proposal,
    And agrees to the betrothal.
He says, "I know the wedding's a disgrace,
But through it I attain high social place
    Plus our king's good graces."
Precisely this occurs in human cases.

The Dog and the Lions
(Pes i l'vy)

A certain dog once came to live in lions' company,
And though he'd heard about the way they were supposed
    to be,
Still, he had never seen one face to face,
And of their way of life knew not a trace.
  How did he get mixed up with lions, then?
    I really can't say how or why—
    Unless I lie.
  Let it suffice: a dog was living in a lions' den.
The dog sees that the lions' life
Is one of cunning and of strife:
Among themselves they know no truth, no friendship from
    the heart;
And what they flatter to one's face, inside they tear apart.
Accustomed to a canine life of frank simplicity,
Which knows no kind of guile, deception, or complicity,
This kind of life he finds surprising.
And soon the dog starts realizing
  That though one dog may quarrel with another,
  And even, it may happen, fight the other,
    Still, no such craft or vicious thoughts
    As lions have, exist with dogs.
So great became his irritation
He left the lions' habitation.

At home again with dogs he made the following pronounce-
     ment:
To have to live with lions he considered was a punishment.
For every moment each would gladly see the next one dead.
And the only reason for it (as the lions themselves had said),
Was every lion wants to be the lion at the head.

The Good Tsar
(Dobryi tsar')

A certain tsar, upon ascension,
Devoted very close attention
To the welfare of his nation
As his prime consideration.
     His first act set up a new basis
          For a better set of laws
     By amending all the places
          Where the standing code had flaws.
So that this new reform might meet with minimal resistance,
Old judges were replaced by new ones at the tsar's insistence.
It was a fine reform, deserving of great praise.
The problem was the judges who new clung to old ways.
          The tsar no remedy could find
               To solve a problem of this kind.
     The only cure for such a situation
     Was time and proper education.

The Hens and the Jackdaw
(Kury i galka)

To make sure that his hens were fed
A man tossed to them bits of bread.
     A jackdaw who was in the mood
     For food
     Thought that he would join the brood.
And yet he did not dare
Approach the tempting fare.
Each time he scattered crumbs, the man would swing his arm,
And then the jackdaw scurried off in great alarm.
Because of all his fright
He never got a bite.

    The hens, meanwhile, were not the least intimidated,
    And pecked and pecked till they were satiated.
By a different sort of daring man attains
His happiness on earth, if he so chooses:
Remember that a bold man always gains
The things a timid fellow loses.

The Spider and the Flies
(Pauk i miskhi)

A certain spider said,
    "I've figured out the reason why
    I never catch a large-sized fly,
But only get the puny kind instead:
I have to spread
My cobweb wider."
And so the spider
Stretched out his cobweb right away
And waited for his prey.
Still only little ones could he ensnare;
A large fly, swooping down, would tear
The tautened web to shreds,
And flying off, would even whisk away some threads.
With people too, this is the case:
For small fry, bad luck's everyplace.

10. On the Death of Prince Meshcherskii

GAVRILA R. DERZHAVIN

One of Derzhavin's finest poems, *On the Death of Prince Meshcherskii* (Na smert' kniazia Meshcherskogo), was first written in 1779 in the form of a poetic letter to Major-General Stepan Vasil'evich Perfil'ev, a friend of Prince Aleksandr Ivanovich Meshcherskii, whose death the ode commemorates. Meshcherskii was a councilor of state renowned for his wealth and his magnificent banquets. Before his recognition as a poet, Derzhavin was a guest in his home, although there is no evidence to suggest that he and Meshcherskii ever entered into a closer relationship. The sudden death of Meshcherskii in 1779 provided Derzhavin with the impetus to write a poem that uses the death of the prince, a well-known epicurean, to comment on the omnipotence of death, the equality of all men before death, and the transitoriness of the pleasures and vanities of this earth.

The poem appeared for the first time anonymously in 1779 in the journal *St. Petersburg Messenger* (Sanktpeterburgskii vestnik) under the title *Ode on the Death of K. M. to * * *** (Oda na smert' K. M. k * * *). In greatly revised form it was published a second time, also anonymously, in 1783 in *The Companion of the Lovers of the Russian Word* under the title *To Stepan Vasil'evich Perfil'ev on the Death of Prince Aleksandr Ivanovich Meshcherskii* (K Stepanu Vasil'evichu Perfil'evu na smert' Kniazia Aleksandra Ivanovicha Meshcherskogo). In the collected edition of Derzhavin's works in 1808 the title was shortened simply to *On the Death of Prince Meshcherskii*, by which it is now commonly known.

The theme of death and human transitoriness so vividly elaborated in *On the Death of Prince Meshcherskii* runs through nearly all of Derzhavin's poetry. It made its appearance for the first time in 1774 in his *Ode to Maupertius. Life Is a Dream* (Oda k Movpertiu. Zhizn' est' son), a prose translation of Frederick II's French ode *À Maupertius. La vie*

A portrait of Gavrila Derzhavin appearing in a book of German translations of his poetry by August von Kotzebue published in Leipzig in 1793.

est un rêve, which Derzhavin had come across in German under the title *An Maupertius. Das Leben ist ein Traum.* (Jean Louis de Maupertius [1698–1759] was a prominent French physicist and astronomer.)

Derzhavin's abiding concern with death and the brevity of man's earthly sojourn, the image of life as no more than a fleeting dream, recalls the predominance of the theme in European Baroque literature. This, together with Derzhavin's use of devices for which Baroque poets had a particular fondness (for example, brilliant colors drawn usually from precious stones and metals, sound, enumeration combined with anaphora, syntactic parallelism, antithesis, and so on), led to attempts to place his poetry within the Baroque tradition. Yet an important distinction must be made. To the Baroque poet concerned with the omnipotence of death, man's life on earth is but a preparation for the eternal life beyond the grave, the only life of man that ultimately has meaning because it is everlasting. The fleeting pleasures of this earth to which man vainly clings bring only sorrow, for time inevitably forces him to part with them. The greater the reluctance to be torn from them, the deeper the pain of separation. The Baroque poet often expresses a yearning for death, that necessary precondition to immortality; life is a trial, a vale of tears, a burden to which man in his vanity and delusion paradoxically permits himself to become too profoundly attached. The emphasis of the Baroque metaphysical poetry is on death, not on life; on man's everlasting existence, not on his brief stay on earth. That is why the opposition of heat and cold, of light and dark appears so frequently in Baroque imagery. The poet sees man's fleeting life on earth as the "cold," the "darkness," before the "warmth," the "light," of eternal life.

Examined closely, Derzhavin's philosophical outlook was not that of the Baroque. His concern with omnipotent death and the fleetingness of earthly pleasures was no less significant, but his emphasis was, finally, not on death but on life, on the necessity for making life—because of its very brevity— as tranquil and good as man can in the short time allotted to him. This is indisputably the sense of the last stanza of the ode on the death of Prince Meshcherskii. In the light of it, Derzhavin appears more within the tradition of Horatian poetry philosophically, despite certain undeniable reminiscences of the Baroque.

Occasional similarities between the poem *The Complaint: or Night Thoughts* (1742–1745) by the English poet Edward Young (1683–1765) and Derzhavin's *On the Death of Prince Meshcherskii* and *God* were also isolated long ago. Young's poem appeared in a Russian prose translation in Novikov's *Morning Light* in 1778. Derzhavin doubtless knew the work, and in a very limited way appears to have been influenced by it. The influence, however, did not extend beyond several textual points of contact.

On the Death of Prince Meshcherskii brings reminiscence not only of Young's *Night Thoughts* but also of other poems by late seventeenth- and eighteenth-century English "graveyard" poets, as for example *A Night-Piece on Death* (1722) by Thomas Parnell (1679–1718), *The Grave* (1743) by Robert Blair (1699–1746), and the *Elegy Written in a Country Churchyard* (1751) by Thomas Gray (1716–1771). Accents of Derzhavin's epicureanism, of his reaffirmation of the preciousness of the gift of life, of his underlying optimism of outlook, are negligible, however, in these works, and they remain spiritually more within the pale of the Baroque than does *On the Death of Prince Meshcherskii*.

In the original, Derzhavin's poem was written in iambic tetrameter, in eight-line stanzas with rhyme scheme: *a b a b c d d c*, with *a* and *c* marking masculine rhymes and *b* and *d*, feminine.

All translations from Derzhavin's poems follow the texts in G. R. Derzhavin, *Stikhotvoreniia*, Biblioteka Poèta, ed. D. D. Blagoi, Leningrad, 1957.

O tongue of time! Cold metal's peal!
Your dreadful voice fills me with anguish;
It calls me, calls me by its moan,
It calls—and brings the grave still nearer.
No sooner did I see this world
Ere Death began to grind his teeth,
And with his scythe, which gleams like lightning,
Cuts down my days as though mere grass.

No creature, nothing can escape,
Find refuge from his fatal talons.
Both king and captive feed the worms,
Fierce elements consume sepulchers.
Time gapes all glory to efface:
Just as there flow to sea swift waters,
Our days and years flow to eternity.
The greedy Death devours kingdoms.

We skirt the edge of the abyss
Into which we shall headlong tumble.
We take death with the gift of life,
And are born just that we may perish.
Death pitilessly strikes down all:
The stars above are shriveled by him,
And even burning suns extinguished;
He threatens every living thing.

The mortal thinks he shall not die
And holds himself to be immortal,
When Death comes to him, like a thief,
And steals his life in just an instant.
Alas! Where we are less in fear
There can Death overtake us faster;
No swifter than Death is the lightning
That flies to lofty pinnacles.

Where have you fled, yourself concealed,
Meshcherskii, child of bliss and pleasures?
You left behind this shore of life
And for the Stygian shores departed;
Your dust is here, but not your soul.
Where is it?—There?—Where there?—We know not.
We only weep and call out sadly:
"Oh, woe to us born in this world!"

Where pleasures, happiness, and love
Together with good health shone brightly,
There now the blood runs icy cold
And sorrow frets the anxious spirit.
A grave now stands where once a feast;
Where shouts of joy attended banquets,
There now resound the wails of mourners,
And pallid Death keeps watch on all.

Keeps watch on all—on potentates
Whose power seeks no limitations;
Keeps watch on those in splendor's lap
Whose deities are gold and silver;
Keeps watch on beauty and on charms,
Keeps watch on intellect exalted,
Keeps watch on might that knows no fear,
And meanwhile hones his scythe's sharp blade.

Death, fear and dread of living things!
While we—but grandeur mixed with nothing:
Today a god, tomorrow dust;
Today deceived by flattering hope,
Tomorrow, though, "Where are you, Man?"
The hours their course no sooner started
Than off they flew to realms of Chaos,
And, like a dream, your age has passed.

Like some sweet vision, like a dream
My youth has disappeared already.
Less am I held in beauty's sway,
Less am I brought delight by gladness,
Less am I frivolous of mind,
Less is my disposition cheerful.
Desire for honors agonizes—
I hear: the voice of glory calls.

But so my manhood will pass too,
And with it all pursuit of glory;
The lust for wealth will also fade,
And all the passions in their tumult
Will pass, will pass each in its turn.
Away all earthly happiness!
You are but false and transitory—
Before me looms Eternity.

Today; if not, tomorrow then,
We finally must die, Perfil'ev!
Why then torment yourself or grieve
Because your friend was not immortal?
Life is a momentary gift
Of Heaven—live it then serenely,
And with a purity of spirit
Give blessings to the blows of fate.

11. *To Rulers and Judges*

GAVRILA R. DERZHAVIN

Derzhavin's poem *To Rulers and Judges* (Vlastiteliam i sudiiam) was conceived as a paraphrase of Psalm 82. The original version of the work was done in 1780; not content with it for various reasons, the poet reworked it completely the same year. The new version was to be published in the November issue (1780) of the *St. Petersburg Messenger*. At the last moment, however, whether on official decree or out of fear of the censors, the editors omitted the page containing Derzhavin's poem and substituted another for it. In a partially revised final draft, in which only the first three stanzas were modified, the ode was published in 1787 in the journal *Mirror of the World* (Zerkalo sveta). Eight years later, in 1795, the poet included it in a manuscript collection of his works that he presented to the Empress Catherine for her review before giving it out for printing. He was forewarned by friends, however, that he was already under suspicion for Jacobin sympathies for his *To Rulers and Judges* because a paraphrase of the psalm on which the poem was based was sung in the streets of Paris during the French Revolution. So advised, Derzhavin hastily penned an "explanation" of the poem stating that in paraphrasing the psalm he had no "evil intention," and sent it to Catherine's favorite Zubov and two other dignitaries of the court. This action spared the poet any greater embarrassment, but the censor still did not allow the poem to be printed in the edition of Derzhavin's works of 1798. The next time it appeared in print was in 1808.

In the original the poem is in iambic tetrameter with alternating feminine and masculine rhymes.

Almighty God to judge has risen
The gods of earth assembled here.
How long, He said, will you continue
To spare the wicked and unjust?

Your duty is: to keep the statutes,
To show no favor to the strong,
To leave not widows or the orphaned
Without assistance or defense;

To save the innocent from hardships,
And shelter the unfortunate;
Protect the weaker from the stronger,
And wrench the fetters from the poor.

They hear not! Yet they see—but know not!
Their eyes are veiled by bribery;
The earth by wickedness is shaken;
Injustice makes the heavens reel.

O sovereigns! Mighty gods I deemed you,
And that no one was o'er you judge.
Yet passions rule you, as they do me,
And you, as I, are mortal too;

And you shall fall, in no way different,
As withered leaves shall fall from trees;
And you shall die, in no way different,
As your most humble slave shall die!

Arise, O God, God of the righteous!
And heed their supplication now;
Come judge, pass sentence on the wicked,
And be alone Thou King of earth!

12. Ode to the Wise Princess Felitsa of the Kirghiz-Kazakh Horde, Written by a Certain Murza, Long a Resident of Moscow, but Now Living in St. Petersburg Because of His Affairs, 1782

GAVRILA R. DERZHAVIN

It was with *Felitsa* that Derzhavin first won fame as a poet. The poem was an immediate success, but because of its originality, its bold flaunting of classicist poetic conventions, it was not long before a controversy swirled about it on the pages of *The Companion of the Lovers of the Russian Word*.

Felitsa was written late in 1782. It was inspired by an allegorical fable, *The Tale of Prince Khlor* (Skazka o tsareviche Khlore), which the Empress Catherine wrote and had published in 1781 in a small number of copies for the benefit of her five-year-old grandson, the future Tsar Alexander I.

Catherine's tale recounts the abduction of the young Prince Khlor by a Kirghiz khan who wanted to discover whether or not the stories told of the prince's uncommon beauty and intelligence were true. In order to test the prince, the khan assigned him the task of finding the rose without thorns—the symbol of virtue. The khan's daughter Felitsa (from the Latin word *felix*, meaning "happy") asked permission of her father to accompany Prince Khlor on his search, but was told that she could not. Instead, she sent her son Rassudok (Reason) to help him on his way. With Rassudok's help, Khlor eventually reached the mountaintop where he discovered the rose. After this the khan sent Khlor back to his parents with the flower. They were overjoyed to see their son again, and soon all heard of Khlor's exploit and came to love him even more.

From Catherine's fable Derzhavin took the name of the khan's daughter Felitsa for that of Catherine herself in his own poems, the names of the *murzas* Briuzga ("Choleric") and Lentiag ("Indolent") for two figures of Catherine's court,

An illustration accompanying the first edition of Catherine II's Tale of Prince Khlor, *1781.*

and in general the Oriental coloration of the fable. Thus his ode, addressed to the "Princess of the Kirghiz-Kazakh Horde," was presented as the work of a certain *murza* (or *mirza*, an Eastern title designating someone of aristocratic origin or distinguished by his learning) that was "translated from the Arabic language."

Because of the light, humorous character of his poem—which was, to say the least, new and daring in a panegyrical ode—and the satirical allusions to several prominent figures in Catherine's court, Derzhavin was reluctant to have *Felitsa* printed, and contented himself with reading it privately to friends. However, in 1783, when the work came into the possession of the Princess Dashkova, who was then the president of the Academy of Sciences and a confidante of the empress (before their later mutual disenchantment), she arranged to have it published anonymously in the first number of *The Companion of the Lovers of the Russian Word*, which she was just undertaking to produce. When Catherine read the ode she was delighted at the novelty of manner with which she saw herself praised lavishly by the poet. Never insensitive to flattery, Catherine insisted on sending Derzhavin a handsome present as a token of her gratitude—a gold, diamond-encrusted snuffbox. Moreover, she invited the poet to a personal audience, which marked the beginning of Derzhavin's state career.

Felitsa was truly something new in the history of Russian literature, and the excitement it evoked is understandable. Although belonging formally to the traditional genre of the panegyric ode, the poem startled by its radical departure from the conventions of the genre. The ode was regarded as the most respected and "elevated" of classicist poetic genres. Its manner was stately, its tone lofty. In eighteenth-century Russian poetry this meant that odic writing would adhere more or less to the patterns established for it by Lomonosov. In writing *Felitsa* Derzhavin kept the formal structure of the Lomonosovian ode: the ten-line stanza and the iambic tetrameter. However, he abandoned the conventional loftiness of style in favor of something light, casual, almost bantering. This is particularly true of the satirical stanzas of the poem, in which Derzhavin also showed no reluctance to introduce lexical and phraseological elements of the "low style" in outright defiance of classicist poetic canon. In the more conventional panegyric parts of the poem, chiefly toward the end of the work, he retreated from this literary audacity to a more conservative position, but even then not entirely.

The second great surprise of *Felitsa* was its satire—the appearance of which in a panegyric ode defied one of the basic principles of classicist poetics; namely, that the hierarchy of genres was not to be violated. The problem of bringing the satire of various members of Catherine's court into a panegyric ode addressed to the empress was handled in a masterly way. Apart from the conventional presentation of Catherine herself as an idealized model of enlightened monarchy, possessing the attributes of a goddess, Derzhavin also showed the empress in a more humble and familiar light—a woman of simple tastes, modest, close to her people, aware of her duties and responsibilities to them, a writer of moralizing works, yet insensitive to the beauties of poetry and devoid of any poetic talent. The essence of Derzhavin's satire lay in the contrast drawn between this image of the empress, idealized yet human, and the slothful, corrupt, self-indulgent, pleasure-seeking, and often low-cultured courtiers around her, whom the author of the poem (that is, Derzhavin himself) represents as a collective portrait. This abandonment of the traditional abstract lyric hero of the classicist ode in favor of the poet himself portrayed as the embodiment of vices satirized in the ode was at one and the same time a bold stroke and a clever maneuver.

This cleverness was not sufficient to spare Derzhavin the attacks of dignitaries who felt themselves humiliated in the poem and who doubtless were peeved at the poet's sudden favor at court. Moreover, there were those who, taking cognizance of Catherine's handsome gift to him, insisted that Derzhavin had written the poem primarily to flatter the empress and thereby improve his own position. They were strengthened in their opinion by Derzhavin's poem of gratitude to Catherine for her present and invitation to court, *Thanksgiving to Felitsa* (Blagodarnost' Felitse), which was written not long after his audience with the empress in 1783. It was published that year in *The Companion of the Lovers of the Russian Word*. In literary circles the poet also had as many detractors as admirers. While some hailed the *Felitsa* as a bold and brilliant departure from conventional poetic practice, there were others who regarded the novelty of the

СОБЕСѢДНИКЪ

ЛЮБИТЕЛЕЙ
РОССІЙСКАГО СЛОВА,

Содержащій разныя сочиненія въ стихахъ и въ прозѣ нѣкоторыхъ Россійскихъ писателей.

ЧАСТЬ IV.

ВЪ САНКТПЕТЕРБУРГѢ,
иждивеніемъ Императорской Академіи Наукъ
1783 года.

The title page of the literary journal The Companion of the Lovers of the Russian Word, *1783.*

work as poor taste, and condemned Derzhavin just for his repudiation of accepted "rules" of literary "behavior."

In May, 1783, Derzhavin determined to answer his detractors. He chose to do so in the form of a poem, *A Murza's Vision* (Videnie murzy). After beginning the work, the poet temporarily abandoned it but returned to it again in 1784. It was finally completed in 1790 and appeared in print the next year in Karamzin's *Moscow Journal*. A month after its publication there it was reprinted in the journal *New Monthly Compositions* (Novye ezhemesiachnye sochineniia). It was translated into German the same year by the dramatist August von Kotzebue (1761–1819) and was published separately in 1792 together with the German translation.

A poetic commentary to *Felitsa, A Murza's Vision* consists of five parts: (*a*) the exposition, containing a superb description of a Petersburg night that the poet observes from within a room of his house. The description of the Petersburg landscape with which the poem begins was the *first*, incidentally, in Russian literature; (*b*) the author's confession—in which Derzhavin expresses his contentment with his lot particularly because his "heart is pure" and he is "a good person." The fact that he receives presents for his poems pleases him because he knows that they were written sincerely and not to flatter out of a desire for personal gain; (*c*) the appearance of Felitsa. The description of the empress in this part of the poem is very detailed, and recalls the portrait done of her during this period by the artist Levitskii. Following the description of Catherine, the poet recalls the circumstances of his first meeting with her; (*d*) Felitsa's speech. Here Derzhavin places in Catherine's mouth his own ideas about poetry and the role of the poet. A poet, insists Derzhavin, should not flatter the powerful, although he recognizes that too often they do. On the other hand, he points out through Felitsa-Catherine that the citizen who lives righteously and responsibly can bring more glory to a ruler than all the praise of poets; (*e*) the poet's reply. In the final part of the poem Derzhavin, speaking directly in a monologue, sharply rebukes all those who attacked him for his *Felitsa*. He concludes by repeating that he did not write *Felitsa* to flatter the empress, that he did not and could never sell "the goods of my heart for money," and that his praise of Catherine was inspired only by the beauty of her deeds.

Apart from its significance as a reply to his detractors, *A Murza's Vision* is also noteworthy in two other respects. First, it is one of the earliest of a number of poems of a largely autobiographical nature in which Derzhavin was to write of his own life and views and was to indulge in personal self-assessment. Second, the poem must still be considered as falling within the tradition of the panegyric ode despite the element of apologia. In this light, it appears in its own way no more conventional than *Felitsa*. Although preserving the iambic tetrameter and a familiar rhyme scheme (alternating feminine and masculine rhymes) it abandons the traditional form of the ode by eliminating stanzaic division and assuming the character principally of a dialogue.

Without doing Derzhavin an injustice, it must be stated objectively that his last poem in the Felitsa "cycle"—*The Image of Felitsa* (Izobrazhenie Felitsy)—represented a certain retreat from the position assumed in *A Murza's Vision*. The poem was written in 1789, when Derzhavin's public career reached a low ebb.

Among the benefits that accrued to the poet from the favorable reception by Catherine of his ode *Felitsa* in 1783 was the governorship of the Olonetsk district, with its seat in Petrozavodsk, which he was awarded in May, 1784. Always a practical woman, it is difficult not to imagine that one of the main reasons for Catherine's assigning Derzhavin to a relatively out-of-the-way post was the desire to remove the controversial poet as far as possible from St. Petersburg because of the enmities created by the satirical thrusts in his *Felitsa*. The point was not lost on Derzhavin himself, who viewed it as something of an exile. To make matters worse, his immediate superior was a friend of his former patron, Prince Viazemskii, who took umbrage to the allusions to him in *Felitsa* and became hostile to the poet.

Derzhavin's position in Olonetsk progressively deteriorated, and after two years' service there his relations with his superior were so bad he was forced to request a transfer. His request was granted, and in 1785 he was made the governor of Tambov. He endured somewhat longer in his new post than at Olonetsk, but it quickly became apparent that his reputation as a "troublemaker" had preceded him. Before too much time elapsed he and his new superior, General I. V. Gudovich, were embroiled in wrangles. The affair came to a head in the middle of 1788 when Derzhavin was summarily recalled and charged with misuse of authority. It was only because of the intercession on his behalf by Potëmkin that the case was settled in his favor and he was declared innocent by the Senate. However, it was to be almost two and a half years before the poet was given the opportunity again of holding a position of responsibility. In 1791 he was made Catherine's personal secretary in charge of the reception of petitions. He remained in this position until September, 1793, when he became first a senator and then president of the "college" (or ministry) of commerce.

During the period that Derzhavin's "case" was before the Senate he was compelled by circumstances to appeal directly to the empress for her intervention. The poet was granted several audiences with Catherine, whose attitude rapidly shifted from a pretense of affection to coolness. Probably just prior to the first of these meetings Derzhavin composed his ode *A Portrait of Felitsa*, which was designed both to secure an audience with the empress and to win her over to his cause.

The longest of the Felitsa poems and the most rhetorical, *A Portrait of Felitsa* is less impressive than the others in the cycle. Calling on the Italian Renaissance artist Raphael to assist him in painting a portrait of Felitsa, the poet then proceeds to a lengthy enumeration of Catherine's many virtues. At the end of the work he discovers that the picture has been painted in his own heart.

Written in the familiar iambic tetrameter and in eight-line stanzas with rhyme scheme *a b a b c d c d* (*a, c*—feminine; *b, d*—masculine), *A Portrait of Felitsa* has only traces of the brilliance of *Felitsa* and *A Murza's Vision*. That it was written for a purpose Derzhavin himself had earlier repudiated cannot seriously be doubted, particularly in the light of the circumstances in which the work arose. It was first printed in *New Monthly Compositions* in 1789 with the dedication: "The author of *Felitsa* ventures to dedicate your portrait to you, O godlike one!" Accompanied by the German translation of the indefatigable August von Kotzebue, it was published as a separate brochure in *Revel'* in 1792.

With *A Portrait of Felitsa* Derzhavin's justifiably renowned Felitsa "cycle" concluded. The close contact with Catherine that his position as her personal secretary afforded him led to a profound disenchantment with the empress the poet had once celebrated as the model of an enlightened monarch. When he left her service toward the end of 1793, he was not to return again to the Felitsa theme in the few remaining years of Catherine's life.

O Princess, fair as a divinity,
Of the Kirghiz and Kazakh horde,
Whose wisdom, which is without equal,
Revealed unto the young Prince Khlor
The true path that he had to follow
To reach the peak of that high mountain
Where grows the rose that has no thorns,
Where virtue has its habitation—
It captivates my mind and spirit,
I beg you help me find it too.

Felitsa, help me with instructions
On living uprightly but well,
On taming passions' agitation
And being happy on this earth!
Your voice is my enthusiasm,
Your son, who led Prince Khlor, my guide;
But I lack strength to follow him.
Of worldly vanity a plaything,
Today I am my own true master—
Tomorrow just a slave of whims.

Not following your *murzas'* custom,
You often go about on foot,
And only have the simplest dishes
Permitted in your dining room.
Not valuing your leisure hours,
You read and write before a lectern,
And grant a true felicity
Unto all mortals by your writings.[1]
Nor do you have a gambling passion,

---

[1] A reference to Catherine's activity as a lawgiver.

Like me who plays from morn 'til morn.[2]
For masquerades you care not greatly
And never set foot in a club;
Preserving ceremonies, customs,
You never act quixotically;
Parnassus's mount you do not saddle,[3]
Nor enter gatherings of spirits,[4]
You leave your throne not for the East;[5]
But following the path of meekness,
Your soul concerned for others' welfare,
You pass your days in usefulness.

But I, not rising until noontime,[6]
Drink coffee and enjoy a smoke;
I make vacations of my workdays
And spin my thoughts in chimeras:
I now steal captives from the Persians,
Or at the Turks direct my arrows;

[2] Card playing was extremely popular throughout Europe in the eighteenth century. Derzhavin recalls in his own autobiography that in 1775 he began a game once with fifty rubles in his pocket, but that in a short space of time he had won 40,000. The most popular card games were faro and omber.

[3] In ancient Greek mythology Pegasus was the winged steed of Zeus. According to legend, the striking of its hoof on Mount Helicon opened up the miraculous stream of the Hippocrene, whose water gave poets inspiration. By saying of Catherine that she does not saddle Parnassus's mount, Derzhavin is referring to Catherine's inability to write poetry.

[4] A reference to Catherine's hostility to Freemasonry and mystic sects, particularly the Rosicrucians and the Martinists (followers of the teachings of the French mystic philosopher Louis-Claude de Saint Martin, 1743–1803).

[5] The Masonic lodges frequently bore such names as East, Eastern Star, Great East, etc.

[6] This stanza, as well as the next four, allude to Catherine's favorite at the time Grigorii Potëmkin (1739–1791), who won renown for his annexation of the Crimea in 1783, shortly after *Felitsa* was written. Apart from his grandiose plans for the collapse of the Ottoman Empire, Potëmkin was also known for his taste for luxury. He heartily enjoyed epicurean feasts, resplendent dress, feminine companionship, and riding about in a magnificently appointed English carriage.

Now dreaming I a Sultan am,
I terrify the world by glances;
Or struck by some fine piece of clothing,
Hop off to have a *caftan* made.

Or I am at a sumptuous banquet,
Which has been tended in my name,
Where gold and silver deck the table,
Where courses by the thousands come;
The famed Westphalian ham is served there,
And fish of Astrakhan in slices;
Pilaff and *pirogi* in mounds.
I wash down waffles with champagne
And leave my worldly cares behind me
'Midst sweetmeats, wines, and nice aromas.

Or 'midst a lovely little orchard,
An arbor, where a fountain plays,
A sweet-voiced harp within my hearing,
Where hardly does a zephyr breathe,
Where everything presents me splendor,
My thoughts ensnares for divers pleasures,
First wearies then awakes my blood;
Reclining on a velvet divan,
A maiden's tender feelings coddling,
I fill her youthful heart with love.

Or in a gilded English carriage,
By truly splendid tandem drawn
With hound, companion, or a jester,[7]
Or with some beauty—better yet—
I go off riding to the Swings;
I stop at taverns for some spirits
Or, if this too becomes a bore—
My nature does incline to changes—
I set my cap at jaunty angle
And fly atop a sportive steed.[8]

[7] The old custom of maintaining buffoons or jesters in the homes of wealthy nobles was preserved in Russia until the end of the eighteenth century.

[8] An allusion not only to Potëmkin, who enjoyed racing horses, but also to Aleksei Orlov (1737–1807), the brother of Catherine's favorite Grigorii Orlov, one of the chief organizers of the palace

Or bring refreshment to my spirit
With music, singers, and with dance,
Accompanied by pipes and organ,
Or pleasure find in boxing bouts;
Or, putting to a side all worries,
I go off to the woods for hunting
And take delight in mastiff's barks;[9]
Or by the banks of river Neva
Enjoy the sound of horns on evenings[10]

---

revolt of 1762 that brought Catherine to the throne. During the Russo-Turkish War of 1768–1774, Aleksei Orlov was nominally in command of the Russian fleet, which dealt the Turkish navy a severe blow at the Battle of Chesmé, for which he became known as Orlov of Chesmé (Orlov-Chesmenskii).

[9] According to Derzhavin's own explanations the allusion here is to Count Pëtr Panin (1721–1789), the brother of the famous politician and diplomat. Pëtr Panin, a devoted amateur hunter, was an army general who distinguished himself in the Seven Years' War. Derzhavin became familiar with him during the Pugachëv campaign, but their relations were anything but cordial. At the time *Felitsa* was written, both Panins were already out of favor.

[10] The Grand Huntsman (*Ober-Egermeister*) of the court at the time, Semën Naryshkin (1710–1755), enjoyed great popularity for the concerts of his orchestra composed solely of hunters' horns. On summer nights a popular diversion of the court consisted of taking boat rides on the Neva River in St. Petersburg to the accompaniment of the music of horns. Grigorii Orlov is believed responsible for arranging such entertainments. That they remained popular into the early nineteenth century is suggested by Pushkin's allusion to them in *Eugene Onegin* (I, 48):

> His soul in rueful agitation,
> Stood leaning on the granite shelf
> Onegin, lost in meditation,
> As once a bard described himself.
> And all is calm save for the trailing
> Calls of a lonely watchman hailing
> Another, and the distant sound
> Of cabs that over pavements pound;
> A lonely boat, its paddles weaving,
> Was on the slumbering river borne;
> And wayward singing, and a horn
> Charmed our ears, the silence cleaving . . .
> Yet, 'mid nocturnal reveling
> Torquato's octaves sweeter sing!

(*Eugene Onegin*, transl. Walter Arndt, New York, 1963, I, 48).

And agile oarsmen's rowing skill;

Or staying just at home make mischief,[11]
Playing "Old Maid" with my lady;
Or both of us climb in the dovecote,
Or sometimes romp in blindman's-buff;
Or have a good time playing ringtoss,
Or have her give my head a scratching;[12]
Or burrowing through books at times
My heart and mind I do enlighten
Polkan and *Bova* reading through,[13]
Or o'er the Bible, yawning, sleep.

You see, Felitsa, my debauchery!
But all the world resembles me.
Someone may be renowned for learning,
Yet every person is a lie.[14]
We travel not by paths of lightness
But chase instead sweet dreams of pleasures.
'Twixt Indolent and Choleric,[15]
'Twixt sinfulness and vain delusion,
Has anyone save by mere chance found
The direct path of righteousness?

And if one found it—can weak mortals,
Can we not err upon this path
Where even Reason may be stumbled
And have to follow passions' way;

[11] The entire stanza is devoted to a description of the amusements of uncultured noblemen.

[12] A popular pastime of such a couple as is described in the stanza was looking through each other's heads for lice.

[13] The reference is to the seventeenth-century Russian *povest'* *Prince Bova* (Bova korolevich). Polkan (from the Italian *Pulicano*) was one of the heroes of the tale. Derzhavin is also alluding here to the reading habits of Count Aleksandr Viazemskii, the *general-prokuror* of the Senate and Derzhavin's patron and later enemy.

[14] A slightly altered quotation from Psalm 116: "All men are liars."

[15] A reference to the characters Lentiag (Indolent) and Briuzga (Choleric) in Catherine's *Tale of Prince Khlor*. According to Derzhavin's own commentary, Prince Potëmkin should be understood for the former, and Prince Viazemskii for the latter.

Where learned ignoramuses
Bedim our sight as mist does wanderers'?
False praise and lures are everywhere
And luxury torments all pashas—
Where then is Virtue's habitation?
Where grows the rose that has no thorns?

To you alone is it behooving,
O Princess, to bring light from dark!
In equal spheres dividing Chaos,
To strengthen them by common bond;[16]
'Tis you alone who have the power
To bring forth harmony from discord
And happiness from savage lusts.
The helmsman thus, the ocean traveling,
A strong wind 'neath his sails ensnaring,
Can keep his vessel on its course.

'Tis you alone who wounds no feelings,
Nor gives offense to anyone;
Toward foolishness you can be tolerant
But suffer evil not a whit.
Misdeeds you treat with condescension;
As wolves do sheep, you choke not people,
But know wherein their merit lies.
To rulers' wills are people subject,
But to their righteous God more greatly,
Who lives within their very laws.

You judge of merits reasonably,
And honor to the worthy give;
You do not rank among the prophets
Who can do naught but spin out rhymes;
But as this mind's fair entertainment
Brings honor, glory to good caliphs,
You do indulge the lyric strain;
Poetic art is pleasant to you,

[16] The reference is to Catherine's administrative reform of 1775, which divided the empire into fifty "governments" (*gubernii*) conforming to a single pattern based on strict division of administrative, judicial, and financial affairs.

Agreeable, and sweet and useful,
Like summer's tasty lemonade.[17]

Of your behavior hearsay has it
That you are not the least bit proud;
In weighty or light matters pleasant,
Agreeable in friendship, firm;
That in misfortune you keep spirit,
But so magnanimous in glory
You did refuse the title Wise.[18]
They also say, and 'tis no falsehood,
That now and always one is able
To come to you and speak the truth.[19]

And 'tis a thing unheard of also,
Though worthy just of you alone,
That you permit the people boldly
To know and think of everything
Both in the open and in secret,
And that you do prohibit no one
To speak of you both true and false;
That you are always prone to pardon
These Zoiluses[20] of your graces,
The snapping crocodiles themselves.

Rivers of joyful tears flow swiftly
From out my dear soul's very depths.
Oh, how those people must be happy
With their fate, who have been bestowed
An angel who is meek and peaceful,
From heaven sent to bear the scepter,
In royal purple's splendor garbed!

[17] A jocular characterization of Catherine's own attitude toward poetry.

[18] In 1767 Catherine refused the title "Great, Wise, Mother of the Fatherland" (Velikaia, Premudraia, Mat' otechestva) that was offered to her by the Senate and Legislative Commission.

[19] Catherine's tolerance and liberalism, of which Derzhavin is speaking here, were already things of the past when *Felitsa* was written.

[20] Zoilus was a Greek critic of the fourth century B.C. He was known for his vitriolic criticism of Homer's works. In time his name became synonymous with unfair, carping criticism.

There one may whisper conversation,
And without fear of being punished[21]
At dinners not toast sovereigns.[22]

There one need have no fear of blotting
Felitsa's name in any line,[23]
Or carelessly permit her portrait
To drop somewhere upon the ground.[24]
There jesters' weddings are not feted,
Nor are there people steamed in ice baths,[25]
Or nobles' whiskers tweeked for fun.[26]
Like brood-hens princes do not cackle,
Nor favorites laugh loudly at them,
And smear their faces black with soot.

You know, Felitsa, what the rights are
Of ordinary men and kings;
While you enlighten all their manners
You turn not people into fools;
In leisure from your busy schedule
You author tales with moral lessons[27]
And teach Prince Khlor the alphabet:[28]

[21] A reference to the practice of informing, which was common in the reign of the Empress Anna Ioannovna.

[22] This is also a reference to the reign of Anna Ioannovna.

[23] Before Catherine, making a mistake or correction in the name of a Russian tsar was an offense punishable by a lashing.

[24] In the reign of Anna Ioannovna it was considered an insult to the empress to drop a coin bearing her image.

[25] A reference to the wedding of Anna Ioannovna's court jester, Prince Golitsyn, which was celebrated with great pomp on February 6, 1740. At the wedding banquet a greeting in verse to the couple was delivered by the poet Trediakovskii. The newlyweds spent their wedding night on the Neva in a house of ice made especially for this purpose. The incident was described in the historical novel *The House of Ice* (Ledianoi dom) by the novelist Ivan Lazhechnikov (1792–1869).

[26] The rest of the stanza refers to the crude jokes, often involving high-ranking dignitaries, which took place at the court of Anna Ioannovna.

[27] Derzhavin has in mind Catherine's *Tale of Prince Khlor* and similar didactic works.

[28] A reference to a Russian ABC's written by Catherine for the future Alexander I, and published in 1781.

"Do nothing bad, Prince, and I promise
The worst of satirists you render
A liar held in base contempt."

Lest you be held in fear and hated
You are ashamed to be called great;
It only suits a savage she-bear
To claw up beasts and drink their blood.
Who ever had a need for lancets,
Except in direst case of fever,
When he could do without their use?
And for one great, like God, in goodness
Is being a tyrant any glory,
A cruel Tamerlane the Great?

Felitsa's glory is the glory
Of a god who brought peace to strife,
A god who sheltered, clothed, and nourished
The orphaned and impoverished;
Who with a radiant eye his light grants
To ingrates, cowards, and buffoons
And also to all righteous men;
All mortals equally enlightens,
Brings comfort to the ill and heals them
And does good just for goodness' sake.

Who has extended all the freedom
To travel off to foreign parts,[29]
And gave permission to his nation
To go in quest of silver, gold;
Who makes the waters of his realm free[30]
And puts no limit on the trees felled;[31]
Who bids that all weave, spin, and sew
And, liberating mind and hands then,[32]

[29] Probably a reference to Catherine's upholding of Peter III's edict permitting members of the nobility to travel abroad, which had been prohibited under previous rulers.

[30] That is, permitted the use of waterways for commerce.

[31] Catherine had withdrawn an earlier limitation on the number of trees landowners could cut down.

[32] In 1775 Catherine permitted the organization of manufacturing enterprises. Previously, only government monopolies existed.

Commands to love both trade and learning,
And to find happiness at home;

Whose statutes and right hand distribute
Both justice and beneficence.
Announce, Felitsa, in your wisdom
Where knaves from honest men are told;
Where old age does not go a-begging,
And merits find due compensation;
Where vengeance drives no one in fear;
Where dwell together truth and conscience;
Where virtues shine in all their splendor—
If not at your own very throne?

But, pray, where shines your throne in this world?
Where do you blossom, heavenly branch?
In Baghdad, Smyrna, or in Kashmir?
But hear: where'er you make your home—
As you receive my praises to you
Think not I wished as payment for them
Some jacket or a cap, perhaps.
To sense the pleasantness of goodness
Is for the soul so great a treasure
As even Croesus did not mass.

I ask that the great prophet let me
Touch just the dust beneath your feet
And revel in your words' sweet current
No less than in your countenance!
The heavenly powers I entreat
That they extend their wings of sapphire
And you protect invisibly
From every evil, ill, and boredom;
That in posterity your deeds' fame[33]
Shine as the stars in heaven do.

[33] In the original Russian Derzhavin has "sounds" (*zvuki*) instead of "fame." As the subject of a verb meaning "to shine" or "glitter," this creates one of the rare instances of mixed metaphor in Derzhavin's poetry.

13. *God*

GAVRILA R. DERZHAVIN

Derzhavin's ode on the Deity became not only his best-known poem, but the first Russian poetic work to gain an international reputation. It has been translated at least fifteen times into French, some eight times into German, and several times into English; there are also Latin, Italian, Spanish, Swedish, Polish, modern Greek, and Japanese versions. How the work came to be translated into Japanese—as early as 1811–1813—has an interesting story behind it. During imprisonment in Japan the Russian traveler Vasilii Golovnin, then a captain and later an admiral in the Russian Navy, was asked by Japanese scholars to familiarize them with Russian poetry. From memory he recited Derzhavin's *God* and helped translate it into Japanese with the exception of the line translated below as "No form, yet in three forms divine," which the Japanese found unintelligible.

Derzhavin began work on the ode on Easter night of 1780. Without completing it he put the poem aside and returned to it only in February or March, 1784, during a stay in Narva. He finished it that year and published it in the April issue of the journal *The Companion of the Lovers of the Russian Word*. It was later published separately, for the first time with Derzhavin's signature.

The poem emerged from the rich tradition of the eighteenth-century religious ode that produced Lomonosov's *Evening Meditation* and *Morning Meditation*. Preserving the formal structure of the ode and written in the traditional "high" style with consistent loftiness of tone, *God* is the shortest and the most laconic of Derzhavin's major poems if we compare it with such works, for example, as *Felitsa* and *The Waterfall*. The prolixity and looseness of organization that weakens the effectiveness of the other poems was avoided here, with the result that the ode with its more sparing and concentrated means succeeds in making a strong impression on the reader.

280

Derzhavin's conception of the Deity as expressed in *God* is essentially traditional. The Deity in all His majesty and greatness is beyond the comprehension of the finite intellect; He is of measureless expanse, the beginning of Beginnings, the Ultimate Cause. The Russian poet's soaring praise of the Deity, however, is not rooted solely in ecclesiastical teaching. The idea of the three faces, or forms, of the Deity springs not only from the dogma of the Trinity but also, as Derzhavin himself explained, from metaphysical considerations. The three aspects of Divinity are seen as infinite expanse, continuous life in the movement of matter, and the unending flow of time.

The arguments the poet adduces for belief in God are also colored by deistic thought. Apart from "innate" supposition, Derzhavin postulates the existence of a supreme being on his own existence; it becomes, as it were, a logical necessity. To Derzhavin God informs all creation. Nature lives with His presence; thus man as a part of nature also partakes of the Divinity. The didacticism of this intimate association of the worlds of man and nature brought Derzhavin close to several eighteenth-century German-language and English poets who dealt with similar themes, particularly the German Barthold Heinrich Brockes (1680–1747), the Swiss Albrecht von Haller (1708–1777), and Edward Young whose *The Complaint: Or Night Thoughts* was mentioned previously in connection with the ode *On the Death of Prince Meshcherskii*. It is often pointed out that Derzhavin's antithetical line in the ninth stanza, "A king—a slave; a worm—a god!" is reminiscent of Young's "An heir of glory! a frail child of dust!/ Helpless immortal! Insect infinite!/ A worm! a god!" Haller's poem *Die Ewigkeit* (Eternity) contains similar reminiscences not only of the above passage but also of Derzhavin's sixth stanza:

> Ich häufe ungeheur Zahlen,
> Geburge Millionen auf:
> Ich wälze Zeit auf Zeit und Welt auf Welten hin,
> Und wann ich auf der March des endlichen nun bin,
> Und von der fürchterlichen Höhe,
> Mit Schwindeln wieder nach Dir sehe,

Ist alle Macht der Zahl, vermehrt mit
    tausend Malen,
Noch nicht ein Teil von Dir . . .

Vollkommenheit der Grosse,
Was ist der Mensch, der gegen Dich sich halt!
Er ist ein Wurm, ein Sandkorn in der Welt,
Die Welt ist selbst ein Punkt, wann ich
    an Dir sie messe.

A Russian translation of Haller's poem appeared in the journal *St. Petersburg Messenger* in 1778, and there is little doubt that Derzhavin knew it. Comparison of Derzhavin with such German-language poets prominent in the first half of the eighteenth century as Brockes and Haller is interesting in view of the fact that, like Derzhavin, they themselves were drawn to certain works of contemporary English poetry, traces of which can be found in their own writing. Brockes, for example, translated Pope's *An Essay on Man* (1733–1734) in 1740 and James Thomson's *Seasons* (1726–1730). Haller had studied in England in 1727 and was familiar with Pope's *Pastorals* (1709) and Thomson's *Seasons*. Derzhavin had a reading knowledge of German; his translations of Frederick II's odes in his Chitalagai cycle were based on the German translations he had obtained, not the French originals. That Derzhavin's interest in English poetry was first stimulated by German-language poets such as Brockes and Haller remains a distinct possibility, and a subject worth further study.

In the original, *God* is divided into stanzas of ten lines each; the meter is iambic tetrameter and the rhyme scheme: *a b a b c c d e e d* with *a c e* indicating feminine rhymes, and *b* and *d*, masculine.

O Thou, of measureless expanse,
Alive in matter's every movement,
Eternal through time's constant passage,
No form, yet in three forms divine.
Spirit informing all, yet single,
Of whom there is no source or station,

Whom none has yet Thy essence grasped,
Who filleth all with Thine own Person,
Embraceth, moldeth, and preserveth,
To whom we give the name of *God*.

Although the lofty mind could measure
The ocean at its deepest depth,
And count the sands and rays of planets,
Thou hast no measure and no count!
Spirits who owe Thee their existence,
And from Thy radiance enlightened,
Can never trace Thy destinies.
No sooner does thought dare rise to Thee
Than it in Thy grandeur vanishes—
An instant in eternity.

From out eternity's abysses
Thou didst the ancient Chaos call,
And life eternal ere time's dawning
Thou foundedst on Thyself alone:
Just of Thyself Thyself consisting,
Just of Thyself unaided shining,
Thou art the light from which light flowed.
Having with mere word all created
And merged into this new creation,
Thou wast, Thou art, and e'er shalt be!

The chain of being dwells within Thee—
'Tis by Thee given breath, sustained.
The end Thou joinest to beginning
And givest life along with death.
As sparks are scattered and surge onward,
'Tis thus that suns are born of Thee;
As on a clear cold wintry day
Small particles of hoarfrost glisten,
'Tis thus in the abyss beneath Thee
The stars, revolving, brightly glint.

Millions of lights illuminated
Flow in the measureless expanse;
They carry out Thy every bidding,
Pour everywhere life-giving rays.
But these enkindled, fiery lampions,

Or multitudes of glowing crystals,
Or boiling mound of golden waves,
Or ethers burning hot with fire,
Or all the glittering worlds together—
To Thee—are like night unto day.

Just like a drop upon the waters
Before Thee is the firmament.
But what the universe seen by me?
And I?—Before Thee what am I?
In that far-off celestial ocean
I multiply the worlds by millions
And add to these a million more—
Yet when I dare compare it with Thee
'Twill no more be than just a dot,
And I before Thee am but naught!

But naught?—Yet Thou within me shinest
By all Thy bounties' majesty;
In me Thou paintest Thine own image,
As sun does in small water drops.
But naught!—Yet life I feel within me;
With some insatiable soaring
I take flight always to the heights.
My soul supposes Thy existence;
It penetrates, thinks, passes judgment:
I am—and therefore Thou must be!

Thou art!—declares the law of nature;
My heart proclaims to me the same,
My mind gives me assurance of it,
Thou art—and I cease being naught.
Of all the universe a fragment
I have my place, it seems, determined
Within Creation's honored midst.
Where Thou didst end terrestrial creatures,
Where Thou beganst celestial spirits,
And with me bound all beings' chain.

I am the bond of worlds existing,
The highest rung of matter's climb;
I am the center of the living,
Divinity's initial mark.

Death turns my body into ashes,
Yet with my mind I order thunders—
A king—a slave; a worm—a god!
But, being thus a wondrous creature,
Wherefrom did I proceed?—I know not.
But by myself I could not be.

Creator, I am your creation!
A creature of your sapience,
O source of life, giver of blessings,
Soul of my soul and sovereign!
To Thy truth was it necessary
That my immortal state of being
Should pass through the abyss of death;
That my soul should in mortal garb dress
And that I should return, O Father,
Through death to Thy immortal realm.

O Thou ineffable, inscrutable!
I know that in my very soul
Imagination lacks the power
Thy shadow even here to trace.
But hast Thou need of exaltation—
Then mortals cannot in their weakness
Revere Thee any other way
Than just to raise themselves to Thee,
To stray amidst eternal variance,
And pour out tears of gratitude.

14. *The Waterfall*

GAVRILA R. DERZHAVIN

The Waterfall (Vodopad) ranks as one of Derzhavin's finest poetic achievements. A work of beauty and majesty despite its excessive length, it was written to commemorate the death of one of the most brilliant figures of Catherine's court, Prince Grigorii Aleksandrovich Potëmkin (1739–1791) on October 5, 1791. Derzhavin's friend the poet I. I. Dmitriev asserted that *The Waterfall* was actually begun before Potëmkin died, but there is no evidence to substantiate such a view, and the assertion seems dubious. The original version of the poem, which has since been lost, consisted of only fifteen stanzas. But Derzhavin grew enamored of his subject and kept working on it until he reached the present length of seventy-four stanzas. By the end of 1794 the composition was definitely finished. Its publication came four years later in 1798.

In its own way *The Waterfall* is no more conventional or orthodox than Derzhavin's ode *Felitsa*. Where *Felitsa* blended the panegyrical and satirical, *The Waterfall* brings together in the same work the panegyrical, elegiac, and philosophical. At the core of the poem is the celebration of the great deeds of Potëmkin and the expression of mourning over his loss. The panegyric and elegiac currents flow from two sources: directly from the author and indirectly from the distinguished statesman and military leader of Catherine's reign. Pëtr Aleksandrovich Rumiantsev (1725–1796), who appears in the poem as an old man close to death himself. It is also through Rumiantsev that Derzhavin expresses the familiar philosophic theme of the work—the transitoriness of all earthly things, the brevity of man's terrestial sojourn, the omnipotence of death and the equality of all men before death. As elsewhere the poet strips death of some of its terror by portraying it as a gateway through which man passes into the eternal. Immortality, for Derzhavin, means two things: the life after death, that is, the immortality of the soul, and the immortality man is capable of achieving among the living through personal glory.

Elaborated throughout the poem as a dynamic metaphoric symbol of the philosophical theme is the waterfall, the description of which Derzhavin based on his own observations of the Kivach waterfall on the Suna River in northwestern Russia. The brilliant turbulent course of the fall as it rushes to crash into the depths below depicts the course of man's life on earth in all its color and vitality—and in the inevitability of its descent, its fall into the abyss of death. But after tumbling into the depths the life of the waterfall is not over; it is merely transformed. The waterfall, as man's life itself, infers the poet, continues to live, but in a different state. The waterfall emerges from the depths to flow on placidly, like a milky way. So too after death does the life of man continue eternally as the immortal life of the soul.

Derzhavin was not the first poet, or the last, to find in the waterfall an appropriate symbol of man's life—terrestial and eternal. The Baroque proclivity for themes to which Derzhavin himself was so strongly attracted led more than a single Baroque poet to write of the analogies between the course of a waterfall and the life of man. The English metaphysical poet Henry Vaughan (1622–1695) included in his collection *Silex Scintillans* (1650, 1655), a poem also entitled "The Waterfall." Considerably shorter than Derzhavin's later work, and devoid of the Russian poet's rich use of color and sound as well as his evocative descriptions of various aspects of nature, Vaughan's *The Waterfall* embraces essentially the same philosophic view, and provides interesting material for comparison:

With what deep murmurs through time's silent stealth
Doth thy transparent, cool and wat'ry wealth
Here flowing fall,
And chide, and call,
As if his liquid, loose Retinue staid
Ling'ring, and were of this steep place afraid,
The common pass
Where, clear as glass,
All must descend
Not to an end:

But quick'ned by this deep and rocky grave,
Rise to a longer course more bright and brave.
Dear stream! dear bank, where often I
Have sate, and pleas'd my pensive eye,
Why, since each drop of thy quick store
Runs thither, whence it flow'd before,
Should poor souls fear a shade or night,
Who came (sure) from a sea of light?
Or since those drops are all sent back
So sure to thee, that none doth lack,
Why should frail flesh doubt any more
That what God takes, he'll not restore?
O useful Element and clear!
My sacred wash and cleanser here,
My first consigner unto those
Fountains of life, where the Lamb goes?
What sublime truths, and wholesome themes,
Lodge in thy mystical, deep streams!
Such as dull man can never finde
Unless that Spirit lead his minde,
Which first upon thy face did move,
And hatch'd all with his quick'ning love.
As this loud brook's incessant fall
In streaming rings restagnates all,
Which reach by course the bank, and then
Are no more seen, just so pass men.
O my invisible estate,
My glorious liberty, still late!
Thou art the Channel my soul seeks
Not this with Cataracts and Creeks.

In the original Russian Derzhavin's *The Waterfall* is written in stanzas of six lines each, in iambic tetrameter and
rhyme scheme *a b a b c c*.

A diamantine mountain pours
Down from the heights in four stages.[1]
A pearl and silver-filled abyss

[1] A reference to the four levels of the Kivach waterfall.

СОЧИНЕНІЯ ДЕРЖАВИНА

ЧАСТЬ ВТОРАЯ.

САНКТПЕТЕРБУРГЪ.

1851.

An illustration based on Gavrila Derzhavin's poem The Waterfall *appearing on the title page of the second volume of the poet's collected works published in St. Petersburg in 1831.*

Boils far below, sends hills of spray up.
The splashing forms a mound of blue,
The roar resounds in distant woods.

Resounds, and 'midst a grove of pines
It later dies out in the thicket.
A ray of light shines 'cross a stream;
'Neath shifting vault of trees flow softly
The waves, all covered as by sleep,
A milky river thus become.

Along the shores the whitish foam
Collects in mounds in shaded thickets;
The sound of hammers fills the air,
The buzz of saws and groan of bellows.[2]
O waterfall! In your deep pit
All drowns in an abyss, in mist!

Are pine trees struck by heavy winds?—
In you they break in tiny pieces.
Are stones by lightning torn asunder?—
Into fine sand 'tis you who grind them.
Does bold ice hold your waters fast?—
Like bits of broken glass they fall.

The fierce wolf prowling 'bout you stops—
For nothing can strike terror in him.
A fire burns inside his eyes,
The fur upon him stands like bristle.
To fight in bloody battles born
He howls, in harmony with you.

The timid deer approaches softly,
Your falling waters' roar perceiving.
She bends her horns upon her back
And takes flight swiftly through the forest.
The noise and howling frighten her,
And brittle leaves beneath her hooves.

The spirited steed greets you next,
Preserving his proud gait, approaching.

[2] An iron foundry was located about 25 miles (40 versts) from
the waterfall. In clear weather, however, sounds emanating from
it reached as far as the Kivach.

His thick mane raised and muzzle hot
He gives a snort and pricks his ears up,
And taking courage, now enflamed,
He boldly hurtles to your depths.

Beneath a sloping cedar tree,
In face of Nature's fearful beauty,
On an old stump which did protrude
From mountain crag o'er eager waters,
I see a certain white-haired man
Bent over with his head in hands.[3]

His lance and sword, his mighty shield,
And helmet all wound 'round with dodder,
One time his fatherland's defense,
Rest at his feet upon the moss there.
Shining in golden armor garbed,
Like evening in a reddish glow.[4]

He sits—and gaze fixed on the stream
He meditates, in deepest thought plunged:
"Does not this waterfall portray
To us the course of man's existence?—
It also with its glittering streams
Sustains the proud, the meek, and wicked.

"Does time not flow from heaven down?
Do not our passions boil inside us;
Glory not shine, nor fame resound;
The happiness of our days glitter,
The beauty and the joy of which
Are gloomed by sorrow, woe, and age?

"Do we not every day see graves,
An aging universe's graying?
Do we not hear as hours toll
Death's voice, the creak of doors beneath us?
Do there not fall into these jaws
The king from throne and friend of kings?

[3] An allusion to Count Rumiantsev.
[4] In the original Russian: *kak vecher vo zare rumianoi.* Derzhavin is playing on the root of the name Rumiantsev—*rumianyi,* "rosey," "reddish," "ruddy."

"They fall—and the unvanquished chief,
'Midst praise in Rome's high Senate, Caesar,
Just as he wished the diadem,
Fell, countenance with mantle veiled.[5]
Gone are the schemes, gone are the hopes—
The eyes that sought the throne are closed.

"They fall—and the incomparable man
Of countless triumphs from his chariot
A model of the world's great souls,
Who scorned the lure of royal purple,
Admired by kings Belisarius[6]
In prison falls, his eyes removed.

"They fall.—And did not dreams entice
When cities long ago did hail me,
When I was in my fullest flower
Bedecked in laurels, olive branches?
Was it long past?—But now in war
My hands no longer lightning hurl!

"My strength is gone, and suddenly
A storm has from my hands the lance seized.
Although my spirit still is proud,
Of victories fate has deprived me."
He spoke—and slumbered quietly
By wings of Morpheus concealed.

October night fell on the earth,[7]
On silent darkness' peaceful bosom.
I hear not anywhere a thing
Except the roaring of the waters,
Dashed from the heights against the rocks
And looking like a snow-capped mount.

The wilderness its eyelids closed,
The crags and cliffs were wrapped in slumber;
And clouds like regiments of waves

[5] A reference to Julius Caesar's assassination.
[6] Belisarius (sixth century A.D.), a Byzantine general convicted of treason and blinded.
[7] Potëmkin died on October 5, 1791, on a journey between Jassy and Nikolaev.

Moved silently by in procession.
From out their midst the moon looked down,
The moon all trembling and pale.

It looked, and barely did it shine,
Its crests before the old man lowered[8]
As though it greeted with esteem
That enemy of days long ended
From whom in fright it had recoiled,
Whom all the world did marvel at.

He slept—and sleep miraculous
Revealed to him the dreams of heroes.
In one it seemed to him that he
Again commanded mighty armies,
That lightning stood by silently
Awaiting him to order it—

That at the pointing of his finger
Artillery squares would follow him;
That on smooth plains, on all sides opened,
At one word from him would rise up
New regiments from hidden placements,
Like hills of clouds upon the ocean—

That just the dewy grass would bear
The imprint of the steps at night;
That 'neath a clear sky in the morning
His foes too late would see his dust;
That by the sharpness of his pupils,
Like hawks their prey he would transfix them—

That laying out his maps and plans
In his tent, like an unseen Magus,[9]
He stations chimeras in vales,
While tigers wait in higher places;
Then suddenly with firm resolve,
On thousands hurls his thunder down—

[8] The poet is also suggesting by this image the humbling of the Turkish crescent (i.e., the Ottoman Empire) before Rumiantsev in the First Turkish War (1768–1774).

[9] A reference to the "wizardry" of Rumiantsev's military strategies.

That crescent's pride and eagle's daring
Where amber waves flow and where black,[10]
He humbled golden-fleeced Colchis,[11]
And losses wrenched from the white tsar[12]
Before the evening's golden borders
Avenged a hundredfold with triumphs—

That, like a reddish ray of dawn,
His country was with glory covered,
And foreign leaders, foreign kings,
Joined his own sovereign and his nation
In praising him for his great deeds
And raising triumphs to his name—[13]

That in the midst of many splendors
Shone bright his image, name, and deeds;
And that his silvery brow's summit
In wreath of lightning's fiery rays
Would glow through future generations
And fill with light the hearts of countless—

That jealousy its pallid glance
Turns from his radiance away,
And groaning in a speechless way
Crawls off and seeks out hidden lairs
Where it can hide itself from him;
And that no one compares with him.

He sleeps—and in these pleasant dreams
Perceives the baying now of hound dogs,
The roar of winds and stout trees' creak,

[10] The "amber waves" refer to the Baltic Sea where Prussian forces were defeated by the Russians in the Seven Years' War (1756–1763). The "black waves" refer to the Black Sea and Russian victories over the Turks.

[11] An ancient country in Transcaucasia, on the eastern shore of the Black Sea. The legendary Golden Fleece was in Colchis. Derzhavin erroneously uses Colchis (Kolkhida, in Russian) with reference to the Crimea, which was "humbled" during the First Turkish War.

[12] A reference to the Russian tsar.

[13] A reference to the celebrations and honors tended Rumiantsev for his victories.

The moaning of the screech and hoot owls
And in the distance animals,
And quiet rustling 'midst the spirits.

He hears: a fir tree has been crumbled,
A flock of ravens taken flight,
A mound of silica cracked open,
A mountain with its riches felled.
The echo rumbles through the mountains,
Like thunder thundering on thunders.

He sees attired in pitch-black raiment
Some kind of winged woman then;
Her hair disheveled, tossing wildly,
She was like news of death or war,
A scythe in hand, a trumpet readied.
He hears her speak to him: "Wake up now!"

Atop the helmet that she wore
An eagle sat with clouded thunder.
He saw in it his nation's arms
And agitated by this daydream
He sighed, he shed a shower of tears,
And said: "Some hero must be dead![14]
"Happy, when in pursuit of glory,
The common weal he kept in guard!
In bloody combat he showed mercy
And spared the lives of prisoners.
For many centuries to come yet
Let blessed be this friend of mankind!

"And let him have for epitaph
The blessed praise that long will ring
If all his life and deeds recall
As dedicated to man's service;
If fame alone lured him not on
And he false glory did not seek!

"O glory, glory—heroes' pleasure!
'Tis you this waterfall portrays.
Through plentitude of flowing waters
And roar of gushing coolnesses,

[14] That is, Potëmkin.

'Tis light, magnificent, and lovely,
Miraculous, clear, strong, and thundering!

"About you crowds of people gather
In constant dumbstruck wonderment;
But if the fall with its rich water
Does not bring nourishment to all,
If it tears shores and in its rapids
There is no gain to mortals—then what?

"Is it not better to be famed less
And be more useful to all men;
Resembling more a lovely streamlet
That waters gardens, groves, and fields,
And with its faraway soft babbling
Attracts posterity's attention?

"Let to a mound grown o'er with turf
Come traveler and take his seat there
And bending his head over read
The writing on the grave, declaring:
'Here rests not famed by war alone
A man whose soul was greater still.'

"O! Be immortal, martial chieftain,
When you have all your duty done!"
So spoke the old man crowned in whiteness
And, gaze on heaven, then grew still.
Grew still—but his wise voice took flight then
And his words everywhere resounded.

But who goes there among the mounds,
Gazing, like moon, upon black waters?
Whose shadow hastens through the clouds
Seeking celestial habitations?
On his dark gaze and on his brow
There sits deep thought obscured by mist.

Who is this wondrous winged spirit
Who soars from Northlands to the South?—
Swift winds pursue, but their pace slackens.
His sudden gaze embraces states;
He roars and flashes like a comet,
A trail of sparks marks his swift journey.

Whose corpse, like mist upon a crossroads,
Lies in the bosom of dark night?
Coarse tatters now his only raiment;
His eyes by two small coins closed;[15]
His hands are clasped on his cold bosom;
His lips are opened, but say nothing!

Whose bed—the earth; whose roof—the azure,
Whose halls the wildernesses 'round?
Are you not fame and pleasure's offspring,
O splendid Prince of Crimea?[16]
Have you not from the heights of honors
Been suddenly 'midst empty steppes downed?

Were you not near the throne and favorite
Of the Minerva of the North?[17]
Apollo's friend—in Muses' temple;[18]
On Mars's field a leader famed;
In war and peace—decision maker,
A potentate—though not in purple?

Is it not you who dared raise up
The power of Russia, Catherine's spirit,
And with support of both desired
To carry thunder to those rapids
On which the ancient Rome did stand[19]
And trembled all the universe.

Is it not you who put to flight
The mighty hordes of vulturous neighbors
And from vast empty regions made

[15] Potëmkin died on the night of October 5, 1791. Sensing the approach of death, he asked to be taken from his coach and laid on the grass of the steppe he was traveling across at the time. When he died, a hussar closed his eyes with two small gold coins.

[16] For his victories over the Tatars and Turks, which facilitated the Russian annexation of the Crimea, Potëmkin was permitted to add the honorific "Tavricheskii" (of Tavrida, an old name for the Crimea) to his name.

[17] A reference to Potëmkin's close ties to the Empress Catherine.

[18] Potëmkin enjoyed the reputation of a patron of the arts.

[19] The reference is to Constantinople (Istanbul). Potëmkin had grandiose plans for the collapse of Ottoman power, and felt himself entrusted with the task of "saving" Europe from the Turks.

Inhabitable towns, and cornfields,
And covered the Black Sea with ships,
And shook the earth's core with your thunder?

Is it not you who knew to choose right
The worthy tests of Russian strength,
The elements themselves to trample
In Ochakov[20] and Izmail,[21]
And by such firm audacity be
The wonder of bravery itself?

'Tis you, the bravest of all mortals!
Mind fertile with a host of schemes!
You did not tread the usual paths[22]
But did extend them—and the roar
You left behind to your descendants.
'Tis you, Potëmkin, wondrous leader!

'Tis you, to whom magnificent
Triumphal arches were erected.[23]
The arts and learning, beauty too,
Wove for you wreathes of laurel, myrtle.
Joy and splendor blossomed 'round you,
And happiness and fame joined hands.

'Tis you, fruit of heaven's bounty,
To whom I was this work to offer,
And thought my humble lyre to tune
In harmony with lofty Pindar.
I celebrated Izmail,[24]
I celebrated—but Death came!

[20] The Turkish fortress of Ochakov in the Crimea was seized
during the Second Turkish War on December 6, 1788.

[21] Izmail, another Turkish stronghold on the Black Sea, was
seized by the Russians on December 11, 1790.

[22] A reference to Potëmkin's frequent use of less orthodox
military strategy.

[23] In honor of Potëmkin's victories in the South, a triumphal
arch of marble was erected in Tsarskoe Selo (near St. Petersburg)
in 1791.

[24] Derzhavin is referring here to his own ode *On the Capture
of Izmail* (Na vziatie Izmaila, 1790–1791, printed 1793).

Alas! My choruses' sweet sound
Has been turned into plaintive moaning.
My lyre has slipped from out weak hands
And I have into bitter tears sunk
Where an abyss of colored stars
Revealed the halls of Paradise.[25]

Alas!—And they have grown dumb too—
The thunders that had roared about you;
Your regiments are orphaned now
And filled the air with their sobbing;
And all that had been near you once
Has grown disconsolate and sad.

Your wreath of laurel has now withered,[26]
Your notched mace has left your hands,[27]
Your sword was half inside its scabbard,
When Catherine broke into tears!
The earthly globe was shaken with her
By your untimely, sudden passing!

Peace brought and threw down from its hands
The branches fresh and green of olives;
The wails and cries of kin and friend
And plaintive sound of Grecian Muses
Resound about this Pericles.
And Virgil his Maecenas mourns,[28]

Who in the rays of homages,
Just as a sovereign on his throne,
In handsome gilded phaeton
By silvery-rose stallions carried,[29]

[25] A reference to brilliantly illuminated celebrations in Potëmkin's palace.

[26] A reference to the laurel wreath of diamonds presented to Potëmkin by Catherine in recognition of his victories.

[27] The *bulava* in Russian was a field marshal's baton. It also indicated the Cossack *hetmanate* that Potëmkin held in 1790.

[28] In his *Eclogues* Virgil glorified the Roman statesman and patron of literature, Gaius Cilnius Maecenas (c. 70–8 B.C.).

[29] A reference to Potëmkin's famous phaeton and tandem of horses.

Shone bright among equestrians—
And fell against a funeral coach![30]

Where are you Splendor? Where is Fame?
And where are you, O mighty earthling?
Methuselah's longevity
Is but a dream, our age a shadow;
Our whole existence is no more
Than just an empty dream by day.

Or no!—A heavy ball our life is,
Suspended on a tender hair,
On which the blows of storms and thunders
And lightning raging from the skies
From all sides beat incessantly,
And which light zephyrs can rend also.

A single hour, a single moment
Can bring down kingdoms of themselves;
By just a puff the elements can
Transform great giants into dust.
They seek their places—and they know not:
They trample heroes in the dust!

They trample heroes?—No!—Their deeds
Shine through the darkness of the ages.
Imperishable memory
And praise fly from their very ruins;
Their graves, like hills in springtime, bloom.
Potëmkin's work will be inscribed.

His theatre—was the Èvksin's border;[31]
Hearts bound by gratitude—his shrine;
The hand extending laurels—Catherine's;
His incense—thundering acclaim;
His life—of triumphs, blood an altar,
A sepulcher of dread and love.

[30] A reference to an actual event in Potëmkin's life. Leaving church after the funeral of the Prince of Wittemberg (the brother-in-law of Paul, the successor to the throne), who died on August 13, 1791, Potëmkin was sunk in thought and actually boarded the hearse instead of his own carriage.

[31] A Russianized form of Pontius Euxinus ("hospitable sea"), the Latin name for the Black Sea.

When through the mist of pitch-black night
The blood-hued moon extends its radiance,
And Danube River's murky waves
Bear glints of blood and through the bushes
Surrounding Izmail winds howl
And groans are heard—what thinks the Turk?

He trembles, and though eyes are closed
Can still see bayonets a-gleaming
Where forty thousand fallen Turks[32]
Lie all about the grave of Weismann.[33]
Their shadows come to haunt his dreams,
And Russians to their knees in blood!

He trembles—and he turns his gaze
Faintheartedly to nearby places.
To heavens burning columns reach
From the Crimea's lands and waters![34]
He thinks again in Ochakov
His blood begins to flow and freeze.[35]

But on a clear day, 'midst a calm sea,
When fishes go among the skies[36]
And striped ensigns flutter gently;
When our ships with their swollen sails
Gleam white in distant estuaries,
What feeling wells up in the Russians?

They are in raptures—but the Turks
Feel only dread and apprehension.
Their eyes know naught but moss and thorns,
While ours see blooming roses, laurels
In mausoleums to our chiefs—
The rulers of the shores and seas.

[32] The Turkish garrison at Izmail numbered 40,000 men.
[33] Baron Otto Weismann von Weisenstein. A general who lost his life in the First Turkish War on June 22, 1773, and was buried in Izmail.
[34] A reference to the fires of Turkish fortresses under siege and the burning of Turkish naval vessels.
[35] Ochakov fell in December on a bitter cold day.
[36] The poet is speaking of the reflections of clouds and naval ensigns on the water on a clear day.

Beneath a tree, by sunset's glow,
Love sits in pensive meditation.
A light spring breeze spreads everywhere
Her sweet voice singing to a zither.
Her pearl-like bosom heaving sighs
A hero's image animates.[37]

In morning when the sun's bright rays
The golden monument enkindle,
And deer lie overcome by sleep,
And vapor curls around the hillocks,
The old man come there reads inscribed:
"Potëmkin's corpse is buried here!"

The dust of Alcibiades!—[38]
Do worms dare crawl about his head there?
And coming 'pon Achilles' helm
Does Tercitus[39] not fear to take it?—
Alas! If flesh and works decay,
Of what then is our glory made?

'Tis Truth alone that gives out laurels,
Which Time can never cause to fade;
'Tis Truth alone the singers sing of,
The thunderings of whose sweet lyres
Will through eternity keep pealing;
The just alone have sacred idols.

Pay heed now, worldly waterfalls!
O heads in turmoil with ambition!
Your sword is clean, your robes unsoiled
If Truth has been your love's devotion,
If your great goal has always been
To bring the world to happiness.

[37] A reference to the medallions of Potëmkin many Russian women wore on their chests.

[38] The Athenian general and statesman in the Peloponnesian War. He lived from c. 450–405 B.C.

[39] A coward who condemned Achilles. Probably here an allusion to Prince Zubov, who was sometimes critical of Potëmkin.

Roar on, roar on, O waterfall!
As you reach to the very heavens.
Delight our hearing and our sight
With your bright sonorous cascading.
And in men's later memory
Live only with your beauty rare!

Live on—and let it be that clouds
Pass seldom through your flowing waters,
And that in minds you be not dimmed
By darkest smoke and blazing thunder;[40]
That all may love you near and far—
As wondrous as you are of use.

And you, mother of waterfalls,
O Suna! Raging northern river—
If from the heights the power is yours
To glitter—and, with dawn's red burning,
You boil and sow a sapphire rain,
A fire ablaze with purple color—

Then when your flow is soft and tranquil
And you are even with yourself,
Not striving, swift, and ever gentle,
Translucent to your very depths,
Not foaming or in tumult stately,
Contained, but no less great and perfect

And unalloyed by alien streams
You nourish shores in cornfields golden;
Your splendid course you then bestow
Upon Onega's luminous gathering.[41]
Oh, what a spectacle to see!
How like the heavens are you now!

[40] The poet is speaking of the ruin personal ambition can cause.
[41] The Suna River flows into Lake Onega in northwestern Russia.

15. *Invitation to Dinner*

GAVRILA R. DERZHAVIN

The *Invitation to Dinner* (Priglashenie k obedu) was written in May, 1795, on the occasion of a reception held in Derzhavin's home. It was printed for the first time in the collected edition of the poet's works of 1798.

The poem expresses the familiar "Horatian" strain in Derzhavin's poetry: the love of life, the pleasure of good food, good drink, good companionship—both male and female—the desire to take the good that life has to offer before death comes. Time again appears an abiding concern of Derzhavin. As in the earlier *On the Death of Prince Meshcherskii*, the poet is ever conscious of the passage of time and the brevity of man's terrestial sojourn. No sooner does one pass his youth, he declares in *Invitation to Dinner*, than he reaches old age and comes face to face with omnipotent, inescapable Death. The image of Death is as concrete as elsewhere in Derzhavin's poetry: here it looks at man "through a fence" (*chrez zabor*) when he approaches his old age. The awareness of death once again leads the poet to preach moderation, temperance in the enjoyment of earthly pleasures so that the cup of life may be drained less quickly in order to be able to quaff from it longer, so that the pain of ultimate separation may be thereby lessened.

In the original, *Invitation to Dinner* is in iambic tetrameter, with the rhyme scheme: *a b a b c c d e e d*, with *a*, *c*, and *d* representing feminine rhymes, and *b* and *e*, masculine.

Gold sturgeon from the river Sheksna,[1]
Kaimak[2] and borsht already wait;
Shining with ice, reflecting crystal,
Wines in carafes and punch allure.
Perfuming pans diffuse aromas,
Fruits gaily laugh among the baskets.
The servants cannot catch their breath
Awaiting you about the table.
The hostess, dignified and youthful,[3]
Is set to take you by the hand.

I beg you come, old benefactor,
Doer of good for twenty years![4]
Come grace my home now with a visit.
Although by no means elegant
And without sculpture, gold, or silver—
Its wealth is pleasantness and neatness
And my firm, honest character.
Come rest yourself from your affairs,
Eat, drink, enjoy yourself a little,
Fear nothing harmful to your health.

[1] A left tributary of the Volga River.
[2] A Turkish borrowing (*kaymak*) used in Russian for cream prepared a certain way for the whitening of borsht.
[3] A reference to Derzhavin's second wife, Daria (Milena), whom he married a few months before writing the poem.
[4] Originally, the stanza was addressed to Count Ivan Ivanovich Shuvalov (1727–1797). Shuvalov had shown Derzhavin kindness on several occasions, and the poet had reciprocated by dedicating a few poems to him. In the first version of the poem Derzhavin had "Doer of good for *thirty years*" in the light of the fact that Shuvalov was a patron of the Kazan' gymnasium where the poet had studied more than thirty years previously. But because the guests he invited to the dinner he celebrates in the poem included Catherine's adviser Count A. Bezborodko, Derzhavin decided not to risk offending so important a dignitary, and changed the "thirty" to "twenty" to enable Bezborodko to consider it an allusion to himself (the two men had known each other since 1761).

Not prominence, nor rank, nor favor
But kindliness alone I asked
To come to my plain Russian dinner,
And whosoever does me harm
Will be no witness to this party.
You guardian angel, benefactor,
Come on—enjoy the good things here,
And let the hostile spirits vanish;
No ill-intentioned step shall darken
The threshold of my humble home.

I dedicate this day to friendship,
To friendship and to beauty too.
I can esteem the worth of others,
And life I know is but a shade;
That we no sooner pass our youthhood
Than to old age we come already
And Death peers at us through a fence.
Alas!—How not to stop and ponder,
For once not covering all with flowers,
Forsaking not a somber look?

I have been privy to the secret
That even kings are sometimes sad;
That day and night they are tormented,
Though others have peace thanks to them.
Although he may have fame and glory,
But oh!—is the throne always pleasant
To one whose life is spent in care,
Whom treachery and downfall threaten?
How that poor sentinel is piteous
Who stands his hours eternally!

And so, as long as nasty weather
Does not cast gloom o'er cloudy days,
And Lady Fortune keeps caressing
And fondling us with tender hand;
As long as frosts are not yet with us
And roses have perfumed the gardens,
Let us not tarry to their scent.
Yes! Let us then delight in living
And take our comforts as we get them—
The cloth says how the coat is cut.

And should it be that you or others
Of the nice guests I've summoned here,
Prefer instead the golden chambers[5]
Or honeyed victuals of kings,
Give up the thought of dining with me,
And pay heed to my explanation:
Bliss lies not in porphyry rays,
Nor in food's taste, or tender converse;
But in good health and peace of spirit—
The finest feast is temperance.

[5] An allusion to Catherine's favorite Zubov, who was invited
by Derzhavin but at the last moment declined on the excuse
that the empress had detained him.

16. *The Monument*

GAVRILA R. DERZHAVIN

Derzhavin's poem *The Monument* (Pamiatnik), written in 1795, is based on Horace's famous ode beginning: "Exegi monumentum aere perennius/ regalique situ pyramidum altius," and so on. Previously, the ode had been translated into Russian by both Lomonosov and Vasilii Kapnist. Of particular interest in Derzhavin's version is the emphasis the poet places on those contributions to literature that he felt earned him the right to immortality: the creation of a "new" type of panegyric ode with amusing or "entertaining" accents (with reference especially to *Felitsa*), and his independence of thought, which enabled him to "speak the truth to sovereigns" without fear.

Written in six-foot iambic verse with alternating feminine and masculine rhymes in the original Russian, the poem was published for the first time in the collected edition of Derzhavin's works in 1798, where it carried the title *To My Muse. From Horace* (K Muze. Iz Goratsiia). It received its present title only in the edition of 1808.

Derzhavin's *The Monument* served as the inspiration for another well-known Russian version of Horace's ode, by Pushkin. Written on August 21, 1836, Pushkin's poem, known generally by the title *Unto Myself I Reared a Monument*, is closely related to Derzhavin's, but develops more profoundly the mission of the poet, of his social responsibility. For the sake of the comparison, Pushkin's version is given after that of Derzhavin.

I raised myself a monument eternal, wondrous,
Firmer than metal, higher than the pyramids;
The whirlwind nor the sudden thunderbolt shall crush it,
Nor will time in its flight succeed in leveling it.

308

Indeed, not all of me shall die; the greater portion,
Having escaped decay, shall live beyond my death.
And fading not, my glory shall continue growing
So long as all the world esteems the race of Slavs.

From White Sea to the Black my fame shall be spread widely
Where flow the Ural, Volga, Don, and the Neva;
All shall remember among peoples without number
How from obscurity I did become renowned

As first to dare proclaim the virtues of Felitsa
In Russian in a light and entertaining style;
To speak sincerely of the Deity, but simply,
And with a smile to tell the truth to sovereigns.

O Muse, take glory in your well-deserved merit;
If anyone should scorn you, scorn him then yourself;
And with a hand nowise constrained or hurried garland
Your forehead with the dawn of immortality.

Unto Myself I Reared a Monument
A. S. Pushkin

Exegi monumentum

Unto myself I reared a monument not builded
By hands; a track thereto the people's feet will tread;
Not Alexander's shaft is lofty as my pillar
    That proudly lifts its splendid head.

Not wholly shall I die—but in the lyre my spirit
Shall, incorruptible and bodiless, survive—
And I shall know renown as long as under heaven
    One poet yet remains alive.

The rumor of my fame will sweep through vasty Russia,
And all its peoples speak this name, whose light shall reign
Alike for haughty Slav, and Finn, and savage Tungus,
    And Kalmuck riders of the plain.

I shall be loved, and long the people will remember
The kindly thoughts I stirred—my music's brightest crown,
How in this cruel age I celebrated freedom,
    And begged for ruth toward those cast down.

Oh, Muse, as ever, now obey your God's commandments,
Of insult unafraid, to praise and slander cool,
Demanding no reward sing on, but in your wisdom
    Be silent when you meet a fool.

(*The Poems, Prose and Plays of Alexander Pushkin*, ed.
Avrahm Yarmolinsky, New York, 1936, p. 88.)

17. *A Nightingale in a Dream*

GAVRILA R. DERZHAVIN

In 1804 Derzhavin published separately a collection of his anacreontic poems under the title *Anacreontic Songs* (Anakreonticheskie pesni). With a number of additions this made up the third volume of the first collected edition of his works, which he himself prepared and the first four parts of which came out in 1808; the fifth and last part was published in 1816, the year of the poet's death.

Written in trochaic tetrameter, which Derzhavin used occasionally for his "light" poetry, the poem is divided into two stanzas of a common pattern: ten lines per stanza and the rhyme scheme *a b a b c c d e e d*, with *a*, *c*, and *e* representing feminine rhymes, and *b* and *d*, masculine. The song echoes the familiar refrain of the joy of life and the poet's wish to enjoy its pleasures while he can.

On a high hill I was sleeping
And your voice heard, nightingale.
Even in my deepest slumber
I could hear it in my soul—
Now it sounded, then resounded,
Now it moaned, and then was laughing
In my ear from far away;
And, while lying with Callisto,[1]
Singing, sighing, whistling, calling,
Brought delight to my sweet sleep.

[1] In Greek mythology Callisto was a nymph in the train of Artemis, the daughter of Zeus and Leto. She was loved by Zeus and became the mother of Arcas, the legendary ancestor of the Arcadians. The poet uses the name here synonymously with "loved one," "beloved."

If, after my life is ended,
In a dull and endless sleep
These songs will, alas, no longer
Reach my ear as they do now,
And if I will hear no longer
Sounds of happiness and joy,
Sounds of dancing, choirs, and glory,
Then let me enjoy my life here,
Kiss my loved one much more often,
Hear the nightingale's sweet songs.

18. *Country Life*

GAVRILA R. DERZHAVIN

The praise of the sweet, idyllic simplicity of country life, of the life closer to nature, far from the bustle of the city with its corrupting and false values, was a popular theme in the literature of European sentimentalism. Its appearance has already been remarked in Emin's *Letters of Ernest and Doravra*, Radishchev's *Journey*, and Karamzin's *Letters of a Russian Traveler*. From the late 1790's it also began to become prominent in the poetry of Derzhavin, but less as a literary convention than as a reality of the poet's life at the time.

After the death in 1794 of his first wife, which affected him deeply, Derzhavin recovered sufficiently from his grief to marry a woman half his age the following year. Although he fell temporarily into disfavor at the very beginning of Paul I's reign (1796–1801), his fortunes soon improved considerably, and he was awarded several high positions. When the throne passed to Alexander I (1801–1825), Derzhavin earned the new tsar's disapproval because of his membership in a group of conservative officials who opposed the liberal policies with which the young tsar enthusiastically launched his reign. Derzhavin was named Minister of Justice in 1802 but was relieved of the post in 1803, after which he put in for retirement from the government service, retaining his ranks of senator and councilor of state.

Despite his early difficulties with Paul and afterward, Alexander, Derzhavin's later years were comfortable. He was esteemed as the foremost poet of his day and was at the same time a man of state. His income was large enough to enable him to acquire an imposing residence in St. Petersburg and the lovely country estate of Zvanka in the Novgorod district about a hundred miles from the capital.

As Derzhavin began to spend his summers at Zvanka regularly, he grew fonder of the country and turned to it more often in his writing. In 1798 he celebrated the rural life in the poem *In Praise of Village Life* (Pokhvala sel'skoi zhizni); in 1802 came *Country Life* (Derevenskaia zhizn'), the poem translated here; in May and July, 1807, he wrote his longest poem on the rural theme *To Evgenii. Life at Zvanka* (Evgeniiu. Zhizn' zvanskaia), which was dedicated to Bishop Evgenii Bolkhovitinov (1767–1837), an eminent historian, archaeologist, and literary scholar who resided in a monastery near Zvanka and with whom the poet was close from about 1804 to 1808; in the summer of 1807 Derzhavin wrote enthusiastically of the peasantry in the poem *A Peasant Holiday* (Krest'ianskii prazdnik).

A short poem but thoroughly typical of those Derzhavin wrote praising rural existence, *Country Life* was written in iambic trimeter, with alternating feminine and masculine rhymes.

What need have I for cities?
The country I prefer.
I need no stars or ribbons,
A magnate I am not.
I make only an effort
To pass life happily;
I'm liked by everybody
And want to like in turn.
Who knows what will come later?
I live just for today;
Tomorrow you're forgotten—
All passes like a shade.
Why should I lose a minute,
Each precious that I have,
And not chase wicked boredom
And sorrow with some fun?
I have no need of treasure:
Peace with my wife is wealth;
If Cupid, Venus, Bacchus
Smile on me, I'm rich too;
If I have health and plenty,
Can eat and drink my share,
I'm rich, and while my strength lasts
To sport with Milena.[1]

---

[1] A reference to Derzhavin's second wife, Daria.

19. *The Gypsy Woman's Dance*

GAVRILA R. DERZHAVIN

The Gypsy Woman's Dance (Tsyganskaia pliaska) also belongs to what may be called Derzhavin's "Zvanka cycle." During the summer of 1804, while at his country estate, the poet thought that his friend and fellow poet I. I. Dmitriev was also in the area and, without signing it, addressed the poem *Summer* (Leto) to him. (It was later published in No. 18 of the *Messenger of Europe* for 1805.) Dmitriev guessed that Derzhavin was the author and penned an answer to him, also in verse. It was printed in the October, 1804, number of the *Messenger of Europe*. When he received Dmitriev's poem, Derzhavin replied to it in turn with *The Gypsy Woman's Dance*. The subject was suggested by Dmitriev's mention of gypsies and dancing in his own work.

The Gypsy Woman's Dance was first published in No. 22 of the *Messenger of Europe* for 1805 with the inscription "D—N." In the original each stanza consists of a quatrain followed by a refrain. The meter is irregular iambic with three stresses or beats per line; the quatrains have alternating feminine and masculine rhymes; the refrains are rhymed couplets.

🌸

Take up your guitar, gypsy woman,
Cry out, strike a chord on the strings;
All filled with voluptuous fever
Entrance everyone with your dance.
    Hurl the fire of your tawny face
    At hearts, set souls ablaze.

Revive at the same time that feeling,
Tempestuous yet full of delight,
The throbbing of nerves and love's languor,
The magic of ancient Bacchantes.

Hurl the fire of your tawny face
At hearts, set souls ablaze.

Like night—from your cheeks flash a radiance;
Like a whirlwind—sweep dust with your cloak;
Like a bird—soar on high with your wings;
And shriek with each clap of your hands.
    Hurl the fire of your tawny face
    At hearts, set souls ablaze.

By the light of the pale shining moon,
At night in a forest of pines,
Awaken the sleep of dead silence
By stamping your feet on the graves.
    Hurl the fire of your tawny face
    At hearts, set souls ablaze.

Let your fearful cry of "euhoe,"[1]
Far off blending with yelps of dogs,
Spread a frightful clamor all over,
And love mingle freely with lust.
    Hurl the fire of your tawny face
    At hearts, set souls ablaze.

No, stop, temptress! That is sufficient!
Spare modest muses further fright,
But decorously, poised, and graceful
Dance on like a Russian maid.
    Hurl the fire that sets souls ablaze
    At a tender poet.[2]

---

[1] According to tradition the cry emitted at ancient bacchanals.
[2] A reference to Dmitriev.

20. "Time's River in Its Ceaseless Coursing . . ."

GAVRILA R. DERZHAVIN

On July 6, 1816, Derzhavin began a philosophical poetic work to which he had decided to give the title *On Mortality* (Na tlennost'). It was inspired by a well-known German wall map, *The River of Time, An Emblematic History of the World*, a Russian translation of which he had in his study. Three days after beginning the new work, death cut short his career. All that remained of *On Mortality* was the fragment beginning "Time's River in Its Ceaseless Coursing . . ." (Reka vremën v svoëm stremlen'i). It was printed for the first time in No. 30 of the journal *Son of the Fatherland* (Syn otechestva) for 1816, and has since been generally included in collected editions of Derzhavin's works as his last poem. Accompanying the verses in the *Son of the Fatherland* was a short note describing the circumstances under which the fragment came to be written. The meter of the original is the poet's favored iambic tetrameter, with alternating feminine and masculine rhymes. Perhaps it was poetically fitting that Derzhavin's career closed with verses dealing with theme that had come to assume the greatest prominence in his poetry.

Time's river in its ceaseless coursing
Bears all men's deeds along with it,
And peoples, governments, and rulers
Drown in oblivion's abyss.
But if, through sounds of lyre and trumpet,
Something should happen to remain,
Eternity's jaws will consume it—
'Twill share the common destiny.

21. *The Brigadier*

A Comedy in Five Acts

DENIS I. FONVIZIN

Fonvizin's *The Brigadier* and *The Young Hopeful* are the high points of eighteenth-century Russian comedy, followed closely by Vasilii Kapnist's *Chicanery* (Iabeda), written probably in 1793–1794. *The Young Hopeful* has been rendered into English a few times, *The Brigadier* never. For that reason the earlier comedy of Fonvizin was selected for translation here.

The Brigadier was begun in the winter of 1768 and finished by the spring of 1769. The play was read in manuscript by Fonvizin in a number of aristocratic homes in St. Petersburg and even before Catherine II at her summer palace in Peterhof. It proved an immense success and at once established the young author's reputation. In his *Plan for a Historical Dictionary of Russian Writers* (Opyt istoricheskogo slovaria rossiiskikh pisateliakh, 1772) Novikov wrote about *The Brigadier* in his Fonvizin entry: "He composed a comedy *The Brigadier* in which clever words and jokes are strewn on every page. It springs right from our customs; the characters are well drawn and the plot is very simple and natural."

Unfortunately, no information has been preserved about the early stagings of the play; the first editions of the printed version are also lacking. The oldest known edition is the one printed in the collection *Russian Theatre* (Rossiiskii Featr), No. 38, St. Petersburg, 1790.

Satire of the slavish, exaggerated imitation of foreign (especially French) ways had appeared in eighteenth-century Russian literature as early as Kantemir's *To My Mind* (in the figure of Medor). The Frenchified Russian fop who despises everything Russian had been satirized by Sumarokov in his comedies *The Monsters* (Chudovishchi, 1750) and *An Empty Quarrel* (Pustaia ssora, 1750). Russian gallomania was also held up to ridicule in the comedy *Jean de Mole, or The Russian Frenchman* (Zhan de Mole, ili russkoi frantsuz), au-

An engraving of a portrait of Denis Fonvizin by E. Skotnikov made in Moscow in 1829 and based on a painting by an unknown artist in Rome. It appears as the frontispiece to the 1830 edition of Fonvizin's works.

thored by Fonvizin's superior at the time in the Ministry of Foreign Affairs, Ivan Elagin, and staged in 1765; the play was an adaptation of Ludvig Holberg's widely popular *Jean de France, or Hans Frandsen.*

It was with *The Brigadier*, however, that the phenomenon of gallomania received its most successful satirical treatment in an original work of eighteenth-century Russian literature.

Although now less well known and far less frequently performed than *The Young Hopeful*, *The Brigadier* is the better structured of the two comedies. There are some fine comic scenes and the tempo is brisker. This is made possible, in part, by the eschewal of lengthy pace-slowing monologues mouthed by a character such as Starodum in *The Young Hopeful*, whom the author has entrusted with the burden of much of the didacticism of the play. With the exception of the conventional young lovers, Sofia and Dobroliubov, the other characters in *The Brigadier* are types, in the tradition of eighteenth-century comedy. However, they are endowed with individual features and individual idioms to an extent that had not been realized in Russian comedy before Fonvizin. Except for the Frenchified jargon of Ivanushka and the Councilor's wife, the individuating characteristics of the language of the other characters unfortunately cannot be conveyed in a translation.

The Brigadier was very popular on Russian stages well into the nineteenth century. In the light of its theme it is little wonder that the comedy continued to be played along with a number of patriotic works in Russian theatres during the Napoleonic invasion from 1812 to 1814. *The Brigadier* was, incidentally, the last play staged in the Moscow Theatre before the French occupation and the first play staged after the resumption of theatrical productions in 1814.

Dramatis Personae

Brigadier[1]
Ivanushka, his son
Brigadier's wife
Councilor of State
Councilor's wife
Sofia, councilor's daughter
Dobroliubov, in love with Sofia
Councilor's servant

---

[1] In the Russian army of the eighteenth century, the rank of brigadier fell between that of colonel and general.

A room furnished in the old style. The Brigadier, dressed in a frock coat, walks about, smoking. His son, in a dressing gown, with very affected gestures, is drinking tea. The Councilor, in a Cossack coat, is looking at a calendar. On the other side of the room stands a small table with a tea service. Beside it the Councilor's Wife, in morning dress and a cornette, is pouring out tea, also striking a very affected pose. The Brigadier's Wife is sitting in the back, darning a sock. Sofia also sits in the back and is sewing in an embroidering frame.

COUNCILOR (*looking at the calendar*). So, God granting, the wedding will take place on the twenty-sixth.

IVAN. *Hélas!*

BRIGADIER. Very fine, my good neighbor. Although we haven't known each other long this hasn't kept me from dropping in on you in the country with my wife and son on our way home from Petersburg. A state councilor like you is worthy of being the friend of a retired army brigadier, and I've already begun getting along with everyone without titles.[2]

COUNC. WIFE. We don't have to stand on ceremony, sir. In the country we ourselves get along with everyone without any formalities.

BRIG. WIFE. Oh! My dear! What formalities are there between us when he (*pointing to the Councilor*) wants to marry his daughter, and you your stepdaughter, to our Ivanushka, with God's blessing? And so as to be able the better to depend on His blessing, you are also giving her your parental endowment. Now what do we need formalities here for?

COUNC. WIFE. Ah! How fortunate our daughter is! She is going to marry someone who's been in Paris. Oh! How

_____

[2] According to Peter the Great's Table of Ranks, an army brigadier and a state councilor (*statskii sovetnik*) were both of the fifth rank, or class, and therefore of equal status.

happy I am! I know well enough how it is to live with a man who's never been in Paris.

IVAN. *(listening attentively, he raises slightly the knob of his nightcap).* Madame! I thank you for your courtesy. I confess that I myself would like to have a wife with whom I could speak in no other language except French. Our life would be a great deal happier.

BRIG. WIFE. Oh, Ivanushka! God is gracious. Of course your life will be better than ours. Thank God, you never served in the army and your wife won't have to drag along on campaigns without any wage or answer at home for what they teased your husband with in the ranks. My Ignatii Andreevich took out on me the guilt of every private.

BRIGADIER. Wife, will you stop talking nonsense.

COUNCILOR. Enough, neighbor. For God's sake, don't sin. Don't anger the Lord. Don't you know how intelligent a mate you have? She's worthy of being the head of a department. That's how wise Akulina Timofeevna is!

BRIGADIER. Wise! Now you've said it, neighbor! You permit yourself to talk that way out of pity for us, but it seems to me that her wisdom is more like stupidity. But your Avdotia Potapievna is another matter entirely. Oh! I can say straight to her face, and behind her back, that her mind is a wonder. I am a man, and a brigadier, but I still tell you, and how, that I'd happily give up all my patents for ranks, which I bought with my own blood, just to have the intelligence of her excellency.

IVAN. *Dieu!* So many lovely compliments, Father! Father-in-law! Mother! Mother-in-law! And so much intelligence, one head is better than the other.

COUNCILOR. And I can also say about you, my dear son-in-law, that your future lies with you yourself. Just apply yourself to matters; read more.

IVAN. To what matters? Read what?

BRIGADIER. What? The military rules and regulations. It's also a good idea for a young fellow to know surveying.

COUNCILOR. Best of all, read the civil code and ordinances. Whoever knows how to interpret them as a judge will amount to something, my dear son-in-law.

BRIG. WIFE. And it's also not bad to run through my household books. That way cheats won't get the best of you. Where you have to give four kopecks and change, then you won't give five kopecks.

COUNC. WIFE. God protect your head from ever being filled with anything except love stories! Throw away all the studies in the world, my dear. You won't believe how such romances can enlighten a person. Without reading them, I'd risk forever remaining an idiot.

IVAN. *Madame*, you speak the truth. Oh! *Vous avez raison.* Besides romances, I've read nothing, and that's why I am as you see me.

SOFIA *(aside).* And that's why you're a fool.

IVAN. *Mademoiselle*, you wish to say something?

SOFIA. Only what I think about you.

IVAN. And what would that be? *Je vous prie*, don't flatter me.

COUNCILOR. Leave her alone, son-in-law. She's going out of her mind, but about what I don't know.

BRIGADIER. Oh! It will pass. For a week and a half before our wedding my wife went about without a mind. But since then, she's been prospering these thirty years now in such perfect sense nobody would ever notice that she was ever any smarter.

BRIG. WIFE. God give you health, my dear. God give you many long years. Living with you, I have not lost my mind.

COUNCILOR. Most certainly, and I am especially pleased that my daughter is going to have so sensible a mother-in-law.

COUNC. WIFE *(sighs).* Why shouldn't my stepdaughter be your daughter-in-law? We're all gentry. We're all equal here.

COUNCILOR. She's speaking the truth. We're equal in almost everything. You, my dear friend and in-law, are in the military service just what I am in the civil. Before you reached brigadier they cracked your head, and before I became councilor I burnt my eyes out in a department. The only consolation I have is that God blessed me with the income I got on the strength of decrees. Perhaps I

would have had my piece of bread and even more if my
wife was not a lover of *cornettes, manchettes*, and other
such nonsense serving neither temporal nor eternal bliss.

COUNC. WIFE.   Are you calling me extravagant, dear? Come
to your senses. Enough being stingy. I am capable of
divorcing you if you keep on abusing me.

COUNCILOR.   It is impossible for us to divorce without the
authority of the Creator and of the Most Holy Synod.
Here is my opinion: What God brings together, man
does not tear asunder.

IVAN.   Does God really interfere in such matters in Russia?
At least in France, gentlemen, He has left such things as
loving, changing partners, marrying, and divorcing to the
human will.

COUNCILOR.   But that is in France, not with us Orthodox
here. No, dear son-in-law! Our wives are in the hands
of the Creator just as we are. He has all the hair on our
heads counted.

BRIG. WIFE.   But, Ignatii Andreevich, you always scold me
for counting money. How is that? The Lord Himself
deigns to count our hair while we, his slaves, are lazy
about counting money—money that is so rare you can
hardly get a wig of this counted hair for some thirty
altyns.[3]

BRIGADIER.   Rubbish! I don't believe that everyone's hair
has been counted. No wonder, though, that ours have.
I'm a brigadier, and if they don't count the hair of
officials of the first five ranks, then whose are they going
to?

BRIG. WIFE.   To God all officers are in the same rank, from
general to lieutenant.

BRIGADIER.   Ah, wife! I am telling you, don't mix in. Or I'll
make sure there really won't be anything on your head
to count. If you knew God better, you wouldn't talk such
nonsense. How can you imagine that God, who knows
all, doesn't know our Table of Ranks? Shameful thing.

COUNC. WIFE.   Leave such conversations. Is there nothing

[3] In Old Russia an *altyn* was a gold coin with a value of three
kopecks.

else to discuss? You've chosen such a serious matter that I don't understand it.

BRIGADIER.   I too don't find it pleasant to talk about a subject that has nothing to do with maneuvers or battles or what—

COUNCILOR.   Or what, at least, had to do with the responsibility of a judge, plaintiff, or defendant. To tell the truth, I myself don't enjoy talking about anything that can't be agreed on either by statutes or by the civil code.

BRIG. WIFE.   As for me, I'm bored by all these speeches from which there isn't any profit at all. (*To the Councilor's Wife*) Let's change the subject, my dear. Tell me, if you please, what do your help get to eat, what's already on the table, or what you have to put out money for? Do your horses eat your own oats or the bought stuff?

IVAN.   *C'est plus interessant.*

COUNC. WIFE.   You're joking, my dear. Why should I know what all this cattle eats?

COUNCILOR   (*to his wife*). Don't embarrass me! My dear Akulina Timofeevna! Our people eat what's already on the table. Don't be angry with my wife. She has no interest in such matters. I myself pass out the bread and oats.

BRIG. WIFE.   Just like with my Ignatii Andreevich: he's not interested in anything. I go alone to the storehouse.

COUNCILOR   (*aside*). A treasure, not a woman! What honeyed lips she has! Just listen to her talk and you're a slave of sin; it's impossible not to become tempted.

BRIGADIER.   What is it you're saying, neighbor? (*Aside.*) The mistress here and my old woman certainly don't make a pair.

COUNCILOR.   I praise the sensible concern of your spouse with household economy.

BRIGADIER.   I am grateful on behalf of her economy. Because of it she thinks more about the cattle than she does of me.

BRIG. WIFE.   How so, my dear? After all, the cattle cannot think about themselves. Shouldn't I then think about them? You, it seems, are a little smarter than cattle, yet you want me to attend you like an infant.

BRIGADIER. Listen, my wife: it's all the same to me if you babble foolishly or you're out of your mind, but in the presence of this honorable company I am telling you not to open your mouth any more. Otherwise, I promise, it'll be bad.

IVAN. *Mon père!* Don't get excited.

BRIGADIER. What? Don't get excited?

IVAN. *Mon père,* I say, don't get excited.

BRIGADIER. Damn it, it's the first part of it I don't understand.

IVAN. Ha, ha, ha, ha! Now I'm guilty just because you don't know French.

BRIGADIER. See how he's opened up his throat. Since you know Russian, why do you chew up what nobody understands here?

COUNC. WIFE. Enough, my good man. Is your son really obliged to speak to you only in the language you understand?

BRIG. WIFE. Ignatii Andreevich, please, let Ivanushka speak the way he likes. As far as I'm concerned it's all the same. Even when he speaks Russian it seems to sound different. For the life of me, I can't understand a word. What is there to say? Knowledge is light; ignorance is darkness.

COUNCILOR. Of course, my good woman! God's grace shines above the person to whom He has granted literacy. Nowadays, thank God, it's not the way it used to be. How many literates we have among us now, and God knows who will be. Before, it happened that whoever wrote Russian well also knew grammar. But these days nobody knows it, yet all write. How many industrious secretaries we have who compose extracts without knowing grammar it's a real pleasure to see![4] I have one in mind who when he writes anything it can never be understood by some learned person even with grammar.

BRIGADIER. But what do we need grammar for, my good fellow? I have lived without it almost sixty years, and even reared children. Ivanushka here is already over twenty, and he knows enough when to open his mouth

---

[4] An extract was a citation from the records of a legal case that served as the basis for a judicial decision.

and when to keep it shut without ever hearing about grammar.

BRIG. WIFE. Of course, grammar isn't necessary. Before you start studying it, you've still got to buy it. So you pay around eight *grivny*,[5] but whether you learn it or not— God knows.

COUNC. WIFE. Devil take me, if grammar is necessary for anything, and especially in the country. At least in the city I could tear one into curlpapers.

IVAN. *J'en suis d'accord*, what do we need grammar for? I myself have written a thousand *billets-doux*, and it seems to me that you can say my darling, my soul, *adieu, ma reine*, without ever looking into grammar.

SCENE 2
   The same and Servant.

SERVANT. Mr. Dobroliubov has arrived.

SOFIA (*aside*). My God! He's come, and I'm someone else's fiancée.

COUNCILOR. Let's go meet my friend's son and we'll take a little walk through the garden with him.

BRIGADIER (*to the Councilor's Wife*). Do you wish to come along?

COUNC. WIFE. No, thank you, I'll stay here. Your son will keep me company.

IVAN. *De tout mon cœur*, I am happy to be alone with you.

COUNCILOR (*to the Brigadier's Wife*). And you, my dear, don't you wish to take a little stroll?

BRIG. WIFE. Certainly, certainly.

COUNC. WIFE (*to Sofia*). And you at least keep your mother-in-law company.

SCENE 3
   Councilor's Wife, Ivanushka.

IVAN. (*seating himself very near the Councilor's Wife*). It seems to me, *madame*, that your spouse knows the world no more than is necessary for a retired state councilor.

5 A *grivna* (or *grivennik*) was a 10-kopeck piece.

COUNC. WIFE. How right you are! He never had anything to do with anyone in his life except secretaries and clerks.

IVAN. I see he's very much like my father, who's run away from intelligent people his whole life.

COUNC. WIFE. Oh, my heavens! I like your frankness. You don't even spare your own father! There's the real virtue of our age.

IVAN. Devil take me if I would even dream of sparing him.

COUNC. WIFE. Actually, my dear, it seems to me that he's no cleverer than my husband. There are, of course, dumber people on earth than he, but not many.

IVAN. Your reasoning is just. Tell me, *madame*, what do you think of my mother?

COUNC. WIFE. What! I'm embarrassed to tell you to your face.

IVAN. Please, say what you wish. I'm indifferent to everything that concerns my father and mother.

COUNC. WIFE. Isn't it true that she doesn't know any more of the world than your father?

IVAN. *Dieu!* What a *connoisseur* you are of people! One can say you see right through people. I see it's best to talk about this without any dissimulation. (*Sighing*) Well, you know that I am the unhappiest person in the whole world. I am already twenty-five years old and I still have a father and mother. You know how it is to live with good parents, but I, damn it, live with animals.

COUNC. WIFE. I myself suffer on account of my monster. My husband's just a line in some official document. I've been living with him several years in the country, and I swear to you that until now I've been deprived of any way of getting even with him. All our neighbors are such ignoramuses, such animals, who do nothing except sit around the house hugging their wives. And their wives—ha, ha, ha! Their wives still don't know what *déshabillé* means, and they think that it's possible to last in this world in a housecoat. The only thing they think about is provisions for the table. Regular swine . . .

IVAN. *Pardieu!* Therefore my mother is included with the rest of your neighbors. And have you been living long with such a creature?

COUNC. WIFE.   My husband retired the same year they issued the statute on extortion. He saw that there was nothing left for him to do in the department, so he took me to the country to torture me.

IVAN.   And his country place he acquired, of course, before the statute.

COUNC. WIFE.   And with all that he's a regular skinflint.

IVAN.   Or like my mother. I can say without flattering her that she'd happily suffer fever with blotches for a ruble.

COUNC. WIFE.   Besides, my monster is a terrible hypocrite. He doesn't let a mass or matins go by, and thinks, my dear, that God is so indulgent that for one vespers He will forgive him for what was stolen during the day.

IVAN.   My father, on the contrary, never did any praying, except for retreat. They say that until his marriage he didn't believe there was a devil. However, after marrying my mother, he soon believed in the existence of an evil spirit.

COUNC. WIFE.   Let us change the subject, *je vous en prie*. My ears can't stand hearing any more about devils and these people who are so much like them.

IVAN.   *Madame!* Tell me, how do you spend your time?

COUNC. WIFE.   Ah, my dear, I am dying of boredom. And if I didn't spend some three hours in the morning making my *toilette*, then I can tell you I wouldn't care if I died. The only thing I live for is the headdresses they often send me from Moscow and which I always wear on my head.

IVAN.   To my way of thinking, lace and gold spots lend the head the best adornment. Pedants think that that's nonsense and that the head should be embellished from the inside, not the outside. What stupidity! Does the devil see what's concealed? But everyone sees what's on the outside.

COUNC. WIFE.   You're quite right, dear; I share your sentiments. I see that you have powder on your head, but for the life of me I can't see if there's anything in the head.

IVAN.   *Pardieu!* Of course, and nobody can see it.

COUNC. WIFE.   After my *toilette*, my favorite pastime is telling fortunes by cards.

IVAN. You know how to tell someone's fortune, *grand dieu*! I too can call myself a prophet. Do you want me to show you my talent?

COUNC. WIFE. Ah, my dear! You'll do me a great favor.

IVAN. (*drawing up a table with cards*). You first tell my fortune, and then I'll tell yours.

COUNC. WIFE. With pleasure. Please read the king and queen.

IVAN. (*reflecting*). Done.

COUNC. WIFE (*spreading out the cards*). Ah, what I see! A wedding! (*Sighs.*) The king is getting married.

IVAN. My God! He's getting married! What's more unbearable to me than that!

COUNC. WIFE. But the queen does not love him. . . .

IVAN. Devil take me if I love her. I simply haven't got the strength to bear any more. I read my own fortune. Ah, *madame*! Don't you see that I don't want to get married?

COUNC. WIFE (*sighing and striking an affected tone*). You don't want to get married? But hasn't my stepdaughter captivated your heart enough? She's so constant!

IVAN. She's constant! . . . Oh, the summit of my unhappiness! She's constant, yes! I swear to you, that if I observe this in her when we get married, I'll divorce her the same minute. A constant wife inspires terror in me. Ah, *madame*! If you were my wife, I would never separate from you.

COUNC. WIFE. Oh, my dear! Why torture yourself about what cannot be? I don't think you would annoy me with empty pretensions.

IVAN. Now, *madame*, please permit me to foretell you something. You think of a king and queen.

COUNC. WIFE. Very well. The king of clubs and the queen of hearts.

IVAN. (*spreading the cards*). The king is madly in love with the queen.

COUNC. WIFE. Ah, what do I hear! I am in ecstasy, I am beside myself with joy.

IVAN. (*looking at her tenderly*). And the queen is not indifferent to him.

COUNC. WIFE.   Ah, my dear! Not indifferent. Say instead, in love to distraction.

IVAN.   I would give my own life, I would give thousands of lives to learn who this queen of hearts is. You're blushing, you're turning pale. Of course, it's . . .

COUNC. WIFE.   Oh! How unbearable it is to confess one's passion!

IVAN.   (*hastily*). So it's you. . . .

COUNC. WIFE (*pretending that the last word costs her dearly*). I, I myself.

IVAN.   (*sighing*). And who is this happiest king of clubs who was able to pierce the heart of the queen of hearts?

COUNC. WIFE.   You want me to tell you everything at once.

IVAN.   (*getting up*). Yes, *madame*, yes. I want you to, and if I am not that happiest king of clubs then my flame for you has been poorly rewarded.

COUNC. WIFE.   What! You are burning for me?

IVAN.   (*going down on his knees*). You are the queen of hearts!

COUNC. WIFE (*raising him*). You are the king of clubs!

IVAN.   (*in ecstasy*). O happiness! *O bonheur!*

COUNC. WIFE.   Perhaps you don't know, my dear, that your fiancée is in love with Dobroliubov and that he himself is madly in love with her.

IVAN.   Sh . . . sh . . . They're coming. If this is true, *Oh, que nous sommes heureux*. We should certainly leave them in peace, so that they might leave us in peace in time.

SCENE 4

The same, Dobroliubov and Sofia.

SOFIA.   You chose to stay here alone with Ivanushka, Mother. I came to you purposely so that the two of you shouldn't be bored here.

DOBROL.   And I, madam, was so bold as to lead her to you.

COUNC. WIFE.   We are not at all bored here. We were telling each other's fortunes by cards.

IVAN.   It seems to me, *mademoiselle*, that you have come here purposely to find out about your wedding.

SOFIA.   What do you mean?

COUNC. WIFE.   We told your fortune, and if one believes the cards, which, by the way, can never lie, then your marriage will not be very successful.

SOFIA.   I know that even without cards, Mother.

IVAN.   If you know that, then why are you risking it?

SOFIA.   There's no risk at all here; but there is my obvious ruin, which my father and mother are leading me to.

COUNC. WIFE.   Please, my dear lady, don't put the blame on me. You know yourself that I never wanted what your father wants.

IVAN.   But why such explanations? (*To the Councilor's Wife*) *Madame*, we understand each other well enough. Don't you want to meet your company now?

COUNC. WIFE.   For me there's nothing more *commode* than freedom. I know that it's all the same, having a husband or being tied down.

IVAN.   (*gives her a sign to leave Sofia and Dobroliubov*). Then you don't intend ever leaving here. . . .

COUNC. WIFE.   Please, my dear.

SCENE 5
    Dobroliubov and Sofia.

DOBROL.   They've left us alone. What does it mean?

SOFIA.   It means that my fiancé isn't very jealous of me.

DOBROL.   And it seems to me that your stepmother wouldn't at all be opposed to your wedding being broken off somehow.

SOFIA.   That's very obvious. It seems that we came in on them at a very inappropriate time.

DOBROL.   All the better if that idiot's fallen in love with her and she's taken by him.

SOFIA.   Her coquetry is very pardonable, when you think it over, and of course she can't find herself a better lover. But I do feel sorry for Father.

DOBROL. Oh, please don't aggravate yourself about him. Your father, it seems to me, is giving the brigadier's wife a most tender eye.

SOFIA. No, I don't think so. My father certainly wouldn't betray my stepmother so as not to anger God.

DOBROL. However, he does know that God is infinitely patient.

SOFIA. If that's so, then apart from the brigadier's wife, it seems that everyone's in love here, to the last man.

DOBROL. True, except that the difference lies in the fact that their love is laughable, shameful, and brings them dishonor. But our love is founded on honorable intentions and is worthy of everyone wishing us happiness. You know that if my small income didn't turn your father against having me as his son-in-law, I would have been happy with you a long time ago.

SOFIA. I assured you and assure you now that my love for you will end with my life. I'm ready to do anything to be your wife. Your small income doesn't frighten me in the least. I'm happy to endure anything in the world for your sake.

DOBROL. Perhaps my income will soon be increased. My case is coming to an end. It would have been finished long ago except for the fact that most of the judges, though they don't accept bribes any longer, don't do anything. That's why my poor position hasn't changed up to now.

SOFIA. We've talked for a long time. We'd better go to them, to avoid suspicion.

CURTAIN

ACT TWO
SCENE 1

Councilor and Sofia.

COUNCILOR. Come here, Sofia. I have a lot I'd like to speak to you about.

SOFIA. What do you wish, Father?

COUNCILOR. First of all, what are you sad about?

SOFIA. About the fact, Father, that your will and my desire don't agree.

COUNCILOR. But can children desire what their parents don't want? Don't you know that a father and his children ought to think alike? I am not speaking about this day and age. Today all sorts of new things have come in, but in my time, whenever the father was guilty, the son caught it, and when the son was guilty, then his father answered for him. That's how it used to be in the old days.

SOFIA. Thank God it's not that way now.

COUNCILOR. All the worse. Now the guilty has to answer for himself, so how can you skin anyone else? Why are rules established if only the guilty party is guilty? It used to be that—

SOFIA. But, Father, why should an innocent person be guilty?

COUNCILOR. Because all people are sinners. I myself was a judge. It used to be that the guilty paid for his guilt, and the innocent for his innocence. In my time everyone was satisfied that way: the judge, the plaintiff, and the defendant.

SOFIA. Please allow me to have my doubts, Father. I think that the innocent is innocent until proved guilty.

COUNCILOR. Rubbish. When the innocent has been charged by judicial verdict, then he is no longer innocent, but guilty. There's nothing for him here to split hairs about. With us, decrees are stiffer than with petitioners. A petitioner interprets a decree in one way only, that is, his own, but our brother, the judge, for the good of all, can interpret one decree more than twenty ways.

SOFIA. Father, what do you really want of me?

COUNCILOR. To interpret my decree—to get married—not according to our judicial practice and to marry whom I order you.

SOFIA. I shall obey you, but just imagine my unhappiness: I'm to be the wife of a fool whose head is stuffed just with French stupidities and who not only doesn't love me but doesn't even have the slightest respect for me.

COUNCILOR.   But why do you demand respect from him? It seems to me that you should respect him, and not he you. He'll be your head, but not the other way around. I see that you're just a young girl and have never read the holy books.

SOFIA.   At least be assured, Father, that he won't even respect you.

COUNCILOR.   I know, I know everything. Nonetheless, your fiancé has a good quality.

SOFIA.   What, Father?

COUNCILOR.   He has some pretty good property. And if my son-in-law won't look after his own estate, then I'll make the direction of his property my own responsibility.

SOFIA.   I don't think my future father-in-law would want to burden you with the supervision of his son's estates. My mother-in-law also likes to run things herself. Besides, I don't win one way or the other. I'm used to seeing a household managed well.

COUNCILOR.   All the better. You won't lose what's yours. Anyway, it's probably little comfort to you that you'll have a mother-in-law, I think, who surpasses every living creature by her goodness.

SOFIA.   In my unhappiness I still haven't been able to notice any in her.

COUNCILOR.   That's just because you're a young girl and you don't know what real virtues consist of. I see you don't know either your mother-in-law or the straight road to your own salvation.

SOFIA.   I'd like to know, Father, what part my mother-in-law can have in my salvation.

COUNCILOR.   I'll tell you. After you get married, treat your mother-in-law with respect. She'll be a mother to you, and a friend and a tutor. Respect her next to God; please her all-penetrating eyes in everything you do and imitate everything good in her. Such accord between you will bring joy to the hearts of people on earth and cause the angels in heaven to rejoice.

SOFIA.   You mean to say, Father, that the angels in heaven have so much to do with my mother-in-law that they'll rejoice if I please her?

COUNCILOR.   Why, of course. Do you think that the name of
   Akulina Timofeevna is not inscribed in the Lord's book
   of life?

SOFIA.   Father! I have no idea if she's in it or not.

COUNCILOR.   And I assure you she is. Go to our guests now,
   dear, and declare to your future mother-in-law, as though
   it were coming from you, that I, I am admonishing you
   to please her.

SOFIA.   May I please ask you, Father, why this is necessary?
   Isn't it enough if I please her without any declaration?

COUNCILOR.   I am ordering you to declare it to her, and not
   to interrogate me. That's my answer. Be off with you!

SCENE 2

COUNCILOR   (*alone*). She's no fool, but with all her brains
   she can't figure out that I'm bound to her mother-in-law,
   bound with my eyes, my thoughts, and all my feelings.
   But I don't know how to reveal my affliction to her. I
   see that I'll destroy my soul by wanting to seduce an
   innocent. Oh, the weight of my sins! Even if she assented
   to my supplication, what would Ignatii Andreevich, who
   protects his wife as much as I do mine, do with me?—
   though it's true we haven't spent a straight two hours
   without arguing. This is where love for someone else's
   wife leads. I am marrying my daughter to her son,
   against her wishes, just so as to have the chance, as part
   of the family, to get together more often with my beloved
   in-law. In her I find something extraordinarily intelligent
   that others are unable to perceive. I am not talking about
   her husband. Although he's always been considered an
   intelligent fellow, he's still a military man and what's
   more a cavalry officer, and you know, sometimes he loves
   his horse more than his wife. . . . Ah! Here she's coming
   now.

SCENE 3
   Councilor and Brigadier's Wife.

COUNCILOR.   Ah!

BRIG. WIFE.   What are you sighing about, sir?

COUNCILOR. About my affliction.

BRIG. WIFE. Pretty soon you'll be like a dead man from fasting and prayer. How much longer are you going to wear out your body?

COUNCILOR. Oh, my good woman! My body is far from worn out. God grant that with my sinner's praying and fasting I could lead it to the point where it would be delivered from the temptation of the devil. Then I wouldn't sin against heaven or before you.

BRIG. WIFE. Before me? And in what way, sir, are you sinning before me?

COUNCILOR. By my eye and my thought.

BRIG. WIFE. How can you sin with your eyes?

COUNCILOR. I sin before you, looking at you with an eye—

BRIG. WIFE. But I'm looking at you, and with both my eyes. Is that sinful?

COUNCILOR. Yes, for me it's sinful, and if I want to be delivered from eternal torment in the next world, then I have to pass through this one with one eye closed until I breathe my last breath. My eye leads me into temptation and I have to poke it out for the sake of my spiritual salvation.

BRIG. WIFE. You really want to knock your eyes out?

COUNCILOR. Since all of my sinner's body offends the commandments, yes, of course. And my hands are not so innocent that they themselves should undertake to fulfill the Holy Writ. But I am afraid of your husband's zealous faith; I am afraid that when he perceived my sin he would carry out God's commandment on me.

BRIG. WIFE. What sin are you talking about?

COUNCILOR. The sin all mortals have committed. Every person has a soul and a body. Although the soul is strong, the flesh is weak. He who bears sin cannot be cleansed by confession. . . . (*Tenderly*.) We sin and we confess.

BRIG. WIFE. But how can we help sinning? Only God is without sin.

COUNCILOR. Yes, my dear. And you yourself are confessing now that you are involved in this sin.

BRIG. WIFE. I always confess myself during first mass at

Lent. But please tell me, if you will, what my sins have to do with you?

COUNCILOR. Your sins have as much to do with me as salvation. I want your sins and mine to be the very same and I want nothing to destroy the copulation of our souls and bodies.

BRIG. WIFE. But what is this *copulation*, sir? I understand the Church language as much as I do French. God sheds His grace on whom He wants. To one He makes known French, and German, and all the reading and writing. But I, a sinner, get along badly even in Russian. I'm talking to you now, and more than half of what you say I don't understand. Ivanushka and his bride I don't follow at all. If I fathom anyone's talk best of all, it's Ignatii Andreevich's. He says all his words so clearly, so loudly, like a parrot. . . . By the way, have you ever seen parrots, my dear?

COUNCILOR. We're not talking about birds now, but about intelligent beings. Do you mean to tell me you don't understand my desire?

BRIG. WIFE. I don't understand, sir. What is it you want?

COUNCILOR. May I ask . . .

BRIG. WIFE. What is it you want to ask me? Just so long as it's not money, then I can lend you whatever you want. You know how money is now: nobody lends it for nothing, and for the sake of it nobody refuses anything.

(*At this point Ivanushka enters, but they do not see him.*)

COUNCILOR. I'm not talking about money; I myself would consent to anything for it. (*He gets down on his knees.*) I love you, my dear. . . .

(*Just at this moment the Councilor sees Ivanushka, and jumps up. Ivanushka bursts out laughing, and applauds.*)

SCENE 4
The same and Ivanushka.

IVAN. *Bravissimo! Bravissimo!*

BRIG. WIFE. What are you jumping like that for, Ivanushka? We were talking about business. You interrupted Artamon Vlasich. I don't know what it is he was going to ask me for.

IVAN.   Why, Mother, he's making you a *déclaration en forme.*

COUNCILOR.   Don't judge and you won't be judged.

(*He leaves, dumbfounded.*)

BRIG. WIFE.   Ivanushka! Explain to me better what you just said.

IVAN.   Mother, he's making love to you! Do you understand at least that?

BRIG. WIFE.   He's making love! Heavens, what's come into your head?

IVAN.   Devil take me if it's not the truth.

BRIG. WIFE.   Cross yourself. What a terrible way to swear! Come to your senses; there's no joking with the devil. Take your hand and cross yourself nicely now, Ivanushka.

IVAN.   Mother! I see you don't believe it. Then why did he get on his knees.

BRIG. WIFE.   How should I know, Ivanushka. Was it really for love? Oh, that damned son of mine! But what got into his head?

SCENE 5
    The same and the Councilor's Wife.

IVAN.   *Madame!* I've just witnessed the funniest scene. *J'ai pensé crever de rire.* Your husband was declaring his love to my mother! Ha, ha, ha, ha!

COUNC. WIFE.   Is it true? (*While the Brigadier's Wife speaks, she draws Ivanushka to a side and whispers something to him.*)

BRIG. WIFE   (*emotionally*). Oh, that dog! What did he really start? Did God take away my tongue? I'm going to tell everything to Ignatii Andreich now. Let him split his head open in his own way. What got into him? After all, I am the brigadier's wife! No, he's just a scoundrel! Don't think he's got a fool here! Thank God, nobody pulls the wool over my eyes! I'm going right away. . . .

(*Ivanushka and the Councilor's Wife grasp her by the skirts.*)

IVAN. Mother, wait, wait . . .

COUNC. WIFE. Wait, *madame*.

IVAN. Couldn't you see, Mother, that I was just joking?

BRIG. WIFE. What a joke! But I heard how you swore it was true.

COUNC. WIFE. Of course he was only joking, my dear.

IVAN. Devil take me if it wasn't a joke.

BRIG. WIFE. What, you're swearing the same way again? What devilishness! Who knows what to believe?

COUNC. WIFE. What are you saying, my dear? Can't you tell a joke from something serious?

BRIG. WIFE. It's impossible, dear. He swears so my tongue gets twisted when I try to say it.

COUNC WIFE. But he was even swearing in jest.

IVAN. Of course, in jest. In Paris I used to know many, and even here there's a great number of intelligent people, *et même fort honnêtes gens*, who don't make anything of swearing.

BRIG. WIFE. Then you were really and truly joking, Ivanushka?

IVAN. Do you want me to swear to you again?

BRIG. WIFE. Maybe you're getting set to joke again! For God's sake, stop making a fool out of me.

COUNC. WIFE. Don't worry, my dear! Be calm. I know my husband. If it were true, I'm myself capable of going into a rage.

BRIG. WIFE. Well, thank God it's a joke. Now my soul is at rest. (*Goes out.*)

SCENE 6

Ivanushka and the Councilor's Wife.

COUNC. WIFE. You almost spoiled everything. If your mother complained to your father, he'd have flown into a fury and taken you right away with her.

IVAN. *Madame!* You can forgive me it. I confess that I'm guilty of *étourderie*, but otherwise I'd badly imitate the French.

COUNC. WIFE. My dear, we must keep quiet about it, and I wouldn't be able to excuse your boldness for anything if caution weren't ludicrous in a young person, especially in one who's been in Paris.

IVAN. *O, vous avez raison!* Caution, fidelity, patience—they were all praiseworthy when people didn't know how one ought to live in the world. But we who know what it's all about, *que de vivre dans le grand monde*, we would certainly be very funny with fidelity in the eyes of all intelligent people like ourselves.

COUNC. WIFE. Those are the real rules of life, my darling. I was never in Paris, but nonetheless my heart feels that you're speaking the very truth. The human heart is always a heart—in Paris and in Russia: it cannot deceive.

IVAN. *Madame*, you enrapture me. I see you have the same subtle understanding of the heart as you do of the mind. *Mon dieu!* How kind fate is! It seeks to unite people of the same mind, the same taste, the same manner. We were created for each other.

COUNC. WIFE. Without a doubt, we were conceived under the same star.

IVAN. All my unhappiness consists of the fact that you're Russian.

COUNC. WIFE. My angel, it is certainly a terrible plight for me.

IVAN. It's such a *défaut* that nothing can make up for it.

COUNC. WIFE. What am I to do?

IVAN. Put your trust in me. I have no intention of dying in Russia. I'm looking for an *occasion favorable* to take you to Paris. There we'll have the pleasure of spending the rest of our days—*les restes des nos jours*—with the French. There you'll see that there are, among others, the kind of people with whom I can have *société*.

COUNC. WIFE. True, my darling! Only, I don't think your father will agree to let you go to France for a second time.

IVAN. But I'm thinking of taking him there along with us. It's never too late to enlighten yourself. I guarantee you that when he goes to Paris at least he'll become a little bit more like a human being.

COUNC. WIFE. That's not what's on your father's mind. I'm quite convinced that he'll prefer our village to paradise and Paris. To put it briefly, he's making eyes at me.

IVAN. What? He's my rival?

COUNC. WIFE. I perceive that he's madly in love with me.

IVAN. Doesn't he know the rights of honest people? Doesn't he know that people get into fights over things like that?

COUNC. WIFE. What, darling, you want to have a fight with your father?

IVAN. *Et pourquoi non?* I read in a beautiful book, for the life of me I don't remember the title . . . *Le nom m'est échappé* . . . Ah, yes, in the book *Les Sottises du Temps*, that in Paris a son challenged his father to a duel . . . and I, what am I, an animal not to imitate what happened in Paris, even though it happened just once?

COUNC. WIFE. Your father is very funny . . . such fools . . . Ah! Speaking of the devil now . . . here he comes.

SCENE 7

   The same and the Brigadier.

BRIGADIER. I have already started managing things here. Came to call you to the table. What have you and this scapegrace of mine been talking about so long, my dear? And you, what are you doing here? You should be with your fiancée.

IVAN. Father, I want to be here.

BRIGADIER. But I don't want you to.

COUNC. WIFE. But what concern is it of yours, sir?

BRIGADIER. It's just that I don't want him to annoy you with his gabbing, my dear. I would prefer to talk with you myself about something.

COUNC. WIFE. Say what you please.

BRIGADIER. It would please me if my son were far from here; he'll get on your nerves.

COUNC. WIFE. Not at all, sir; we've spent a very pleasant time together without you.

BRIGADIER. But I am bored without you. (*Looking at his son*) Get out of here, nuisance!

COUNC. WIFE (*to Ivanushka*). Since it's time to go to the table, let's go. (*She gives him her hand and he leads her out, striking an affected pose. The Brigadier, going after them, speaks.*)

BRIGADIER. Fine, Ivan! There'll come a time when you won't be twisting about so.

CURTAIN

ACT THREE
SCENE 1

The Brigadier and his son.

BRIGADIER. Listen, Ivan. I've rarely blushed since I was a young fellow. But now, in my old age, I could have burned up on account of you.

IVAN. *Mon cher père!* Can I tolerate hearing that they want to marry me to a Russian girl?

BRIGADIER. Why, what are you, a Frenchman? It seems to me that you were born in Russia.

IVAN. My body was born in Russia, that's true, but my soul belonged to the crown of France.

BRIGADIER. Nevertheless, you're more bound to Russia than to France. You do have more bonds in your body than in your head.

IVAN. There, Father, you're already beginning to flatter me when you see that sternness hasn't helped you.

BRIGADIER. Well, aren't you a regular idiot? I called you a fool and you think I'm flattering you. What an ass!

IVAN. What an ass! (*aside*) *Il ne me flatte pas.* . . . I'll tell you again, Father, *je vous le répète*, that my ears aren't accustomed to such terms. I beg you, *je vous en prie*, not to treat me as you used to treat your privates in the army. I'm a member of the gentry the same as you, *monsieur*.

BRIGADIER. Idiocy! Idiocy! Whatever you say, you lie like a trooper. Is it proper for a father to be considered with his son in the gentry? But even if you were a stranger to me, at least you shouldn't forget that I am an army brigadier.

IVAN. *Je m'en moque.*

BRIGADIER. What's this "manmok?"

IVAN. Just what I think of your brigadiership. I disregard it, and you disregard the fact that your son knows the world, that he was in Paris. . . .

BRIGADIER. Oh, if only it were possible to disregard it! Oh, no, my friend! You remind me of it every minute with new stupidities for the smallest of which you'd be made to run the gauntlet, according to military regulations.

IVAN. Father! You act about everything as though you were at the front and issuing orders left and right. What are you making so much noise about?

BRIGADIER. The truth, that's what. But from now on, as soon as you spill out some nonsense, I'll slam two hundred Russian sticks into your back. Understand?

IVAN. I understand, but do you understand me? Every man of the world, and especially one who's been in France, can't wager that he'll never in his own life have anything to do with a person like you. Consequently, he also can't wager that he'll never be beaten. And if you go into a forest and succeed in coming across a bear, he'll handle you the way you want to treat me.

BRIGADIER. What a freak! You've compared your father to a bear; am I really like one?

IVAN. There's no "really" here. I told you what I think: *voilà mon caractère.* And what right do you have to lord it over me?

BRIGADIER. Idiot! I'm your father.

IVAN. Tell me, Father, aren't all animals, *les animaux*, the same?

BRIGADIER. Meaning what? Of course they are. From human beings to cattle. What nonsense is it you're trying to give me now?

IVAN. Listen: if all animals are alike, then I can include myself here also, can't I?

BRIGADIER. Why not. I told you: from human beings to cattle. So why shouldn't you also put yourself in with the rest?

IVAN. Very well. Then if a puppy isn't obliged to respect the dog who was his father, must I you, even in the slightest?

BRIGADIER. That you're a puppy, nobody has any doubts. However, I swear to you, Ivan, as a swearing man, that if you insist on comparing me to a dog, then soon your own mug won't have any resemblance to a human being's. I'll teach you how you have to talk to a father and a person who's been honored. A pity I don't have a stick with me—what a saucy rascal he's become!

SCENE 2
    The same and the Brigadier's Wife.

BRIG. WIFE. What's the noise here? What are you so angry about, dear? Have you caused us some loss, Ivanushka? Have you lost anything?

BRIGADIER. A great deal. No small loss.

BRIG. WIFE (*out of breath*). What a calamity! What did he lose?

BRIGADIER. He lost his mind, if he had one.

BRIG. WIFE (*relaxing*). Phoo, what a misfortune! Thank God, I almost fainted I was so scared. I thought: What if he really had lost something?

BRIGADIER. And his mind is nothing?

BRIG. WIFE. How nothing?! Who told you that? It's bad to live without a mind. What could you get without it?

BRIGADIER. Without it! But without it you got this freak here. Didn't I keep telling you: Wife, don't spoil the child. Let's enroll him in a regiment. Serving in a regiment he'll get sense the same as I did. But you always nagged: Oh! My husband! No, my dear! What do you want to do with the boy? Don't destroy him, dearest!— Well, there you are, my good woman! See how he's prospering! Why a moment ago, he likened me to a dog. Do you want to hear about it?

IVAN. (*yawns*). *Quelles espèces!*

BRIGADIER. See, talk to him, if you like, but he'll just open his yap. Ivan, don't get me mad. You know I can crack two of your ribs at the same time. You know the kind of a person I am.

SCENE 3

The same and the Councilor's Wife.

COUNC. WIFE. What is it you've stirred up here, sir? Do you expect me to tolerate such *barbarie* here?

BRIGADIER. I just want to teach my Ivan a little lesson.

COUNC. WIFE. What? You just want to teach your son a little lesson, breaking two of his ribs?

BRIGADIER. Well after all, my dear, he doesn't have just two ribs. Even if I break them, he still has something left. Anyway, it's all the same to me whether he has these two ribs or not.

BRIG. WIFE. You see, dear, how he talks about his own off-spring?

IVAN. (*to the Councilor's Wife*). *C'est l'homme le plus bourru, que je connais.*

COUNC. WIFE. Do you know, sir, that your rudeness to your son disturbs me?

BRIGADIER. And I thought, madam, that his rudeness to me disturbs you.

COUNC. WIFE. Not at all. I can't bear partiality. A person's merits should always be respected. But of course you don't see any merits in your son.

BRIGADIER. I do not. But tell me, what merits do you see in him?

COUNC. WIFE. Don't you know that he's been in Paris?

BRIG. WIFE. Only in Paris, my dear? Why, he was even in France. The idea!

BRIGADIER. Wife, don't you ever get tired of yapping?

BRIG. WIFE. Nobody can talk the truth to you.

BRIGADIER. Talk, but not yap.

COUNC. WIFE (*to the Brigadier*). I'm sure you haven't heard how he was received in Paris.

BRIGADIER. Up to now he hasn't dared tell me that.

COUNC. WIFE. Say instead he didn't want to. But if I beg

you now, *monsieur*, to tell us something about your *voyage*, would you consent to content me?

IVAN. *De tout mon cœur, madame.* But in my father's presence I am unable to fulfill your request. He'll start making noise, he'll disturb me, stop me . . .

COUNC. WIFE. For my sake he certainly won't do it.

BRIGADIER. For your sake, yes, but not for anyone else's on earth do I agree to keep quiet, that is, as long as I have the strength to. Talk, Ivan.

IVAN. Where should I begin? *Par où commencer?*

COUNC. WIFE. Begin with what you liked about Paris, and what Paris, *monsieur*, liked about you.

IVAN. I liked Paris first of all because there everyone is distinguished by his merits.

BRIGADIER. Hold on, hold on, Ivan! If that's true, then how is it Paris liked you?

COUNC. WIFE. Sir, you promised not to disturb him. You shouldn't, at least out of consideration for the ladies who want to listen to him, and not you.

BRIGADIER. I am guilty, my dear, and for you and not anyone else I'll keep quiet.

COUNC. WIFE (*to the Brigadier's son*). Go on, *monsieur, continuez.*

IVAN. In Paris everyone treated me as I deserve. Wherever I went, I either spoke alone, or all spoke about me. Everyone was delighted with my conversation. Wherever I was seen, happiness shone on people's faces, and often, unable to conceal it, they declared it with such extraordinary laughter as showed immediately what they thought of me.

COUNC. WIFE (*to the Brigadier*). Shouldn't you be delighted too? I'm in ecstasy over his words, and I'm not in any way obliged to be.

BRIG. WIFE (*weeping*). I am out of my mind with joy. In my old age God has let me see Ivanushka with such intelligence.

COUNC. WIFE (*to the Brigadier*). Why don't you say anything?

BRIGADIER. I am afraid to upset you, but if it weren't for

that I'd certainly either start laughing or crying, one or the other.

COUNC. WIFE.   *Continuez*, my dear.

IVAN.   In France the people are not at all like you; that is, not Russian.

COUNC. WIFE.   See, my dear, I was never there but still I already have a very good idea of what France is like. Isn't it true that mostly Frenchmen live in France?

IVAN.   (*ecstatically*). *Vous avez le don de déviner.*

BRIG. WIFE.   How's that, Ivanushka?! Are the people there really not like all us Russians?

IVAN.   Not like you, and not like me.

BRIG. WIFE.   But why?! After all, you're my offspring.

IVAN.   *N'importe!* Every person who's been in Paris has the right, speaking about Russians, not to include himself in their number because he has already become more a Frenchman than a Russian.

COUNC. WIFE.   Tell me, my dear, is it possible for those of us who've been in Paris to forget completely that they're Russians?

IVAN.   *Totalement impossible*. It is not the kind of misfortune that can soon be eradicated from one's thoughts. However, it's impossible to say that it would be vivid in our memory. It appears to us as a dream, as an *illusion*.

BRIGADIER   (*to the Councilor's Wife*)   My good woman, please allow me to say one little word to him.

IVAN.   (*to the Councilor's Wife*). *Cela m'excède, je me retire. (Goes out.)*

BRIG. WIFE   (*to the Councilor's Wife*). What was it he just said? Did Ivanushka dash out of here like that because he got sick? I'd best have a look.

SCENE 4
   Brigadier, the Councilor's Wife.

COUNC. WIFE.   See what you've done? You've deprived me of the pleasure of hearing the story about your son and all of Paris.

BRIGADIER.   And I would have thought that I saved you from

the displeasure of hearing nonsense. Unless you really like making fun of my son, eh?

COUNC. WIFE.   Or do you really like making fun of me, sir?

BRIGADIER.   Of you?! God forbid. I want to be shot the same moment I think anything bad of you.

COUNC. WIFE.   I thank you for your esteem, sir.

BRIGADIER.   That's quite all right, my dear.

COUNC. WIFE.   Your son, I see, suffers from your rudeness.

BRIGADIER.   I'm letting him off now for your sake. But sooner or later I'll knock this French soul out of him. I see he's already become a bore to you too.

COUNC. WIFE.   You're quite wrong. Stop being rude to your son. Do you know that his words simply delight me?

BRIGADIER.   Which ones?

COUNC. WIFE.   Are you deaf? Were you really without feeling when he was telling about himself and about Paris?

BRIGADIER.   I would like to be just this once, my dear. I see you want to joke. His stories—gibberish. Although he's my son, there's nothing to hide. Where was he? In what campaigns? In what action? And if you really want to hear something nice, then ask me, and in a moment I'll tell you how when we were putting the Turks in their place I didn't spare Muhammadan blood. And as rough as it was then, still everything wasn't as dangerous as it is now.

COUNC. WIFE.   What do you mean "now"? What are you talking about?

BRIGADIER.   About something I wanted to talk to you about for a long time, but my damned son kept getting in the way each time with his nonsense. If it pleases you then tomorrow I'll put him out of his misery for it.

COUNC. WIFE.   But what do you want to destroy him for?

BRIGADIER.   For the fact that without him, perhaps, I would have told you my secret long ago and already had your answer.

COUNC. WIFE.   What secret? What answer?

BRIGADIER.   I don't like ceremonies. I want either a Yes or a No.

COUNC. WIFE. But what is it you want? Why have you changed so?

BRIGADIER. Oh, if you only knew the anxiety I feel when I look into your bright eyes.

COUNC. WIFE. Anxiety, for what?

BRIGADIER. The anxiety I fear much more than when I go against a whole enemy army. Your eyes are more terrifying to me than all the bullets, shells, and buckshot. My heart has already been pierced by their very first shot, and before they annihilate me, I surrender as your prisoner of war.

COUNC. WIFE. I don't understand a thing you're saying, and for that reason, with your permission, I'll take my leave of you now.

BRIGADIER. Wait a moment, please. I'll explain everything to you much more clearly. Imagine to yourself a fortress that a bold general wants to capture. What does he feel in himself then? Exactly what I do now. I'm like a bold general, and you're my fortress in which, no matter how strong, it's still possible to make a breach.

SCENE 5
The same, the Councilor, Dobroliubov.

COUNCILOR (*to Dobroliubov*). So your case is already settled, is it?

DOBROL. Settled, sir.

BRIGADIER. Oh! Damn them all! No sooner do I start than they never let me finish!

COUNC. WIFE. Finish what?

BRIGADIER. My dear woman! It's not the sort of matter I would discuss in the presence of your husband. (*Going out.*) I'm bursting from anger.

SCENE 6
The Councilor, Dobroliubov, the Councilor's Wife.

COUNCILOR. You found out about your case so early?

DOBROL. At once.

COUNC. WIFE   How's that? You've won your suit?

DOBROL.   Yes, ma'am. My situation has improved greatly. I've got two thousand souls now.

COUNCILOR.   Two thousand souls! Oh, my God, great heavens! And with all your other virtues! Ah, how worthy you now are of esteem.

COUNC. WIFE.   By the way, weren't you really ever in Paris?

DOBROL.   No, ma'am.

COUNC. WIFE.   A pity. This one thing can darken all your other merits.

COUNCILOR.   Nevertheless, if a person has two thousand souls it seems to me that they can more than make up for all his vices. Two thousand souls even without a landowner's virtues is always two thousand souls, but virtues without them—devil with such virtues. However, just between the two of us, it's a wonder to me that you could bring up your case so soon, chase after it, and not lose what you got.

DOBROL.   You're quite right. The self-interest of our extortioners went beyond all bounds. It seems that there just aren't any restraints to hold them back.

COUNCILOR.   I always used to say that it's impossible to prohibit bribes. How can you settle a case for nothing on just your salary? Have we ever heard of it from the time we were born? It's against human nature. . . . How did you finally manage to get your case settled?

DOBROL.   We're lucky that each of us who doesn't find justice in the designated places, can go, in the final analysis, straight to the highest court of appeals. I was bold enough to take recourse to it, and my judges were forced by strict decree to decide my case.

COUNCILOR.   It's good that your case was just and you could go higher up. But what would it have been had it not been such and you couldn't have gone further with it?

DOBROL.   Not only would I not have gone further with it; I wouldn't have bothered the courts with it in the first place.

COUNCILOR.   Was your case so good? In my day every person with a just or unjust case went to the department and could, once he got friendly with the judge, receive a favorable resolution. In my day you didn't poke your nose any further. We used to have a saying: To God it's high, to the tsar far.

COUNC. WIFE (*to Dobroliubov*). I think it's already time for you to settle down, time for you to get married.

DOBROL. I don't want to marry anyone, if you don't consent to let me have your daughter's hand.

COUNCILOR. My dear friend, you were in poor straits, and my circumstances, besides, aren't that good.

COUNC. WIFE. For my part, I never opposed your courtship.

DOBROL. Does that mean that I can still hope . . .

COUNCILOR. Right now I can't say one thing or another. Better let's go and have a glass of tea. After dinner it's inconvenient to talk about business. I always used to decide the interesting cases in the mornings.

CURTAIN

ACT FOUR
SCENE 1

Dobroliubov, Sofia.

DOBROL. I have great hopes for the fulfillment of our wishes.

SOFIA. I still don't dare count on it. I can speak frankly with you. If it's true that my father is betraying my stepmother, then the change in your situation can't alter his intentions.

DOBROL. Nevertheless, I saw with what feeling he received the news of the settlement of my case in my favor. I, too, can't hide my thoughts from you. You yourself know that your father loves wealth, and self-interest works even such miracles as love in people.

SOFIA. Even so, love rarely conquers self-interest. I don't know if I'll be so lucky as to have our destinies united. Nevertheless, I am happy that your situation has improved.

DOBROL. My situation will be unfortunate until my greatest desire is fulfilled. You know what that is. My heart's an open book to you. . . .

SCENE 2

The same and the Brigadier's Wife.

DOBROL. (*seeing the Brigadier's Wife wiping her tears away*).
What were you crying about, ma'am?

BRIG. WIFE. This isn't the first time in my life I'm crying.
The Lord alone sees the kind of a life I have!

SOFIA. What's the matter?

BRIG. WIFE. I'll order a friend and an enemy to get married.

SOFIA. How's that? Can you say that at a time when you
want me to be your son's wife?

BRIG. WIFE. Why shouldn't you want to get married to him?
I just said it to myself.

DOBROL. No, you wanted to say it to all of us.

BRIG. WIFE. And no wonder.

SOFIA. I don't understand: now to yourself, now to others?
Tell us what's on your mind.

BRIG. WIFE. You talk instead. What can I say?

DOBROL. What did you want to say?

BRIG. WIFE. Nothing. I just came here to lament my fate.

SOFIA. What for?

BRIG. WIFE (*crying*). Because I'm sad. Now go ahead,
Ignatii Andreevich, let me have it again for no reason
at all. He kept on cursing me and cursing me, and Lord
knows for what. I've already become a pig and a fool as
far as he is concerned. You yourselves see, am I a fool?

DOBROL. Certainly, we see, ma'am.

SOFIA. Why did he attack you so?

BRIG. WIFE. You know, one word led to another. He's got
such a bad temper, God forbid! I have to watch out or
he'll butcher me with the first thing that comes his way.
Just consider, my dear, how quickly trouble comes. He'll
crack open my skull with a blow. Afterward he may
regret it, but then it will already be too late.

DOBROL. And that's why your life is in danger every
moment?

BRIG. WIFE. Does it take long for trouble to come?

SOFIA. Can he really have treated you so barbarously that you've suffered something like that from him?

BRIG. WIFE. Oh, no, my dear. It hasn't come to the point yet where he'll beat me to death. No, not yet.

DOBROL. Nobody is asking you about that, ma'am.

SOFIA. It's enough that he had the barbarity to use the law of force.

BRIG. WIFE. Oh, he's strong enough, dear. Once, and just joking, you know, without any quarrel even, he poked me in the chest with such force, believe me, my dear, for God's sake, I could hardly breathe. My eyes spun around in my head so, everything just went black.

SOFIA. And that was in jest!

BRIG. WIFE. I could hardly catch my breath, while he, my dear husband, was bursting his sides with laughter and having a good time.

DOBROL. Fine laughter.

BRIG. WIFE. Five or six weeks later, I laughed at it myself, but when it happened I almost gave my soul to God without even having had time to confess.

DOBROL. But how can you go on living with him, when he almost sent you off to the other world just joking around.

BRIG. WIFE. You get on somehow. After all, dear, I'm not the only woman married. God knows, my life's bad enough, but not as bad as our officers' wives used to have it. I saw enough of it all. We had an officer nick-named Grozdilov who was captain of the first company in our regiment. His wife was such a nice young woman. He used to get really angry at her, and most of all when he was drunk. And, so help me God, how he used to give it to her and give it to her, it's a wonder anything was left of her, and for no reason at all. Well, even though it wasn't any of my business, I couldn't help crying looking at her.

SOFIA. Please, madam, don't talk any more about such disturbing things.

BRIG. WIFE. You mean you don't want to hear about what the captain's wife had to go through?

SCENE 3

The same, Ivanushka and the Councilor's Wife.

COUNC. WIFE (*to Ivanushka*). Do you feel like playing cards?

IVAN. With great pleasure, *avec plaisir*.

COUNC. WIFE. Then I'll have them set things up. (*To a servant.*) A table and cards, please. (*To Dobroliubov.*) Wouldn't you like to play a hand of quadrille?[6]

DOBROL. If you like.

(*A table with cards is placed between them.*)

IVAN. (*shuffles the cards and distributes one each for the places. To the Councilor's Wife*). Madame! (*To the Brigadier's Wife*) Madame!

BRIG. WIFE. What's that for, Ivanushka? If you're going to play, then give out all of them. Unless they're playing now with just one little card apiece.

IVAN. That's for the places.

BRIG. WIFE. Oh! There'll be a place for me, too, thanks to the hostess's courtesy.

IVAN. Mother, will you please take it.

BRIG. WIFE. But what use is one card to me?

COUNC. WIFE. Do you play quadrille, my dear?

BRIG. WIFE. I never even heard of it.

COUNC. WIFE (*to Sofia*). So you take it, then.

IVAN. *Mademoiselle!* (*He hands it to her, and all take their places while he distributes the rest of the cards.*)

BRIG. WIFE. Well I'll just sit down, dear, and see how you amuse yourselves.

SCENE 4

The same, the Brigadier and the Councilor.

BRIGADIER. Aha! So they've got gambling here too!

[6] Quadrille was a four-handed form of omber (ombre, hombre) —a three-handed card game of Spanish origin played with forty cards and popular in Europe in the seventeenth and eighteenth centuries.

COUNCILOR. Wouldn't you like to have a little game of chess with me?

BRIGADIER. By all means, come on. (*They sit down at the other end. The Councilor and the Brigadier play, and one says to the other: "I'll move so," and the other: "And I so."*)

COUNC. WIFE. I'll play hearts.

IVAN. *Passe!* (*And all pass.*)

COUNC. WIFE. Nil and nil.

BRIG. WIFE. Nil and nil? What sort of nonsense is that? Who's this "nil"?

COUNCILOR (*hearing her question*). Now, my dear, don't you go investigating all the games people like to amuse themselves with.

BRIG. WIFE. My heavens, what won't they think of next? Nil and nil! That's what's become of intelligent people! (*Taking a look at her son's cards.*) Ah, Ivanushka, all the clubs you've got in your hands!

IVAN. Mother, I'll toss the cards down, *je les jette par terre!*

COUNC. WIFE. You really should have kept that in your mind, my dear woman. . . .

BRIGADIER (*listening carefully to what the Councilor's wife says*). In your mind? That would be something! . . . Check!

COUNCILOR. It's going badly for me, I see.

BRIGADIER. No joking, my dear in-law.

IVAN. (*showing his cards*). *Sans prendre* six matadores.[7]

BRIG. WIFE. What did you say, *madadury*? Now they've started to play *dury*, and it used to be that everyone played *duraki*.[8]

[7] In quadrille, or omber, a "matador" was the principal trump. Ivanushka means in this line that without taking any more cards he has a full hand of trumps, i.e., a hand of six matadors.

[8] This is an untranslatable pun in the original Russian. The brigadier's wife does not understand what Ivanushka means when he says "matadores." She hears *madadury* for this, and assumes that her son is talking about a new kind of game: *dury. Duraki* ("fools," nominative plural of *durak*) was a popular game. *Dury*, however, is just the equivalent feminine form ("lady fools"), and was not the designation for any game.

COUNCILOR. Yes, my dear, what used to be isn't any more—
and what is didn't used to be.

BRIG. WIFE. How right you are. I used to be among people,
but now, what's the good of talking, old age has come,
and I don't even have a memory any more.

BRIGADIER. But you never used to have a head.

IVAN. (*sings a French song. The Councilor's wife joins him.
To the Councilor's Wife*) Madame! We've both lost.
Mother, won't you sing some air for us?

BRIG. WIFE. What do you mean "sing?" I don't even have a
voice any more. The spirit's willing . . . But what kind
of a game is that you're playing? I won't go examining
it, for the life of me. In the old days, when we wanted
to play games, it was either *mariage* or *duraki*. Best of
all, though, was *khriushki*.[9] Three cards apiece were
given out. Whoever got a spade, went out; whoever
remained got such a thumping you just burst your sides
laughing.

COUNCILOR (*laughs gently*). Ha, ha, ha! I myself used to
play it and I can still remember the different kinds of
amusement we used to have with each card.

DOBROL. *Mediator*.[10]

BRIG. WIFE. Yes, my dear! (*She takes some cards and runs
up to the Councilor.*) Here's the way it was: if someone
lost, they'd say don't ask for help from this side or from
that one. Afterward, you can ask whatever you want.
(*Holding the cards in one hand, she flips them with one
finger while the Councilor stops his game of chess and
looks at her tenderly.*) The person would peek at
his card and until they got to it in the deck he'd get a
good thumping for each one that wasn't his. All kinds of
blows he'd get: a slap in the face for a queen, a pull by
the ear for a jack.

BRIGADIER. Come, my wife, let's play *khriushki* together!
(*Gets up.*) As you like, we won't ever finish this way.

IVAN. *Pardieu!* Mother, where did you put the cards?

BRIG. WIFE. Here, Ivanushka.

---

9 *Khriushki* ("piggies") was another old Russian game of cards.
10 A card term in quadrille.

IVAN. (*jumping*). *Il est impossible de jouer.*

(*All get up.*)

BRIG. WIFE. But how did I disturb you? You still have cards, and even in threes.

BRIGADIER. Listen, wife! Wherever you go you cause mischief.

BRIG. WIFE. How did I bother you? If you knew how to play your game you'd have gone on. After all, I went up to him (*indicating the Councilor*), and not you.

BRIGADIER. When you don't have a brain you can disturb everyone when you go up to one person.

BRIG. WIFE. There you are: I'm already to blame.

IVAN. Well, Mother, am I to blame? (*Pointing to Dobroliubov.*) *Ou ce monsieur?* (*Pointing to the women.*) *Ou ces dames?*

COUNCILOR. Enough, son-in-law. It's sinful for you to upbraid the woman who brought you into the world.

COUNC. WIFE. And shameful for you to mix into what isn't your business.

BRIGADIER. My dear in-law, I am very fond of you, but please, if you will, don't reconcile me with my wife. You probably know the saying: When your own dogs fight, don't let someone else's join in.

IVAN. Yes, Father, all proverbs are right, but especially the French ones. (*To Dobroliubov.*) Isn't that true, *monsieur?*

DOBROL. I know many Russian ones are right, too. (*To Sofia.*) Isn't that true, ma'am?

SOFIA. True.

IVAN. (*to Sofia*). Which, for example?

SOFIA. For example: Let a fool blab what he wants, there's no tax on nonsense.

BRIGADIER. Right! Ah, I love that one, my dear! There's a proverb and riddle for you. And if you want me to unravel it for you, Ivan, you'll come out a fool.

IVAN. *Par quelle raison?*

COUNC. WIFE. For what reason?

BRIGADIER. For the reason that he talks nonsense free of duty.

BRIG. WIFE. Thank God, for heaven's sake, that there is no tax on nonsense. That would really be the ruin of all of us!

BRIGADIER. You've no worry there. In five or six hours you'd be going around begging.

COUNCILOR. Don't be angry with your husband; he's just in a bad mood today.

BRIG. WIFE. And just because he gets angry, do I have to? My job is to get farther away now. (*She goes out.*)

SCENE 5

The Brigadier, Councilor, Councilor's Wife, Dobroliubov, Ivanushka, and Sofia.

BRIGADIER. So she's done her job.

COUNC. WIFE (*to Sofia*). Go to your mother-in-law, dear. It's not nice for her to sit alone there like that.

SOFIA. I'm going. (*She goes out.*)

SCENE 6

The Brigadier, Councilor, Councilor's Wife, Dobroliubov, Ivanushka.

COUNCILOR. Have it your way, old man. But you do treat your wife very badly.

BRIGADIER. And she treats me very badly.

COUNC. WIFE. How, may I ask?

BRIGADIER. How, you ask? By being sad when she should be happy, and happy when she should be sad. She's lived too long, sinned too much: she's out of place.

COUNCILOR. What do you mean, "out of place"? You think you're always right, is that it? God grant her health and happiness for many years to come. Are you out of your senses? Whom are you wishing death?

IVAN. It's not proper to wish anyone death, *mon cher père*, not even a dog, let alone my mother.

BRIGADIER. Ivan, don't you teach me. Even though I said what I did, I want much better for her than you do for the both of us.

IVAN. I'm not teaching you, I'm only speaking the truth.

BRIGADIER. Speak it when you're asked.

COUNC. WIFE. Then why are you speaking to him when he doesn't ask you?

BRIGADIER. Why, because he's my son, my dear. How will it be for me when people start saying that such a brigadier, a person of status, has a good-for-nothing son?

IVAN. Father! I a good-for-nothing! *Je vous demande pardon*. I'm the kind of a son for whom you'll be more acclaimed than for your being a brigadier! (*To Dobroliubov*) You, *monsieur*, of course, must know many children who do their fathers honor.

DOBROL. And still more who do them dishonor. The truth of the matter is that upbringing determines everything.

BRIGADIER. Yes, sir, that's exactly what I think too. His mother's a fool, and that's the reason why he's become a ne'er-do-well, and worse, a French ne'er-do-well. The Russian ones are bad enough, but the French still worse.

COUNCILOR. Eh! Don't you have any fear of the Lord, my good fellow? Why are you cursing your own wife, who could be called a repository of human virtues?

BRIGADIER. Which?

COUNCILOR. She is humble, like an angel; industrious, like a bee; lovely, like a bird of paradise (*sighs*); and faithful, like a turtledove.

BRIGADIER. Or intelligent, like a cow; lovely, like I don't know who . . . like an owl.

COUNCILOR. How dare you compare your wife to a night-bird?

BRIGADIER. It seems to me that it's possible to liken a day-time fool to a nightbird.

COUNCILOR (*sighing*). Still she stays faithful to you in all ways.

COUNC. WIFE. Actually, she has many virtues, if she loves you.

BRIGADIER. Well, who else would she love, if not me? It's silly for me to praise myself, but the truth is that, thank

God, it seems I've earned my rank by loyalty and truth.
The fact is that because of me she became a brigadier's
wife. I didn't get to be a brigadier through a wife. In
today's world this is something to take note of. So how
could she fall in love with someone else? If I weren't the
kind of a man I am, then we'd see how virtuous she'd be.
Especially if someone of our brothers also from the first
five ranks took an interest in her.

COUNCILOR. No, old man, don't say that. Your wife really
isn't that kind of a woman. All flesh certainly cannot be
praised before God, but even if a worthy man, or the
worthiest, took an interest in her, he truly would not find
it returned. After all, my friend, we're not talking
about a city—you won't take her by storm.

BRIGADIER. You say that, but I know the kind of man I am.

IVAN. What's that, Father? Ha, ha, ha, ha! Are you really
thinking of taking a heart by storm?

BRIGADIER. Ivan! Are there storms in that head of yours?
Can't you talk a little quieter?

COUNC. WIFE. You yourself like to make more noise than
anyone else. I don't know why you don't want your son
to say what he thinks. You're so *bizarre*! (*To the Brigadier's son and Dobroliubov.*) *Messieurs!* I want to leave
them to continue their discourses further, and I ask you
to do likewise.

IVAN. I'm going with you. *Adieu, messieurs!*

DOBROL. I bow to your will.

SCENE 7

The Brigadier and Councilor.

COUNCILOR. My wife has already noticed that you attack
your spouse.

BRIGADIER. No, but I noticed that she takes my son's part
too zealously.

COUNCILOR. I don't notice it.

BRIGADIER. So much the worse.

COUNCILOR. What do you mean?

BRIGADIER. Nothing. Nonetheless, I wouldn't advise my wife to take some other fellow's part in front of me like that.

COUNCILOR. Do you think, my friend, that I'd allow my wife if I noticed that she had something capricious on her mind . . . Thank God! I have eyes. I'm not one of those husbands who look but don't see.

BRIGADIER. For my part, I'm calm. My wife won't fall in love with another man.

COUNCILOR. Her chastity is known to the poor fellow who's blinded by her charms.

BRIGADIER. However, there's no such fool on earth who'd take it into his head to chase after her.

COUNCILOR. But what are you calling him names for?

BRIGADIER. Whom? No, my friend. I say the animal hasn't been born yet who'd think of looking for anything in my wife.

COUNCILOR. But what are you calling him names for?

BRIGADIER. Am I really calling anyone names when I say that a person would have to be a first-class skinflint to be tempted by my wife.

COUNCILOR. You're not calling names, are you? (*Emotionally*) Why should the person be a fool who's attracted to Akulina Timofeevna?

BRIGADIER. Because she's a fool.

COUNCILOR. Why, she's so smart you could publish everything she says.

BRIGADIER. Why not publish it?! I've heard that in the books they print today they lie no more intelligently than my wife.

COUNCILOR. Can it be possible that they lie in books? Don't you know, my dear fellow, that all we Orthodox should believe everything that's printed? It's evident that your faith has been shaken. The number of heretics has increased.

BRIGADIER. And it seems to me that much of our printed nonsense is not because there are more fools. But talking about my wife, I'm not saying that she's dumber than everyone else.

COUNCILOR. But I am talking about your wife and I'll always say that nobody's smarter than she.

BRIGADIER. Even if I were bursting from envy, I still couldn't deny that your lady is very intelligent.

COUNCILOR. The grass always seems greener in the other fellow's yard. I see much in my wife that you don't see.

BRIGADIER. Let's suppose that that's true. Nevertheless, it's also no lie that I see much in your spouse now that you don't see.

COUNCILOR. What would that be?

BRIGADIER. What you, perhaps, will see, but too late.

COUNCILOR. I know what you're getting at, brother! You think that I don't look after my wife enough. However, for the happiness of husbands, God grant that all wives were as chaste as mine.

BRIGADIER. Women are usually chaste with men of substance, but rarely with ne'er-do-wells.

COUNCILOR. They'd have to be pretty ingenious to deceive me, my dear Ignatii Andreevich.

BRIGADIER. And most ingenious of all to dupe me.

COUNCILOR. We're both, it seems, not the kind of men whose wives would give us up for others. I lived with my first wife for some fifteen years and I can say, thank God, that she was no different than my present wife. With wives I'm not unlucky.

BRIGADIER. I understand.

COUNCILOR. A wife wouldn't be that way if she didn't have a good husband, so the thought would never even enter her head to love someone else.

BRIGADIER. Don't talk, my friend. There was a lieutenant-major who served with me in the same regiment—his name doesn't matter—and he was no fool and looked like a pretty solid fellow. Almost twice my size.

COUNCILOR. That couldn't be, old man. . . .

BRIGADIER. But I'm not lying. In my time, when I was a little younger, people were much bigger.

COUNCILOR. But certainly not as big as you're saying. It's true that in our bureau once there was a clerk who was almost five times as fat as I. . . .

BRIGADIER. That couldn't be, my dear fellow. . . .

COUNCILOR. Of course it was. When I was in the bureau, from the chairman down to the watchman, all the people were corpulent.

BRIGADIER. You interrupted what I was going to say. What the devil was it I wanted to tell you?

COUNCILOR. I really don't know.

BRIGADIER. I don't know either . . . what the devil . . . ah, yes, about the lieutenant-major. He was the dearest fellow. The whole regiment knew that his wife loved our colonel, our lieutenant-colonel, our premier-major, or, better said, everyone knew that of our staff and junior officers she didn't love him alone. But he, the son of a bitch, didn't want even to think that she could ever love anyone but him.

COUNCILOR. What in heaven's name have we been talking so long for?

BRIGADIER. I'm never too tired when it comes to talking about sensible things. However, we'd best join the others. (*Going out.*) Indeed, if we didn't stop talking about how people make mistakes we' wouldn't move from this spot for the rest of our lives.

COUNCILOR. Let's go, let's go.

CURTAIN

ACT FIVE
SCENE 1

The Brigadier's Wife and her son.

BRIG. WIFE. Don't be stubborn, Ivanushka. Why don't you want to get married?

IVAN. Mother! It's enough to see you and father to develop a complete aversion to marriage.

BRIG. WIFE. Why, what's the matter, my dear? Do we really live so miserably? It's true we don't have very much money, but still we have enough for our needs.

IVAN. Little or nothing, *c'est la même chose*, for me it's all the same.

BRIG. WIFE.   What do you mean, "all the same"?! Sometimes
it'll happen you need ten kopecks and you won't even
pluck that out of the ground. My, how frivolous you've
become lately! Why ten kopecks even is just so much
manure to you, but don't forget that you can get by on
a ten-kopeck piece a day.

IVAN.   Mother! I'd rather be hungry than be satisfied with a
ten-kopeck piece.

BRIG. WIFE.   You'll see how it hurts, Ivanushka! Don't eat
today, don't eat tomorrow; then you'll see how happy
you'll probably be just with our bread crumbs.

IVAN.   In case of hunger, I dare to think that even a native
Frenchman would lower himself to eat our bread
crumbs. . . . Mother, when you speak about something
Russian I would like to be a hundred French miles away
from you, and particularly when it concerns my marriage.

BRIG. WIFE.   What do you mean, Ivanushka? Why, we've
already given our word.

IVAN.   But I haven't.

BRIG. WIFE.   What does that have to do with us? Our job is
to find you a bride, and your job is to get married. This
isn't your business any longer, so don't poke your nose in.

IVAN.   What?! *Ma mère*, I'm getting married and I have no
say in the choice of a bride?

BRIG. WIFE.   Certainly. After all, how did your father get
married? And how did I get married to him? We never
even heard about each other before. Until the wedding
I didn't exchange a single word with him, and it was
only some two weeks after the wedding that somehow
I began to begin to talk to him little by little.

IVAN.   That's why afterward you talked to each other too
much.

BRIG. WIFE.   God grant that you should live the way we have!

IVAN.   *Dieu m'en préserve!*

BRIG. WIFE.   God's grace and my blessings be with you.

IVAN.   *Très obligé.*

BRIG. WIFE.   Either I've become deaf or you have.

IVAN.   *Ni l'un, ni l'autre.*

BRIG. WIFE.   What will I do with you, Ivanushka? What way
can you really talk to me?

IVAN. My fault. I just forgot I have to speak Russian with you.

BRIG. WIFE. Ivanushka, my dear, either you teach me French or I'll study it myself. I see that otherwise it's completely impossible for me to listen to you or talk myself. (*Goes out.*)

IVAN. As you wish.

SCENE 2

Ivanushka and the Councilor's Wife.

COUNC. WIFE. Know what, dear? I think your father is very angry at us for the way we try to conceal our love for each other.

IVAN. *Madame*, is it possible to conceal a conflagration? And so great a one, *car je brûle, moi*.

COUNC. WIFE. I'm afraid that when they find out about our flame your father and my fool of a husband will try to extinguish it.

IVAN. Yes, *vous avez raison*. They are the kind of people who love mixing into others' affairs.

COUNC. WIFE. And especially my husband. He likes nothing better than to be *mal à propos* mixed up in some affair that has nothing to do with him. The less our flame concerns him, the more he'll get interested in it.

IVAN. *Vous avez raison*. And what concern of his would it really be?

COUNC. WIFE. I'll tell you. He says, my dear, that it's as though a husband and wife constituted a single person.

IVAN. All the better. *Par consequent*, if it is pleasant for you to love me, so should it also be pleasant to him that you love me.

COUNC. WIFE. Of course; he's contradicting himself.

IVAN. *Madame*, you were never in Paris, but you know all the French words. (*They both sit down.*) *Avouez* (*with a happy expression on his face*), didn't you ever have *connaissance* with some Frenchman?

COUNC. WIFE (*embarrassed*). No, my dear. When I was living in Moscow it was impossible for me to get to know anyone.

IVAN. *Pourquoi?* Are there few Frenchmen there?

COUNC. WIFE. I didn't know anyone (*contemptuously*), except teachers.

IVAN. Don't you know how our French teachers are? Even though the greater part of them are illiterate, nevertheless they're the best people in the world for the upbringing of children. Do you know that I, I whom you see before you know—that I lived here at the *pension* of a French coachman before my departure for Paris.

COUNC. WIFE. If that is true, dearest, *je vous demande pardon.* From this hour I shall preserve in my heart a true esteem for French coachmen.

IVAN. I advise you to. I am grateful to one of them for my love for the French and my coldness to Russians. A young person is like wax. If, *malheureusement,* I had fallen into the hands of a Russian who loved his country, perhaps I wouldn't be the way I am.

COUNC. WIFE. It is your good fortune and mine, dear, that you fell into the hands of a French coachman.

IVAN. However, let's forget the coachman and talk about my father and your husband.

COUNC. WIFE. Is it possible, my darling, to pass suddenly from such an exalted subject to such a low one?

IVAN. For intelligent people nothing is impossible.

COUNC. WIFE. Then talk.

IVAN. We have to take steps; *prendre nos mesures.*

(*Enter the Brigadier, from one side, and the Councilor, from the other. Not seeing them, the Councilor's Wife and Ivanushka continue as before.*)

COUNC. WIFE. I love you and agree to everything.

IVAN. To everything! (*Gets down on his knees.*) *Idole de mon âme!*

SCENE 3
    The same, the Brigadier and the Councilor.

BRIGADIER. Aha! What's this? Is it for real or am I just dreaming?

COUNCILOR.   God be with us! Haven't they just been pulling my leg?

IVAN.   (*jumping up and looking bewildered*). *Serviteur très humble.*

BRIGADIER.   Now, Ivan, I want to have a little talk with you in Russian.

COUNC. WIFE   (*to the Councilor*). You're beside yourself, my dear. What's happened to you?

COUNCILOR   (*in a rage*). What's happened to me, damned one?! Didn't you, talking to this ne'er-do-well here, agree to everything?

IVAN.   But what are you scolding me for? Let my father scold me, if he has to.

BRIGADIER.   No, my friend. I'm getting ready to give you a good thrashing.

COUNC. WIFE.   What?! You want to beat him just because he was on his knees before me out of *politesse*?

BRIGADIER.   Yes, my good woman. I saw, I saw. I congratulate you, my dear fellow, for having changed a son-in-law into a lover.

COUNCILOR.   Oh, my God, good heavens! Did I ever think I'd live to see such a loathsome thing!

BRIGADIER.   I seem to recall telling you, brother: watch out for your wife, don't give her her way. Here's what came out of it. We've become related to each other, but not quite the way we planned. You're offended, your daughter also, (*aside*) and I no less.

IVAN.   (*to the Councilor*). Isn't it all the same, *monsieur*? You want to have me as a relation—I willingly . . .

COUNCILOR.   Oh, you scoundrel! You have stripped me of my honor—of my last treasure.

BRIGADIER   (*getting angry*). If that's the last treasure you had left, then you're not very wealthy. It's nothing to chase after.

COUNCILOR.   You yourself are an intelligent person. Just consider what hands I placed this little treasure of mine in (*indicates his wife*).

SCENE 4

The same, the Brigadier's Wife, Sofia, Dobroliubov.

BRIG. WIFE.   Treasure?! What treasure? Don't tell me you found buried treasure! God grant it!

BRIGADIER.   Buried treasure or no buried treasure, we did find something we didn't expect.

BRIG. WIFE.   What is it?

BRIGADIER   (*pointing to the Councilor*). He's making a profit.

COUNCILOR   (*to the Brigadier's Wife*). My damned wife, having no fear of the Lord, not ashamed before decent people, fell in love with your son, my future son-in-law!

BRIG. WIFE.   Ha, ha, ha! What nonsense, my dear Councilor. Ivanushka has a fiancée, so how can he love your wife? That's not the way it's done.

IVAN.   Of course it isn't. And even if it were, it's impossible for honorable people to get angry about such a trifle, *pour une bagatelle*. Among people who know the world, it's just something to laugh at.

BRIGADIER.   If someone had the stupidity to dangle after my old lady, I wouldn't wait for more talk from him—I'd pound his ribs in wherever I met him.

COUNCILOR.   No, my good man, I know what to do with your son. He dishonored me, but I know how much this dishonor will cost you according to the statutes.

BRIG. WIFE.   What?! You want us to pay for your dishonor? For God's sake, what for?

COUNCILOR.   For the fact, my dear lady, that my honor is dearer to me than everything. . . . All the money due me according to my rank I shall take from him and I shall not settle for a kopeck less.

BRIGADIER.   Listen, brother. If the matter goes as far as paying off, then my son should pay one half, and let your wife pay the other half. After all, they both dishonored you.

BRIG. WIFE.   And you know, sin is a two-way matter.

COUNC. WIFE   (*to her husband*). Don't you want him for your son-in-law?

COUNCILOR.   Shut your mouth, damned one!

SOFIA. Father! After what my fiancé has done, let me assure you that I'd never marry him as long as I live.

COUNCILOR. I agree to that.

DOBROL. (*to Sofia*). My hopes are getting brighter and brighter.

BRIGADIER. And I don't want my son to have such a chaste mother-in-law. And as for you, Ivan, here's what I'll do with you (*shakes a stick at him*).

COUNCILOR. Yes, old man, you with a stick, and I with money.

IVAN. Father, don't listen to him. He's not worthy of having such a wife.

COUNC. WIFE. Traitor! Barbarian! Tyrant!

COUNCILOR (*dumbstruck*). What is it, what's the matter?

IVAN. (*to the Councilor*). After all, didn't I see how you were on your knees in front of my mother?

BRIGADIER. Who was on his knees? Aha! In front of whom?

IVAN. He was—in front of my mother.

BRIGADIER. You hear, my friend? Ah! What's the meaning of that?

COUNCILOR. I can't dare look up to heaven.

BRIGADIER (*to his wife*). He was courting you, and you, you fool, didn't say anything to me about it!

BRIG. WIFE. Ignatii Andreevich, my husband, as God is my witness, I didn't know anything about it myself. The good people told me about it only afterward.

BRIGADIER. Brother, I'll take care of Ivan myself; but I see I also have to deliver a petition to you, but not over morality so much as murder.

COUNCILOR (*trembling*). Your excellency! Even God accepts a repenter. Forgive me for sinning before you.

IVAN. *Mon père!* Out of decency . . .

BRIGADIER. Don't you teach me, Ivan; don't forget that I'm getting ready to give you a good thrashing.

COUNC. WIFE. What have you started here? (*Going up to him.*) Didn't you declare your own love for me on this very spot?

COUNCILOR. What? What is the meaning of this, sir . . .

BRIGADIER   (*quieter*). What do you wish?

COUNCILOR.   Of whom was she speaking?

BRIGADIER.   Of me.

COUNCILOR.   So you, my good man, entered my home really to seduce my wife?

BRIGADIER.   If that's so, then I'll go back.

COUNCILOR.   Without delaying an hour.

BRIGADIER.   Not a minute. I see I've fallen into the hands of honorable and substantial people here. Ivan, order the carriage brought around at once. Wife! This minute we're getting out of this house where I, an honest man, almost became a ne'er-do-well.

BRIG. WIFE.   Dear, at least let me put my things away.

BRIGADIER.   You'll leave here in what you've got on!

COUNCILOR.   And what remains is mine.

IVAN.   (*throwing himself at the Councilor's Wife*). Forgive me, *la moitié de mon âme*!

COUNC. WIFE   (*throwing herself at Ivanushka*). *Adieu*, my soul!

(*The Brigadier and Councilor rush to separate them.*)

BRIGADIER.   Away, you dog!

COUNCILOR.   Away, you damned one! O God!

BRIGADIER   (*mocking him*). O God! No, brother, I see by that, that the more someone has God on his tongue, the more he has the devil in his heart. . . . Let's be out of here, people!

COUNCILOR   (*following the Brigadier's Wife, his hands clasped*). Forgive me, Akulina Timofeevna!

SCENE 5

The Councilor, his wife, Sofia, Dobroliubov.

COUNCILOR.   O God! You shall punish us for our deeds. And you, Sofiushka, why did you deprive yourself of your fiancé?

DOBROL.   If your will agrees with our wish, then I, becoming her fiancé, will consider myself the happiest man in the world.

COUNCILOR. What?! After receiving two thousand souls you still haven't changed your mind?

DOBROL. Nothing on earth could make me change my mind.

COUNCILOR. And you, Sofiushka, do you consent to marry him?

SOFIA. If your wishes and Mother's don't oppose it, then I am happy to be his wife.

COUNC. WIFE. I never opposed your happiness.

COUNCILOR. If that is so, then the two of you are engaged as of now.

DOBROL. (*to Sofia*). Our desires are fulfilled; how happy I am!

SOFIA. I can be happy on earth only with you.

COUNCILOR. Be happy, then, while I, for all my sins, am punished sufficiently by the Lord. Here is my Gehenna.

COUNC. WIFE. I wish you good fortune, but I have been sentenced to suffer until death. Here is my Tartarus.

COUNCILOR (*to the parterre*). They say that it is hard to live with one's conscience. But I have learned for myself that living without a conscience is worst of all.

CURTAIN

22. *Misfortune From a Coach*
A Comic Opera in Two Acts

IAKOV B. KNIAZHNIN

Remembered primarily for his controversial *Vadim of Novgorod* (1789), Kniazhnin was also the author of one of the best Russian comic operas of the eighteenth century, *Misfortune From a Coach* (Neschastie ot karety, 1779). Thoroughly sentimental in its idealization of the peasant and its treatment of the love theme, *Misfortune From a Coach* also implies a harsh condemnation of the frivolous landowner who sees his peasants as nothing more than objects to be traded in exchange for imported French baubles. The motif of the selling of a peasant into the army (the fate that threatens Lukian in Kniazhnin's work) is one that appears frequently in Russian literature of the eighteenth century (for example, Radishchev's *Journey*, Chulkov's *Bitter Fate*, and so on).

The music for *Misfortune From a Coach* was written by V. A. Paskevich (c. 1742–c. 1800). The opera was staged for the first time on the stage of the court theatre in St. Petersburg on November 7, 1779, before an audience that included Catherine II and her son Paul. When the French Revolution erupted and Kniazhnin fell into difficulties with the empress (who earlier had expressed great admiration for his work) over his *Vadim of Novgorod*, *Misfortune From a Coach* was withdrawn from the stage, as well as Kniazhnin's tragedy *Rosslav* (1784). From 1789 to 1801 the opera was performed only once. It returned actively to the boards at the beginning of the nineteenth century and remained popular to about 1820. The role of Firiulin was one of the earliest played by the brilliant nineteenth-century Russian actor Mikhail Semёnovich Shchepkin (1788–1863).

The translation follows the text in Ia. B. Kniazhnin, *Izbrannye proizvedeniia*, Biblioteka Poèta, ed. I. I. Kulakovaia, Leningrad, 1961.

Се образъ Княжнина! кого за лирный гласъ
И сами Граціи украсили короной
Напрасно мыслимъ мы что въ Греціи Парнассъ,
Онъ здѣсь воздвигъ его Росславомъ и Дидоной.

A portrait of Iakov Kniazhnin appearing as the frontispiece
to the first collected edition of his works published in St.
Petersburg in 1787.

Dramatis Personae

Mr. Firiulin
Mrs. Firiulin
Aniuta, daughter of Trofim
Lukian, her lover
Trofim, father of Aniuta
Afanasii, a jester
Klementii, a steward
Crowd of peasants

The action takes place in the village of Mr. Firiulin, not far from St. Petersburg.

ACT ONE
SCENE 1

A valley, surrounded entirely by mountains. On one side peasants' huts can be seen in the distance.

Lukian (*alone*).

LUKIAN (*holding a package in his hands*). Phew! How tired I am after running all the way from the city. I've been gone just since yesterday, but it seems like a year that I haven't seen my Aniuta. . . . I can't rest. . . . But I raced like this for nothing. The sun is still high. This is the day I am to become a happy man. In an hour . . . yes! In an hour . . . you will always be with me wherever I go. . . . In an hour you'll be my wife. Aniutushka will be mine. . . . What a joy! Aniuta, here are presents I bought for you in the city.

Aria

Here's a pink shawl just for you.
When you kiss me and you blush
You've such color in your face.
Here's a pearl, and white like snow;
But no match for dear Aniuta's
Fair complexion in its whiteness.
O my splendid city-dwellers,
Whom I saw this very hour,
How much happier than you am I.

I'll be off now to dear Aniuta . . . ah! Here she is now.

SCENE 2
Lukian, Aniuta.

ANIUTA. I could hardly wait for you to come back.

LUKIAN. How are you, Aniutushka, my darling!

ANIUTA. Did you have to spend so much time in the city?

LUKIAN. If you yourself were not the reason, I would be guilty. I bought everything we need.

ANIUTA. Am I definitely to be yours today?

LUKIAN. Today! I love you so much I can hardly believe my own happiness.

ANIUTA. What is there to doubt? My father saw how you ran into the village. He's already gone to the priest and I think he'll soon come to tell us that the priest is in church, and afterward not only the steward but the master himself won't be able to separate us.

LUKIAN. How happy I am!

ANIUTA. Tell me, what did you see in the city?

LUKIAN. Tumult, splendor. Gold flows in rivers, but there's not a drop of happiness. In a word, I saw everything the two of us saw when we lived there with the old master who raised us as his own children until we were thrown out after his death. But I love you and am loved by you. I can get along without the whole world. Aniutushka, do you love me as much as I love you?

ANIUTA. Do I love you? Aren't you ashamed to ask? I'm getting married to you today, and you doubt it! You grieve me when you ask me a question like that. And I would even get angry with you for it if it weren't such a time.

Aria

You wound my heart's tenderness
With your doubts and questions.
And you darken all the bliss
Of this happy day.
If, as you keep telling me,
Loving me so very much,
Only I can make you happy,
None is happier than you.

LUKIAN. Don't be angry, Aniutushka! I'm wrong . . . but why am I wrong? My very great love for you has annoyed you. It seems to me that nobody should love as much as I love you.

Duet

LUKIAN.	Please do love me, As I love you, As I love you truly,	
ANIUTA.	That is why I want to live, So that I can love you, So that I can love you always.	*(Together)*
LUKIAN.	Even in my dreams I fear to See you taken from me.	
ANIUTA.	Loving you is happiness Nothing means a thing without you.	*(Together)*

Here's your father coming! Why is he so sad?

SCENE 3
    Trofim, Lukian, Aniuta.

ANIUTA. What happened to you, Father?

LUKIAN. Is the priest in church already?

TROFIM. Not yet.

LUKIAN. What are you so sad about?

TROFIM. Oh, my friend, Lukianushka—trouble!

ANIUTA. Tell me, Father, what is it?

TROFIM. Trouble! What more do you need—trouble!

ANIUTA. What is it, the priest doesn't want to perform the
    ceremony?

TROFIM. Not that!

LUKIAN. For pity's sake, tell us what it is!

TROFIM. Don't be alarmed: the steward has arrived.

LUKIAN. What kind of trouble is that?

TROFIM. That he came is no trouble, but that he stopped at
    the priest's is.

ANIUTA. And what is the trouble with that?

TROFIM. That he stopped at the priest's is also no trouble,
    but the trouble, Aniuta, is that he's angry. And he is
    never angry without a reason.

LUKIAN. Well, we'll just pay him to stop being angry.

TROFIM. I'm afraid that it may be too costly for us. I never

saw him so angry. I went to the priest and, greeting both
of them with a bow, I said: "Father, if you please, let us
be off to the church—Lukian has already returned from
the city. And Your Grace, Master Steward, we invite to
the wedding banquet." But, like a wild animal he looked
at me and shouted: "Hold on, that won't do, and there
will be no wedding today."

LUKIAN. No wedding!

TROFIM. Yes, Lukianushka.

ANIUTA. But why?

TROFIM. I don't know, Aniutushka.

LUKIAN. I'll go to that scoundrel who is putting off my
happiness. I'll go to him, let him take what he wants.
I'll give him everything I have, just so long as he doesn't
prevent me from being happy today. My God! How
unlucky we are! We have to eat, drink, and marry according to the will of those who delight in our suffering
and who would die of hunger without us. Let's go,
Trofim, and you too, Aniutushka. Help me prevail upon
him.

ANIUTA. Here's the steward now. Why are there so many
people with him?

TROFIM. Oh, my! He looks even angrier than before.

SCENE 4
Trofim, Lukian, Aniuta, and the steward Klementii with
several peasants.

STEWARD. Take him.

TROFIM. Master steward!

STEWARD. What is it?

TROFIM. Please, sir, I implore you with a sheep.

STEWARD. Fine. Take him away.

TROFIM. Please, sir, and with a ram too.

STEWARD. Very good. What did you stop for? Yes! Take
Lukian.

TROFIM. And I thought it was me you wanted. If what I
offered was too little, you could have taken all my live-
stock.

LUKIAN. And what do you want to take me for?

STEWARD. I know what for.

LUKIAN. You know, but I don't know.

TROFIM. Don't argue, Lukianushka—after all, he's the steward. He knows what he's doing.

LUKIAN. He may be the steward, but we have a master still.

STEWARD. Well, why would I be doing this if it weren't for the master's orders. He sent me an order. Here, I'll read it to you now. (*The Steward reads.*) "O you, who until now have been disgraced with the stupid and barbarous name of Klementii, out of my personal affection for you for your having clothed the greater part of the peasants in French style, I bestow the name of Clément." (*As he pronounces the last word, the Steward looks at all, and the peasants bow.*)

TROFIM and the PEASANTS. } God grant you happiness in your new rank!

STEWARD (*continues reading*). "And henceforth I order everyone not to off—ah!—end." (*Stops reading.*) Not to offend. It seems it's no rank. I still don't understand, though. (*Reads.*) "Not to offend you by the name Klementii, but to call you Clément." (*Arrogantly looking at all*). But to call you Clément! You hear?!

TROFIM and the PEASANTS. } We hear, sir. God be praised, we are all happy!

STEWARD (*continues reading*). "Meanwhile, know that I have a desperate need of money. For the holidays I absolutely have to have a new coach. Although I have many coaches, this one I have in mind has been imported from Paris. Imagine, Mister Clément, the disgrace it would be not only for me but for all of you if your master did not ride in this beautiful coach; and if your mistress did not buy those lovely headdresses that are also imported directly from Paris. An honorable man should hang himself for such shame. You wrote me that the harvest was poor; that is not my business, and I am not to blame for it if our soil is poorer than the French. I order you and I beseech you, do not ruin me: find money wherever you can. You already bear the name of Clément now, and wear, thanks to my seigneurial grace, the clothing of a French bailiff. And so, you should be wiser and more expeditious. There are several ways you can obtain money for me. For example, you must have suitable people who could be sold as recruits. Thus, seize them and sell them. Firiulin." Well! Don't you see that I'm not guilty and that I'm just carrying out the master's wishes? Lukian, I congratulate you on becoming a soldier.

ANIUTA. I'm ready to go everywhere with you. I will be happy wherever you are so long as I'm with you.

TROFIM. And whom will I be left with—everyone wants to leave me.

STEWARD. Don't make a fuss, Trofim. After all, he still isn't married. Aniuta is yours and we need her. There are people who love her no less than Lukian.

ANIUTA. But I cannot love them.

STEWARD. You mean you can't love the steward? Love Clément?

ANIUTA. Not only the steward, but the master and anyone else. Lukian is dearer to me than all.

STEWARD. We'll see, we'll see.

LUKIAN. And what will you do?

STEWARD. What will I do? Just make Aniuta mine.

LUKIAN (*taking Aniuta by the hand, with threatening mien*):

Aria

As long as I live,
That will never be!
Only when my soul and I part
Will I give her up, then only!
But no sooner, no it can't be!
If you want to take her from me
Dare approach me any closer.
Then you'll see, who's losing all
Has contempt for everything!

SCENE 5
    Steward, Trofim, Aniuta, Lukian, Jester.

STEWARD.   What are you doing here, Afanasii?

JESTER.   What do you mean *what*?! The master and mistress
    are out hunting and will soon be here. Hello, Trofim,
    how are you? . . . Say! Lukian, what are the peasants
    holding you like that for?

STEWARD.   Because he's going into the army—and the master
    needs a new coach.

JESTER.   Oh, he's wrong!

LUKIAN.   You forgot to mention another wrong.

JESTER.   What?

LUKIAN.   That he wants to take Aniuta away from me.

JESTER.   He's right.

LUKIAN.   I can't live without her.

JESTER.   And what has that to do with the steward? It would
    be good for him. And I, if I weren't married, I'd be
    strongly tempted to turn over not only you but all the
    stewards in order to be master of Aniuta.

STEWARD.   Now Afanasii's talking sense.

Aria

    As a fresh flower in a bush,
    Which a light wind has not touched,
    Hides its petals from the sun,
    While all wish to pluck it—
    Our Aniuta's such a flower
    Dear to all and liked by all.

STEWARD   (*to the peasants*).   I'll go meet the master, and you
    look after him.

SCENE 6
    Aniuta, Lukian, Trofim, Jester.

LUKIAN.   I thought that you'd take our side, but instead you
    defended the inhuman steward.

JESTER.   What am I to do? You yourself are to blame. You

grew to such an extent that nearly a third of a coach could be bought on you. You shouldn't have grown so expensively.

LUKIAN.   You're making jokes, while I have anything but joy in my heart. You have it good. Even though you don't know French, the master loves you just the same, and only we are unfortunate.

TROFIM.   We're poor wretches, and unfortunate.

JESTER.   It wouldn't be bad for you if you really knew how to joke.

Aria

To be useful—nothing worse.
It's this way in life:
He who jokes and he who cheats
Does all right indeed.
He who makes his way by work
Suffers, nothing more.
Why be sad and why go moan—
Everything be damned!
It's all knowing how to dance to someone else's tune—
The trick's to be a jester and a knave.

TROFIM.   Please, intercede for us with the master.

ANIUTA.   Have pity on us, Afanasiushka!

JESTER.   I'd have pity on you if I could, but our master is the sort of person who can't be softened by anything Russian.

TROFIM.   What kind of a wonder is that?

JESTER.   He even hates Russian names. After dressing me in his father's holiday outfit, he even baptized me Buffon from Afanasii.

TROFIM.   What need has he of that?

JESTER.   Oh, a great one!

TROFIM.   Will he be any richer because of it?

JESTER.   Why does he have to be any richer? He's satisfied as he is. The only thing left for him now is to play a fool.

LUKIAN.   Stop talking nonsense. Afanasii, help us; you can do a lot with the master, and I'll make it up to you.

JESTER.   Well, Lukian talks like a smart man should.

ANIUTA   (*giving away Lukian's gifts*). Take everything I have. All I have is what Lukian bought me. Take it; I don't need anything, but just save him.

JESTER   (*taking them*). She's talking even more sweetly than Lukian.

TROFIM   (*taking out money*). And here's something from me, and later on . . .

JESTER.   More.

LUKIAN   (*showing money*). Here's the last money I have; if you help us, all of it will be yours.

JESTER.   Phew, my heavens, what kind of people are these— you can't excuse yourself from them! Lukian, you can give me the money now. I assure you I'll leave you alone. (*Lukian hands the money over to him.*) Go, calm yourself. I hear hunters' horns. Our master is nearby.

SCENE 7
   The same and the Steward.

STEWARD.   Take him and put him in chains.

TROFIM.   For what? What have I done?

STEWARD   (*to Trofim*).

> I have business not with you
> But your son-in-law.
> You are old, thus innocent.
>   (*To the peasants.*)
> Lukian put in chains, yes, him!

LUKIAN
and   } (*together*). They put scoundrels in chains; have
JESTER   } yourself chained.

STEWARD.

> So it's insolent you want to be, eh?
> I'll teach you to be respectful!
> I'll take you into my own hands!

LUKIAN.   Of what am I guilty, why these torments?   }
TROFIM.   Of what is he guilty, why these torments? } (*Together*)
ANIUTA.   Let me share in all his torments.   }

ANIUTA. Let me be chained with him.
I am ready to suffer and to die with him.
(*She falls at the feet of the Steward.*)
I beg you, take pity on me.

LUKIAN. Don't cry, take yourself in hand.
Stop your suffering and groaning.
What can he do?—I'm not guilty.

PEASANTS.
TROFIM.
ANIUTA. } Very much, he's after all a steward!
LUKIAN.

JESTER. Is it very much that he's a steward?

CURTAIN

ACT TWO
SCENE 1

Lukian (*alone, in chains*).

Amidst hope and fear
I'm hesitant and doubtful. . . .
Ah, if I lose her!
What unbearable punishments!
I'm growing numb, I'm trembling. . . .
But maybe it's for nothing that I grieve;
Perhaps my fortunes will yet change.
But if no other way is left me,
I'll turn to death to find my refuge.

SCENE 2
Trofim, Lukian.

LUKIAN. What have you to say, Trofim?

TROFIM. What can I say—nothing. Poor Lukian! Poor Lukian!

LUKIAN. Talk faster; I've prepared myself for everything.

TROFIM. It's bad, Lukianushka!

LUKIAN. Of course, Afanasii couldn't do anything.

TROFIM. He did implore on our behalf, but won nothing.

The steward overpowered him. And the master is giving Aniuta to him.

LUKIAN.   Well, everything is finished now!

TROFIM.   How sorry I am for you!

LUKIAN.   So no hope is left?

TROFIM.   It's obvious there's none. Afanasii has already left to give us back what he took from us. Don't worry, he's bringing back your money too.

LUKIAN.   From him I don't need anything!

SCENE 3
    Trofim, Lukian, Aniuta.

ANIUTA   (*running in in haste*). Lukian! Oh, what can we do?

Tercet

LUKIAN.   O miserable fate!

ANIUTA.   O fatal passion!

TROFIM.   The steward's power!

ALL.   I am perishing with you,
    And losing you forever.
    Oh, farewell, farewell forever!
    Is it possible to bear this?

SCENE 4
    Trofim, Lukian, Aniuta, Jester.

JESTER.   I'll bring you right back what I took from you.

TROFIM.   But I thought that you already brought it.

JESTER.   Not yet. After all, it's not so easy to return as it is to take. All people have the habit of taking what they grab, and finding it hard to give back. But why should you get your money back, Lukian? After all, you want to die. . . . I heard you. . . . So you don't need money! The world is already hateful to him. Spit on it all, die; that's the best way. You can't imagine how bad this world is. Truly, it's not worth living in. You see the woe that comes from such trifles? You're in love with Aniuta,

Aniuta with you, the steward with Aniuta, the master
with a coach, and the coach loves nobody impecuniously.
And because of that go give up everything. As a friend,
I advise you to die.

Aria

>Damn this world of ours,
>Where woes so plenty are—
>From coaches or
>From cuffs—
>Or from Aniutas too—
>And where the steward is a knave!

Nevertheless, I'm still not despairing. The master himself
will be here soon. You ask him yourself; I'll help you.
Let's see now . . . Lukian! Do you happen to know
French?

LUKIAN.   For what?

JESTER.   It would be very good if you did.

LUKIAN.   I learned a few French words when I lived with the
old master. Aniuta also knows a few.

JESTER.   How good! Now, if you please, don't die; your
money will truly be mine.

SCENE 5

Firiulin, Mrs. Firiulin, the Steward, and the Jester. In
the distance Trofim, Aniuta, Lukian.

FIRIULIN.   Nation of barbarians! Savage country! What ignorance! What coarse names! How they offend the
delicacy of my hearing! I see I have to look after things
myself and change all the names that hurt the ears. That
will be my first task.

MRS. FIRIULIN.   I'm surprised, my dear! Our village is so close
to the capital, but nobody speaks French here. But in
France, no more than a hundred versts from the capital,
everyone talks French.

JESTER.   Now there's something to wonder at! I think you
and your husband will soon begin being amazed that dogs
bark and don't talk.

FIRIULIN.   Ha, ha, ha! Well said! To be honest, here they bark when they talk. What chatterboxes! Isn't it so?

JESTER.   That's so, when one looks at you.

FIRIULIN.   When one looks at us, he'll see a great difference—isn't that so? But even we, we, ah!—We're nothing compared to the French.

JESTER.   It was worth traveling to France to bring back just contempt, not only for one's fellow countrymen, but for one's self.

FIRIULIN.   To tell the truth, it would be worth it even for that. But my wife and I brought back many wonders for the enlightenment of the ignorant masses: I, red heels,[1] and she, caps. . .

MRS. FIRIULIN.   Almost none of which are left, and now I have to buy some more . . . but the money . . .

FIRIULIN (*to the Steward*).   Clément, dear Clément will help us.

STEWARD.   Please rest assured that there will be money.

FIRIULIN.   And the girl you asked me about will be yours.

JESTER.   You brought back many wonders from your trip to France, but no pity for your own servants. I guess there's none of that there.

FIRIULIN.   Pity for Russians? You've gone mad, Buffon. All my pity has remained in France and now I can't restrain my tears remembering . . . O, Paris!

JESTER.   That's fine! Crying over the fact that you're not there, and torturing your servants without pity. And for what? Just so as to be able to buy a French coach.

FIRIULIN.   Stop talking about that! To unfortunate people like us who have returned from France to this savage country one pleasure has remained, and that is after making a decent turnover on this Russian trash one can get some respectable French thing. But they want to deprive us even of that pleasure.

JESTER.   Live the way you want now. I'm only saying that I'll leave you. For could I stay with you? I'd always be afraid that you'd exchange me for a little red French heel.

[1] A mark of the nobility in France at the time.

FIRIULIN.   No, no, I wouldn't give you up.

JESTER.   Are you really selling someone worse than me? (*Pointing to Lukian.*) Take a look at that young fellow there who even knows a little French.

FIRIULIN.   French? *Mon Dieu!* What am I hearing?

MRS. FIRIULIN.   Ah! *Mon cœur!* He knows French, and he's in chains! That simply will not do.

FIRIULIN.   It's terrible, *horrible*! Remove his chains. *Mon ami!* I am guilty before you.

STEWARD.   But the French coach . . .

JESTER.   Be quiet, scoundrel!

FIRIULIN.   And who is the young girl here? She's not bad.

LUKIAN.   Oh, master! She is the one whom I love more than myself, who loves me and whom you are giving away to the steward.

FIRIULIN.   What can be done? I've already given my word.

ANIUTA.   Your father loved us, but his son torments us. The cruel one takes my life away with Lukian.

LUKIAN.   Have me taken out and killed this very minute. And then only give Aniuta to another.

ANIUTA
and   } (*together*).   Look upon the tears
LUKIAN   Of your servants here.
                                End the suffering
                                Of those you've brought grief.

FIRIULIN.   *Parbleu!* I never would have believed that Russian people could love so tenderly. I am beside myself with wonderment! Am I not in France? That he feels love comes as no great surprise to me—he does speak French. But you, girl, what about you?

JESTER.   She understands it too.

FIRIULIN.   She too? Now I am still more amazed.

LUKIAN   (*on his knees*).   *Monseigneur!* Have pity on us!

ANIUTA   (*on her knees*).   *Madame!* Intercede for us.

FIRIULIN.   *Monseigneur! Madame!* Get up, you have moved me to such pity by your words that I can't keep from crying.

JESTER.   Two French words have extracted the pity left in

France. You see what a treasure the steward scoundrel was depriving you of?

FIRIULIN (*threatening the steward*). *Monsieur* Clément, you're a good-for-nothing.

MRS. FIRIULIN. *Mon cher!* Let us unite them. They are worthy of each other and worthy of being with us.

STEWARD. Have you given up all thought of buying the coach?

FIRIULIN. No, but I still have many people even without him. Besides, I need a servant who knows French to travel with me. (*To Lukian.*) Do you consent never to speak Russian again?

LUKIAN. I swear to you that these are my last Russian words.

JESTER (*to Lukian*). Look and don't talk. (*To Firiulin.*) See how necessary a person he is to you.

Aria

What happiness it is,
What sweetness to the heart,
If, standing there behind you,
Not speaking any Russian,
Instead of shouting—come!
He'll shout instead in French!
What happiness it is,
What sweetness to the heart,
When he begins to shout and roar,
No one will understand a word!

FIRIULIN (*to Lukian*). Well, *mon ami!* Marry her, *mariez vous*, I now give you my permission.

MRS. FIRIULIN. It makes me very happy! They love each other so that I would be bored without them, to be honest.

TROFIM (*bowing to Firiulin*). You're the father . . .[2]

FIRIULIN. What kind of a creature is it dares address me as father? Perhaps my father was your father, but I don't want to be father to such a swine. Don't ever dare do this again.

[2] Merely a conventional peasant's manner of address for a master; Firiulin, however, takes it literally.

JESTER.   Imagine, crawling here and not knowing a word of
French.

TROFIM.   Not I, but the blood in me speaks, Afanasiushka.

FIRIULIN   (*to Lukian and Aniuta*). Well, now you are happy,
and I am glad. We'll be off. When you get married, come
to us in the city.
                    (*Mr. and Mrs. Firiulin go out.*)

JESTER   (*to the Steward*). Steward! Why don't you have the
wedding at your place?
                    (*The Steward leaves angrily.*)

SCENE 6
    Jester, Lukian, Aniuta, Trofim, and peasants.

JESTER.   Well, you see, when I want something, there isn't
anything I can't do.

LUKIAN.   You gave me back my life. Rest assured that I shall
never forget your kindness.

ANIUTA.   Nor I.

TROFIM.   Nor I.

JESTER.   What were you crying about? Wherever the jester
Afanasii is, you have to laugh and be gay. You see, there's
nothing to worry about in life at all, and you never have
to die before your time.

        Though in life there is much evil,
        Should we bow and let it crush us?
        You were ruined by a trifle,
        But it was a trifle saved you.

LUKIAN.   Never shall I stop forgetting
        How much in your debt you've placed me.
        Every hour that I see her,
        You I'll know gave me my life back.

ANIUTA   (*to the Jester*).
        I am also grateful to you
        That our woes have now been ended.
            (*To Lukian*)
        All we had we lost for good,
        But you're mine and I am yours.

TROFIM   (*to the Jester, bowing*).
           Thanks to Afanasii,
           My Aniuta is alive.
           Oh! The master would have chained us!
           Oh! A French head just makes trouble!

CHORUS.
           Though in life there is much evil
           Should we bow and let it crush us?

JESTER.   You were ruined by a trifle. ⎫
PEASANTS. You were ruined by a trifle. ⎬ (*Together*)
TROFIM.   You were ruined by a trifle. ⎭

LUKIAN.   We were ruined by a trifle. ⎫
                               ⎬ (*Together*)
ANIUTA.   We were ruined by a trifle. ⎭
ALL.   But it was a trifle saved you.

CURTAIN

23. *Dimitrii the Impostor*
A Tragedy in Five Acts

ALEKSANDR P. SUMAROKOV

The first real dramatist in the history of the Russian theatre, Sumarokov authored nine tragedies between 1747 and 1771: *Khorev* (1747), *Hamlet* (Gamlet, 1748), *Sinav and Truvor* (Sinav i Truvor, 1750), *Aristona* (1750), *Semira* (1751), *Iaropolk and Dimiza* (Iaropolk i Dimiza, 1758), *Vysheslav* (1768), *Dimitrii the Impostor* (Dimitrii samozvanets, 1771), and *Mstislav* (1774). These were complemented by twelve comedies, the best of which were *Tressotinius* (1750), *The Guardian* (Opekun, 1765), and *The Imaginary Cuckold* (Rogonosets po voobrazheniu, 1772).

Among the most interesting eighteenth-century Russian tragedies, particularly in the light of Pushkin's later drama on the same theme, *Boris Godunov* (1823–1825), *Dimitrii the Impostor* was staged for the first time on February 1, 1771, at the Imperial Theatre in St. Petersburg. It proved immensely popular, and remained a standard item in the Russian repertoire down to the 1820's.

The tragedy deals with one of the most turbulent episodes in Russian history—the so-called Time of Troubles (*Smuta*, in Russian), which endured from 1604 to 1613. Upon the death of Tsar Boris Godunov (1598–1605), the throne passed to his son Fëdor. His claim was challenged, however, by the False Dimitrii, or Dimitrii the Impostor, a pretender who claimed to be the supposedly murdered son of Tsar Ivan IV (the Terrible, 1533–1584). With extensive support among the Poles and Cossacks, Dimitrii's claim was accepted by many of the boyars. Following the deposition and murder of Fëdor, Dimitrii advanced to Moscow and established himself on the throne. In 1606 a boyar faction led by Vasilii Shuiskii succeeded in driving out the Impostor and murdering him. Shuiskii thereupon became tsar. The appearance of new pretenders, Cossack risings, and the inroads of the Poles kept Russia in a state of turmoil until the Poles were expelled from Moscow in 1612 and the first Romanov, Mikhail, was elected to the throne by a national assembly (*zemskii sobor*) on February 21, 1613, thereby bringing to an end the Time of Troubles.

The subject of Dimitrii the Impostor captured the imagination not only of Russian writers; and many works have been written on it, beginning as early as Lope de Vega's *El gran duque de Moscovia* (1617). Sumarokov's *Dimitrii the Impostor* was the first important Russian literary work devoted to it; the greatest, however, remains Pushkin's *Boris Godunov*.

Pushkin's desire to follow the "freer" path of Shakespearean dramatic technique in *Boris Godunov* is well known, and requires no further elaboration here. Shakespeare was one of the great "discoveries" of European romanticism. By imitating Shakespeare the romantics believed that they could free themselves from the rigidity of classicist dramatic conventions.

But Sumarokov, in the middle of the eighteenth century, was also interested in Shakespeare, although obviously in a very different way than the Romantics were to be. In 1748 Sumarokov wrote his own version of *Hamlet* in conformity with the principles of classicist poetics. The play was staged at the court theatre in St. Petersburg in 1750—the first appearance of Shakespeare on a Russian stage.

Dimitrii the Impostor also manifests Sumarokov's interest in Shakespeare. We find, for example, that—as Pushkin was to do after him, following Shakespeare—Sumarokov introduces the crowd as an active force in the action of the tragedy. However, it does not actually appear onstage, as it was to do in *Boris Godunov*. The echoes of tumult, of mobs running riot, and the tolling of bells—of sound emanating from offstage—further reflect Shakespearean dramaturgy. Yet Sumarokov's borrowing of such "devices" was insufficient to lead him to any meaningful break with the established canons of classicist tragedy. This is particularly apparent in the design of Sumarokov's central character, Dimitrii. Consonant with classicist practice the character is little more than an abstraction, the embodiment of some single trait or aspect of personality. The other characters are also drawn simply; they are divided into two groups, the virtuous and the evil. The dramatist's purpose is not subtle delineation of character using all the colors of his palette, but the heightening of contrast between opposing camps. His colors are only two: black and white. Sumarokov also took no pains to present a realistic picture of the epoch of the Impostor. Dimitrii, for example, was murdered by a throng. The presentation of such violence was ruled out by classicist dramatic theory; thus we find instead that in Sumarokov's version Dimitrii ends his own life by suicide.

More important an aspect of the play is the easily isolated allusions to the political program of the Panin group: the expression of the progressive conception of the monarch as the servant of the people, and the idea that a sovereign's powers and privileges are not limitless. This does not mean that the tragedy should be read primarily as a political drama, especially in the light of Sumarokov's conservatism and strong class feelings. But keeping in mind the activity of the Panin group in the first decade of Catherine's rule, and a certain sympathy on Sumarokov's part with some of their goals, most notably as regards monarchic power, enables us to appreciate the enthusiasm for the play in Russian liberal circles, well into the nineteenth century. Though somewhat denigrating Lomonosov's position, Radishchev did not hesitate to speak highly of Sumarokov in his *A Journey From St. Petersburg to Moscow,* where, in his "Eulogy on Lomonosov," he declared: "And this is your crown of victory, O Lomonosov: you brought forth Sumarokov!" Radishchev had further praise for Sumarokov in his philosophic tract *On Man, His Mortality and Immortality* (O cheloveke, o ego smertnosti i bessmertii, first printed in 1809). Although later times were to be less kind to Sumarokov's dramatic talent, his tragedies exerted an immense influence on Russian tragic writing virtually down to Pushkin's *Boris Godunov.*

Like all of Sumarokov's tragedies, *Dimitrii the Impostor* was written in a twelve-syllable iambic verse with caesura after the sixth syllable and in alternating rhymed masculine and feminine pairs.

Dramatis Personae

Dimitrii the Impostor
Shuiskii
Georgii, Prince of Galicia
Ksenia, daughter of Shuiskii
Parmen, confidant to Dimitrii
Captain of the guard
Boyars and others

The action takes place in the Kremlin, at the royal palace.

ACT ONE
SCENE 1

    Dimitrii and Parmen.

PAR. I am your true friend, Sire; keep me no more in darkness.
    For thirty days and more I hear but heavy sighing,
    And see my troubled lord in torment on his throne.
    What is the hidden woe that waits upon the tsar?
    What hidden cloud prevents contentment for Dimitrii?
    And can a monarch's throne no longer bring him joy?
    Wretchedness, once your lot, lies now all in the past,
    And heaven has restored what Boris took away.
    It was not granted him to open up your coffin.
    From swift, untimely Death by Fate you've been delivered.
    Since truth has raised you, then, up to your fathers' throne,
    Why now this woe that weighs on you so heavily?

DIM. Deep, deep within my heart an evil fury rages.
    Unto the wicked man there comes not peace nor calmness.

PAR. Unutterable violence, ferocious savagery
    Your subjects have endured while you have scourged the land.
    You wallow in the blood of deeds both dark and beastly;
    People you send to death—doomed, though guilty of nothing.
    Your wrath against our land is boundless, limitless.
    Fair Moscow has become the boyars' charnelhouse.
    All Russia's faithful sons share the same bitter fortune.
    The Poles—the Poles alone—stand guardians of our monarch.
    The Eastern Church's rule—behold, it droops and fails,
    And our own Russian tsar would yield us to the Pope.
    If something in your heart entices you to error,
    Rise over it—become a father to your people.

DIM. But I have sworn an oath that binds me to the Pope.
    The Polish nation serves me faithfully and well.
    Thus Russia shall not find the favor of its ruler
    Until it will submit to papal domination.

PAR. It seems to me that man seeks brothers of his kind.

False teachers—risen up—have fed our people's minds
Fables, depravities. From their unholy teachings
They find a rich reward; they reap their selfish harvest.
The pastors of our flocks, in silence, and confused,
Fall tumbling with the fallen, counting themselves as
    blessed.
England and Holland have sloughed off the loathsome
    burden,
And half of Germany. The time is pressing forward
When all of Europe will rise up above its fears
And from his throne will fall the haughty Roman
    prince
Who sets himself apart from men and all things mortal
And sees mobs cringe as though Himself God moved
    among them.

DIM.   A little more respect! Parmen, you're impudent!
This luminary's praised by princes, tsars, and kings.

PAR.   From honest hearts alone comes not this adulation.
From many, sheer hypocrisy calls forth this honor.
Some call him patriarch—among his equals, first;
But not the world's sole judge; not highest prince, not
    God.
The Pope must realize men are not witless cattle.
Men with intelligence will find God's truth through
    reason.

DIM.   In sophistry you waste your words, and all in vain.
If you would go to heaven, be no philosopher!
Wisdom can lead to ruin even though it but flatters.

PAR.   But how shall wisdom be offensive to the Almighty?
Filled with eternal wisdom, He made the universe.
He gave both life and reason to that which was but
    dead.
In all that we behold we see his holy wisdom.
Hate we then in ourselves what we in God still honor?

DIM.   The wisdom of the Lord so far beyond us lies!

PAR.   Then it must also lie beyond the Pope as well.
The confines of the mind can't reach its understanding;
But in His acts we find our God in His creation.
And if we use our minds, whet our God-given wits,
Then we may know as much as he, the Pope, can
    know.

DIM.   For insolence like this you'll find a place to suffer

　　　　　Where there are thirst and hunger, anguish, fiery rivers;
　　　　　Where there are pain of soul and wounds without a
　　　　　　　cure.

PAR.　　And there we'll find you too, unless you change your
　　　　　　ways.

DIM.　　I know that I've been cruel, a witness of much evil.
　　　　　I've perpetrated deeds unspeakable and shameless.

PAR.　　Then shun them, run from them; flee from these
　　　　　　wicked deeds.

DIM.　　If I but had the strength to overcome myself!
　　　　　But Russia's honor must descend to utter darkness.
　　　　　My armies will accept the Pope father of fathers;
　　　　　For him will I subdue the Church with tools of war.
　　　　　This the tsar wishes; this—then suits Dimitrii Tsar!

PAR.　　You're setting sail, my tsar, upon a stormy ocean,
　　　　　And with the grief you bring to Moscow and the
　　　　　　Russians
　　　　　You're beating down a path that leads but to your
　　　　　　doom.
　　　　　Your throne is tottering; the crown falls from your
　　　　　　head.

DIM.　　Down from my throne descends my loathing for the
　　　　　　people.
　　　　　My power grows secure with their increasing bondage.
　　　　　A father shall I be to this rebellious land
　　　　　Which by opposing me goads me from wrath to wrath?
　　　　　I rule, and ruling find a singular amusement
　　　　　In meting out to Russians death and execution.
　　　　　The Poles will be the sons of the new fatherland.
　　　　　The Russians will submit to Polish domination.
　　　　　Let victory follow victory—until I find in triumph
　　　　　Full state of majesty, full regal exultation,
　　　　　Obtaining for my own, possessing as my prey,
　　　　　That for which my soul has longed for many days.
　　　　　Should this not come to pass—this, all my heart's
　　　　　　desiring,
　　　　　No peace of mind will come unto the Tsar Dimitrii.
　　　　　What torment! Oh, what pain my conscience must
　　　　　　endure.
　　　　　My love for Ksenia, what pain this also brings.

PAR.　　You have a wife, my tsar, and Ksenia is betrothed.

DIM.　　Parmen, you have my trust. I count upon your friend-
　　　　　　ship.

Hear then my thoughts outright. My marriage I'll
dissolve.

Poison will send my wife to everlasting gloom.

PAR. What terror seizes me!

DIM. Your fear, Parmen, is idle.

PAR. To think of such a deed is an abomination.

DIM. I have grown used to horrors. Evil is my friend.

The paths of wickedness have stained my soul with
blood.

PAR. In nothing stands your wife before her husband guilty.

DIM. Before the tsar stands truth in silence, Parmen, silence.

I, not the truth, am tsar! The law, the power are mine;

And how to use the law is for the tsar to say.

That monarch is a slave who will deny such pleasures

As are proscribed by law; the monarch is above them.

If this were such an age wherein who bore the crown

Were subject to the law, then he would be no tsar.

And he who wears the purple vainly for his subjects

Would labor if like them their judgment were his
judgment.

PAR. (*Aside*). His wife must be advised of his barbaric
scheme.

(*To Dimitrii.*) Your ways will plunge you, Tsar, into
the pits of hell.

DIM. Oh, Clement! If in heaven there waits for me a room,

For whom then waits the pain of dread Gehenna's
doom?

SCENE 2

Dimitrii, Parmen, and the Captain of the Guard.

CAP. Great Sovereign and King! The people are aroused

Like waters in the wind; like seas moved by a storm.

Some have been stirred to say, transported by their
fury,

What lies within their hearts concerning tsar and
scepter.

DIM. What mischief do they weave there in the marketplace?

I know of ways to deal with witless, raving mobs.

CAP. Sovereign, what I have heard, I do not dare repeat it.

DIM. Say it! I know of ways to quiet restless Russians.

CAP. They say that you are not the true son of the tsar;

That he who was his son in Uglich murdered lies.
Among the common folk Otrepev have they named
you,
And this is how they tell the Tsar Dimitrii's story.
They say that, once a monk, you fled your cloister walls
And sanctuary found on foreign Polish soil.
In Poland you deceived your betrothed and her father,
And did not fear to seize the throne with craft and
cunning.
The shadow of the Poles falls now upon the throne,
And you are bringing in the church law of the Romans.
They say you have become with recklessness and
boldness
Moscow and Russia's foe—a butcher to your subjects.

DIM. We must increase my guard of true and trusted Poles.
Stir me no more to rage. My spirit is inflamed.
I lack the strength to hear more treason from these
monsters.
Bring now before my eyes Prince Shuiskii and his
daughter!

SCENE 3
Dimitrii and Parmen.

PAR. When by decree of fate you climbed to Russia's throne,
Ancestry mattered not; we needed then a tsar.
And if you had not ruled with such an evil spirit,
It would be all the same, were you or not Dimitrii.

DIM. Prince Shuiskii brews the plot. I see it in his face.
And when an enemy will not become my friend,
Upon that day the earth will swallow up his carcass
And coffin lids will slam on him and on his daughter.

PAR. My blood stops at this talk. Your love for Ksenia
Is such a love as none has seen on earth before.

DIM. Love that is most sublime will stoop to crudest ven-
geance
If it is not returned, but burns up unrequited.
And if the princess choose to laugh away this fear
We'll watch a blooming rose wither and turn to dust.
If she is obstinate and spurns the monarch's passion,
Then she defies the tsar's authority and power.

SCENE 4

Dimitrii, Parmen, Shuiskii, and Ksenia.

DIM.   The rumors of revolt have fallen on my ears,
And I've been made aware whence come these trea-
    sonous thoughts.
High-placed respected men are making here in Moscow
Assertions that are bound to harm our throne and
    welfare.

SHU.   The murmuring of the mob is but an empty sound.
The wind sweeps up the noise, and soon it disappears.

DIM.   Enough dissembling! Stop! There's nothing more to
    fathom.
Your secret wish is clear: my throne is what you covet!

SHU.   The thought of being tsar—tsar in this glorious land—
Has never once occurred within my loyal mind.
You only are the tsar; son of the monarch Ivan.
For us your noble head was crowned in the cathedral.
The villain Godunov was ever tyrannous.
Stern you are, but just—and so your father was.
Only dishonest men against you groan and grumble,
Drunkards and thieves, no more; but all the rest do
    love you.
Though harsh today through need, you'll yet be merci-
    ful.
Great Sovereign, your throne in Moscow stands secure.

DIM   Don't play me for a fool with words that soothe and
    flatter.
Your looks betray your thoughts. If you would keep
    my friendship,
Then be a friend to me, a true and faithful friend.

SHU.   I am your loyal slave.

DIM.   Parmen, you may withdraw.

SCENE 5

Dimitrii, Shuiskii, and Ksenia.

DIM.   To rid my mind of doubts, I must have more assurance.
I crave the guarantee of loyalty unquestioned.
My blood with fiery love has destiny inflamed.

Let Ksenia be my own as pledge of friendship true.

KSE. I yours?

SHU. You have a wife.

DIM. She is by law a Roman.
I need a Russian wife, a true and loyal Russian.

KSE. My heart was long ago unto another joined.

DIM. Then it is not your wish to be a monarch's wife?

KSE. Not for the radiance of golden crowns and scepters,
Not for the royal thrones of all this world's fair king-
doms,
Would I turn from the one who is my only love.
The fire that flames my heart, there shall it ever burn.
It fills my mind and soul; it melts into my senses;
Georgii in this heart shall dwell now and forever.

DIM. But Death can cut you down, both you and him you
love;
And Death can quench the flame that blazes in you
both.

KSE. Then it may be that each to each will be forgotten,
But not before that day will either one be faithless.

DIM. You do perhaps forget the one to whom you speak.
Have you no fear of death—of execution?

KSE. No!

DIM. Prepare yourself then, Ksenia, with your vaunted
courage.
The very dust of you will fade from earth and vanish.
O heaven! How my path to vengeance speeds its way.
I only grieve that death will free you from all pain.
Could I but now move hell, the land and all the ocean!
Could I torment your soul from now until forever!

SHU. Be not enraged by Ksenia's obstinacy, Sire.
Even from childhood days she has been always so.
If in her body's charms your eyes find their desiring,
Her father shall persuade. Entrust me with this matter.
Over my daughter's thoughts my judgment will prevail.

KSE. I shall preserve my faith unto the very grave.
Is this the parent's task, is this the father's duty,
To lead his child astray, to make his child unfaithful?
Persuade me as you will; your words are all in vain.

SHU. What I have promised you, that will I see performed.
A little while and you will see the foolish maiden
Restored to reason. Calm your justly heated anger.

DIM. If it lies in your power, persuade this stubborn shrew.
KSE. Imagine not, O Tsar, I shall be wife to you!

SCENE 6
    Shuiskii and Ksenia.

SHU. Arise, O truth, defend the honor of your people!
    O enemy of Moscow––not long is yours the scepter.
KSE. Yet moments past you spoke quite differently to him.
SHU. Think not I spoke the truth to one so villainous.
    Your foolishness, my child, your daydreams of the springtime,
    Have in your bosom sown but seeds of first love's sweetness.
    Your goal you would attain by a straightforward path;
    But we must walk the way of cunning and deceit.
    When we are forced to deal with such a wicked tyrant,
    We dare not contradict or outrightly oppose him.
    It was by craftiness that he attained the crown.
    So truth must not speak out till the appointed hour
    When the oppressor's might is overthrown in Russia.
    O God, a time of peace give to this land and Moscow!
KSE. The vicious tyrant saps my very life from me.
SHU. Pretend to yield, my child, deceive him, flatter him.
    Excite, inflame his heart with words of love, and tokens
    Of your affection; thus, you'll pacify his baseness.
    Watch then his anger melt, dissolve in amorous sighs.
    Even tigers and snakes are conquered by love's charms.
    The wildest of the beasts leaves his accustomed fierceness
    When bound beneath the yoke of a much longed-for pleasure.
KSE. There is no basilisk or asp more vile than he.
SHU. Suppress these thoughts, my child, if you can banish them,
    These thoughts that frighten now and terrify your spirit.
    Remember you shall save your father and your lover,
    And, saving us, you also save your fatherland,
    Moscow, all Russia. . . .
KSE.   Father, this I realize.

Hard lies the way ahead! May heaven spare this nation!
O God! Let Russia find through me at last salvation!

CURTAIN

ACT TWO
SCENE 1
Georgii and Ksenia.

GEO.   I must dissemble now and force my tongue to speak
       Words strange to me when truth must sleep a painful sleep.
       I must put on the guise of hypocrites and liars.
       Here's how one must behave with false and evil tyrants.
KSE.   Let blessed be on earth that purple-wearing man
       Who does not bind in chains the freedom of our souls;
       Who glories in the good he brings to his dominion;
       Who with humility exalts the rank of monarch,
       His subjects granting days of peace and plenty,
       By those men feared alone whose ways incline toward wrong.
GEO.   O Kremlin, you have seen with tears of woe and sorrow
       Cast from her throne today the broken corpse of virtue.
       Behold how Moscow droops and trembles in despair,
       How happiness has fled in exile from its walls.
       The brightest of our days seem darker than the night;
       The fairest of our groves in shrouds of gloom lie buried.
       When through the city sounds the solemn mournful bell,
       It seems but to repeat the sorrow of us all.
       It tells us that our Church is crumbling down before us,
       Falling before the Pope and Roman subjugation.
       From this calamity good Lord deliver us!
       The rumor now is heard, is spreading through the squares,
       That Clement promises a rich reward in Heaven
       For those who will betray the city of their fathers;

Assures them in advance forgiveness of their sins.
Now Moscow must endure what the New World endured.
There by the papal might the land was drenched in blood;
And those who were not slain were left in desolation.
In their own fatherland they burned the innocent.
While one hand held a cross, the other held a sword.
The fate that came to them, sudden and unexpected,
Will visit you today—from Rome it comes, O Russia!

KSE.   Not all the fiendish host—Dimitrii, Clement, Hell—
Will take you from my heart, or wrench you from my soul.
O heaven, lift from us the dreaded scourge of Rome;
And with it make an end to Ksenia's wretched torment.
Oh, let it come to pass that Russia raise her head,
And Ksenia be the bride to him who has her love!
Grant that we see once more upon the throne a monarch
Submissive to the truth, not evil inclination.
For justice has grown pale. The tyrant would become
A law unto himself; this is his highest wish.
Our former tsars were just, who for immortal glory
Made laws that led the way to joy for all their subjects.
The sovereign should be God's deputy on earth.
Strike down, destroy me, Tsar—cold and unmerciful!
From Tartarus you came, hurled upward by Megaera.
The Caucasus gave birth to you; Irkania fed you.
Blaspheming heretics, surrounded by their slaves,
Will desecrate the graves of Russia's holy saints.
Their names on Russian soil will be no more remembered;
The houses of our God will stand in Moscow empty.
People! Rip off the crown from the tormentor's head!
Make haste, pry loose the scepter from his barbarous hands.
Deliver, free yourselves from his unending fury.
Crown with the diadem a man who's fit to wear it.

SCENE 2
Dimitrii, Georgii, and Ksenia.

DIM. Ksenia, listen to me! Georgii, hear me now!
      You are but crawling things, worm-dwellers of the earth.
      Listen as slaves to that which I, the tsar, command you;
      Or should I say to what has been decreed by heaven.
      This maiden was not born to be betrothed to you.
      It has been so ordained that she shall be my bride.
      If you've no wish to meet a sudden, swift disaster,
      Then cease your tenderness toward Ksenia, my princess.

GEO. I do not contradict your claim, O Tsar.

KSE.   Nor I.

DIM. Tomorrow then with me you'll be forever joined.

KSE. How shall I tear my thoughts from what was once so pleasant?
      How then shall I prepare so quickly for this marriage?
      The tsar's command is strong; this is well known to me.
      But love's emotion, Tsar, should not be thought less strong.
      It is not possible to break its spell so quickly,
      Nor to leave him I love without a time of sorrow.
      Give a few days at least, let passion spend itself,
      That I may grow accustomed to leave a cherished dream.
      The wound within my heart first needs a time for healing.
      You would not have me come despairing to this marriage.
      When I lift up my eyes unto the altar's lights,
      I shall relinquish life, and fall before you dead.

DIM. Suppress this insolence; this brooding passion still,
      Or else Georgii's life will be abruptly ended.
      Vanish, pitiful man, an offering to the tsar!
      He is but earthly dust—I, the annointed king!

GEO. I have endured enough—

KSE.   Be still!

GEO.   Humiliation
      Like this cannot be borne!

KSE.   My prince!

DIM.   The monarch's mildness
To anger has been stirred, transformed to righteous
     wrath.
Death the all-ravenous has opened up his mouth.
Summon the guards!
          (*The guards enter.*)

GEO.   I stand ready for any torture
If into barbarous hands I am by fate delivered.
O robber of the crown! Tyrant and murderer!
Glut yourself on my blood, and on your people's blood;
Ascending to the heights from hell's most darksome
     valley,
Till the appointed hour when from your throne you
     topple.

DIM.   Away with him!

SCENE 3
     Dimitrii and Ksenia.

KSE.   Be cruel! Torment me, torture me
With your barbaric acts; perform all infamies!
Your sight cannot abide the happiness of others.
O God, look down and see the deeds of our tormentor.
See how his evil hand lies heavy on his people.
Each hour brings forth new cries of suffering to your
     ears.
How evil are these days! How horrible these moments!
Look down from heaven, God, look down and see our
     sorrow.
Behold my trembling hands, the tears that flood my
     eyes.
Hear now my prayer of woe; hear now my weary
     voice.
Send to the torturer the punishment he merits;
To me most miserable grant still a little comfort.

DIM.   I'll show you solace soon, and comfort for your grief.
You'll know me; you will see what I am truly like.
Before your very eyes your lover ripped asunder
Will your own doom foretell that with him you'll be
     sharing.

KSE. I'd rather die with him, with honor at the square.
Than see myself in shame upon Dimitrii's throne.

DIM. I shall have carried out what you have here requested.
Your love for him will be inexorably ended.
Thus shall I have avenged the scepter, state, and crown.

KSE. Impatiently I wait that all may be fulfilled.
You have shown no regard for rank, for sex or kinship.
But know one thing, O Tsar: your days on earth are numbered.
You cannot hope to rule much longer in this world.
The blood that you have shed cries to Almighty God.
Your heart has never known compassion, kindness, pity.
Boyars and city walls—the people all are wailing.
Death does not frighten me; your threats are all in vain,
Tyrant, so strike me down! What are you waiting for?
(*Shuiskii arrives before the last line.*)

SCENE 4

Dimitrii, Ksenia, and Shuiskii.

SHU. You should be put to death for such impertinences.

DIM. Her insolence surpasses all imagination.
Hearing such things, the world would surely be amazed.

SHU. Is this how Ksenia heeds her father's admonitions?

KSE. In desperation, I—

SHU. In such unseemly matters,
Leave us immediately! Out of our sight at once!

SCENE 5

Dimitrii and Shuiskii.

SHU. When the ascendant moon has reached its highest peak,
By then she will repent and humbly will submit.
Forgive a maiden's youth, her brashness and her folly.

DIM. My heart is made to melt by love's much-sought-for sweetness.

How I have longed for her, though she has made me
    groan,
Until this very moment I don't understand.
The tender pangs of love are strangers to my feelings;
My heart's adorned itself with dreams alone of glory.
The simple folk, they say, to tenderness are given.
But I have found my joy and gloried in the thought
That my bright diadem shone to fill them with terror.
Moscow with awe is filled; before me Russia trembles.
The most distinguished men lie prostrate at my feet.
The greatest of their chiefs shudder like prisoners.
And what has tenderness to do with royal purple?
Proud soul! Then it must be—to love you too are
    subject.
Command your daughter now to kneel before the tsar;
And if she wishes so, she'll be my humble wife.
Let her accept this ring in token of my friendship;
Or let her choose to go where she shall die in torment.

SHU.   If she dare disobey, she disobeys the heavens.
And I myself approve the wisdom of your choice.
We must conform our wills and subjugate our wishes
Unto the law of God and to our monarch's power.

SCENE 6
    Dimitrii, Shuiskii, and Parmen.

PAR.   The rumors still increase. A storm is brewing fast
As when a bitter wind comes howling from the North.
The people soon will break their angry stifled silence.
News of Georgii's death, the constant chains and
    prison,
The same atrocities descending from the throne,
All Moscow has aroused to fury and revolt.
As great as is your state, so great is now your danger.
A dire and dismal doom stands now before Dimitrii.
You did not choose to rule with justice and in peace.
You have not tried to check or to restrain your rage.
If you had brought some joy and comfort to your
    subjects,
The people would have been your throne's most sure
    defenders.

SHU.   To make your throne secure I'll try to calm the mob.
       I'll turn their loyalty again unto the tsar.
       Sire, you may rely with confidence on Shuiskii.

DIM.   Are there still remnants in my heart of idle mercy
       That I endure the mob, Georgii and his kind,
       And do not spatter blood upon the city streets?
       The tiger gapes and I—I pet the gaping tiger.
       Go, calm the people down! Increase the guards around
       me!

SCENE 7

       Dimitrii (*alone*).

DIM.   The crown no longer lies secure upon my head.
       My days of greatness draw to an untimely close.
       Each moment brings the threat of unexpected changes.
       O sturdy Kremlin walls! Why do you terrify me?
       Deep in my mind it seems you're whispering to me:
       "You are our enemy—the foe of all our land!"
       The citizens cry out, "You've brought about our ruin!"
       The churches call to me, "Behold us stained and
       bloody!"
       All vanished is the cheer of Moscow's fairest groves.
       And Hell from its abyss opens its jaws for me.
       I see the gloomy stairs that lead to nether regions,
       And I behold the shades in Tartarus tormented.
       My body even now burns in Gehenna's fire.
       I look up at the heavens and see a holy place
       Where sainted tsars of old beam with celestial beauty;
       And angels sprinkle them with dew of Paradise.
       But what of my despair? What hope is left for me?
       I'll suffer there forever as I here suffer now.
       I am no more the tsar in a resplendent city,
       But groveling in hell I live, an evil outcast.
       I perish for the ones—the many—I've destroyed.
       Run, tyrant, run! . . . From whom? . . . Shall I run
       from myself?
       For no one else is here. There's no one here beside me.
       Run! . . . Where shall I run? . . . Your hell goes with
       you always.
       Here's an assassin, run! . . . But I'm the murderer.
       I've grown to fear myself! My shadows frighten me.

I'll seek revenge! . . . On whom? . . . Myself? How
shall I hate me?
I love myself . . . I love . . . For what? . . . I under-
stand not.
All cry against me now—injustice, robbery;
All of the base, foul deeds, together all cry out.
I live for wretchedness; I'm dead to joy of near ones.
Better now seems the lot of my most humble subject.
The lowly beggar—he—even he sometimes is tranquil,
While I reign here as Tsar, and know but misery.
I'll live and I will die for my ill-gotten throne!
I'll drive till driven out—a tyrant to the end!

CURTAIN

ACT THREE
SCENE 1
Shuiskii and Parmen.

PAR. I've tried to chase away the villain's gloomy thoughts,
To keep within control his new outbursts of wrath.
The tyrant has agreed to grant Georgii freedom.
Through reasoning at last I've overcome his anger.
He trusts me. I would be always his faithful friend
Were he a man in whom some virtue could be found.
But he who rules this land, son of the Russian
people . . .

SHU. His birthright gives the throne and scepter to Dimitrii.

PAR. If in those qualities a tsar should have to rule
He is found lacking, then his birthright counts for
naught.
Suppose the rumor's true; suppose he is Otrepev.
If he rules well, then he is worthy to be monarch.
What meaning does his high-born background have
for us?
Suppose he really is a Russian monarch's son;
If in the qualities of tsar he is found wanting
Then we must hate his blood—this is our bounden
duty,
Then must the father lose his children's former love.
When from the scepter come no benefits, no help,

When from the innocent fall tears of bitter weeping,
Widows and orphans drown in wretched lamentation,
And flattery in place of truth is by the throne,
When honor, life, estate lose all security,
When truth is bartered for with pounds of gold and
  silver,
And justice finds its scales with heavy bribing tilted,
When virtue sees its mark of honor blotted out,
While evildoers live and prosper without fear,
And mankind sees its lot unbalanced by upheavals—
Then all the monarch's praise is but an idle fancy,
A vain and empty dream that rises and declines—
A useless thing that sits like dust upon the throne.

SHU.   The people and the tsar have my most earnest bless-
         ings.
PAR.   And I send up this prayer to God Who is in Heaven—
         Have mercy on this land, Georgii, and yourself,
         And on poor Ksenia, your most unhappy child!

SCENE 2
    Shuiskii (*alone*).

SHU.   Whether you scheme or not, I will destroy Dmitrii.
         He shall not rise again when from the throne he's
         fallen.
         If I must die, I die—let come to me what will.
         But Moscow will I first stir up against the tsar.
         I'll save the Fatherland, and our beloved city;
         And if I die, I leave my name with the immortals.
         A hero he may be who vanquishes the foe,
         But he who frees his land from the oppressor's yoke
         Is even more revered. He is the greater man
         Who will lay down his life and perish for his people.

SCENE 3
    Shuiskii, Georgii, and Ksenia.

SHU.   Our common enemy would talk with you again,
         Desiring brazenly to reconcile himself.
         But even though his proposition loathsome be,
         Try to behave yourself both modestly and humbly.
         This is the same advice I gave you once before;

But what I had built up, you recklessly undid.
Who knows not how to yield when need compels us harshly,
Knows not this wicked world nor how we must live in it.

GEO. Prince, I was greatly wronged by hateful words that touched
My honor—they cut deep into my anguished spirit.
Discretion, reasoning, at once together vanished.
Never in all my life did I once think to hear
Such words of insolence from any living soul.
The unexpected blast left all my reason shattered.
My self-control and all my patience disappeared then.
And though his marriage plans had threatened me with less,
I'd still have plunged my sword into the tyrant's breast.
If he appears today unscrupulous and godless,
I will restrain myself—I'll promise to be cautious.
For Ksenia alone the cursing I'll endure.
Now, Ksenia, can you see the love I have for you?

KSE. And how should I stay still, and how should I keep silent,
Seeing Georgii doomed to die upon the scaffold?
What would life mean to me? What care I for the world?
O my beloved prince! My soul belongs to you.
In you I live and breathe, through you my life has meaning;
You are my source of joy, you only are my comfort.
I'd be content with you in poverty if need be.
In the most humble home with you I'd gladly live.
Not by the hand of Death, not by the direst judgment,
Will he—the evil one—take me from you, beloved!

SHU. But for a time conceal this love that joins you both.

GEO. One fear alone I have—he may resort to force
To consummate his wish, to bring about this marriage.
This in Georgii's sight would be ten times more loathsome
Than all the pains of hell, all torment without end.
A heart of stone would even break at such a sight!
My breast trembles within, my soul is numbly stricken,
Whenever in my mind I see this dreaded vision.

KSE.   Georgii, cast off fear. It shall not come to pass.
        Not triumph, but by death his marriage would be
            crowned.
        And if it cannot be that we in life together
        Be joined, then lay me down beside you in the coffin.
        United we shall fade to particles of dust.
        The marriage shall not be. Death only is your fear.

GEO.   O my beloved Ksenia, I alone shall die
        So that I may not see the day of your declining.
        But you live on and dress perpetually in black;
        Live—and an angel be—angel all-beautiful!
        The clergy still retain some remnant of their power.
        They still dare to oppose the Patriarch Ignatii,
        And still are vigilant against the heresies
        Which have misguided some to yield unto the Pope.

SHU.   Let us yet hope in God; in grief and still in sorrow.
        He is all-powerful and wise; His bounties, many.
        Now follow my advice in everything you do.

KSE.   We're ready to obey; we'll follow your command.

SCENE 4
        Georgii and Ksenia.

KSE.   Pass quickly, days of woe; pass, days of lamentation!

GEO.   Pass, time of wretchedness, our bitter time of sorrow!
        Stay hidden in my heart, my all-consuming love.
        Cease to inflame my blood with fires that can't burn
            out.
        Look not upon her eyes, upon her tender glances,
        Lest they become to you a draft of lethal poison.
        Passion, be still! Submit, obey necessity!
        Ardor, conceal yourself behind a veil of frost!
        Away, sweet tenderness—if it lie in your power.

KSE.   Eyes, look no more on him with gentle love and
            longing—
        Remember not the hours, sweet hours of yesterday—
        But try now to conform with what I must pretend.
        Let memory cease to dwell upon those joyful moments
        Which once were dear to me, as dear as now they're
            painful.
        Let not my eyes betray the happiness I knew.
        Let them not stir the pool that murmurs in my heart

Wherein Georgii's love is evermore reflected.

GEO. Look down on us, O Heaven, and number all my
    sighing!

KSE. And reckon all the drops of these, my bitter tears!

GEO. Soften my fate, O Tsar that rules the sun and skies,
    Restore once more to me of all my hopes the sweetest
    Or from the face of earth blot out my life forever!
                (To Ksenia).
    The love I have for you can never be destroyed.
    I shall be always yours, and you—forever mine,
    Whatever destiny decrees that we must suffer.

KSE. Ksenia is prepared to go to death beside you,
    And loving you far more than even life itself
    Will suffer all for you, endure all things for you.
    Though to an evil state our city now has fallen,
    It still is Paradise when in it lives Georgii.
    You fill all places here. I see you everywhere.
    Without you, Moscow seems forlorn and desolate:
    The many streets, the lanes, the byways of the city,
    All of the roads upon which you have walked so often,
    Those nearby villages where once I lived with you,
    The groves where we have strolled even if only once,
    The meadows and the fields where we together
        wandered
    And laughed and listened to the murmur of the waters.

GEO. It seems to me the towers and all the city walls,
    The little streams meandering among the hills,
    Singing a joyful song in first days of the springtime,
    The sunbeams when they fall from bright clear skies
        of heaven,
    The darkness of the night enwrapped in deepest
        sleep—
    All, all depict for me the Ksenia whom I love!
    I see not in your soul unrest or any trouble,
    And all our paths and all our hours are filled with
        fondness.
    Until my dying breath, I live within your realm.

KSE. In the same way, beloved, my prince, rule over me.

SCENE 5
>   Dimitrii, Georgii, and Ksenia.

DIM.   To the decrees of fate have you at last surrendered?
GEO.   In all things stand we both before the tsar submissive.
DIM.   In recompense for this, I shall forgive you all.
>   But henceforth sterner means I'll use with brazen
>   slaves.
>   O fruits of justice, you enhance the taste of vengeance
>   Even as you are loathsome to a woman's weakness.
>   The basest creature can for something be of use;
>   But he, the tsar, alone can torment a whole realm.
>   Behold in all the world the acme of perfection!
GEO.   But he who rules the land and guides a noble nation
>   Should build their happiness; this he alone can do.
DIM.   Eternal happiness ill suits a monarch's subjects.
>   A tsar ought to be wealthy; the state, however, poor.
>   The monarch should rejoice; and let his subjects groan!
>   The lean horse for its work is all the better fitted,
>   Subdued by stinging whip, made strong by frequent
>   riding,
>   And always held in check by sturdiest of bridles.
GEO.   The law and diligence are labor's steadfast help.
DIM.   For him who rules alone, what need has he of them?
>   The wishes of the tsar—these are the monarch's
>   statutes.
GEO.   Autocracy it seems is better far for Russia.
>   Where there is found to lack the rule of one supreme,
>   Ambition falters there, and, persecuted, dies.
>   The mighty tyrannize subordinates with pride,
>   And for their arrogance in turn are paid in hate.
>   The Fatherland's true son sits not upon the throne
>   Seeking of those he rules judgment for what he does.
>   Though it seems novel now—the rule of one sole
>   monarch—
>   Without it we would find authority in bondage.
>   Unhappy is that land where many nobles rule.
>   Truth must keep silent there, and liars reign supreme.
>   Prosperous is to us the power of the monarch
>   When the tsar's regal hand is not to us a burden.
>   And if in Moscow you shall choose to rule us thus,
>   Your throne all Russia will hold blessed, as your reign.

DIM. I oftentimes have heard such idle women's fables.
      Let Moscow shine today or be snuffed out forever.
      Let all my peoples here in Moscow weep and wail.
      Not for them I exist; but they exist for me.
      And you are wheedling me, seeking the monarch's
          graces,
      Because of Ksenia—whom you still wish to marry.

GEO. But do I vex the tsar when I speak out this truth,
      Even though it be said when passion bids me speak?
      I know that in all things I'm subject to the monarch.
      But though my love still burns, this does not touch
          the scepter.
      How then shall I release what nature's laws have
          bound?

DIM. You have no property, no land, and no estate.
      Scion of Constantine, you prince, Prince of Galicia,
      Before me you are but a shadow and a cobweb.
      All that is God's is mine.

GEO.   Am I not then my own?

DIM. You too belong to me—to me and to the Heavens;
      And being mine, yourself your own you cannot reckon.

GEO. My heart, blood, soul, and mind—are these not my
          possessions?

DIM. They are not yours to hold. For every part of you
      Is subject to your God and equally to me.

GEO. But God gave to the last of all His creatures freedom.
      Of that how may a monarch legally deprive him?
      The monarchs have the power to read and change the
          laws;
      But even with their power can falsehood be excused?

DIM. Alarm my soul no more. Vex me, O prince, no longer.
                      (*To Ksenia.*)
      Go now, go under guard to the appointed chambers,
      My very dearest Ksenia, lovely princess mine,
      And on the morrow you will be Dimitrii's wife.
      You weep?

KSE.   It is my wish to be to you obedient
      No matter how much I, alas, still love Georgii.
      Submitting to a fate that we could not foresee,
                      (*To Georgii.*)
      Try to subdue yourself as much as you have strength.

SCENE 6
   Dimitrii and Georgii.

DIM.   Poorly indeed I see you heed her admonitions.
        Are you so troubled then?
GEO.   I seek to still my feelings.
DIM.   Are you becoming weak?
GEO.   No, strong . . . strong as I can.
        My Sire, you know full well how dear I am to her.
        I cannot leave her thus without a troubled spirit.
DIM.   Try to correct your heart, this insolent vexation!
        Hold fast within your mind where full authority
        And the monarchal rank rule higher than all men.
GEO.   The caesars and the tsars, no matter how exalted,
        In tenderness of love—they and their slaves are equal.
        'Tis flattery alone that deifies a man.
        Duties are not alike; honors are different,
        Rewards are measured out according to the worth.
        The tsar our father is; the subjects are his children.
        We all are born and live a short while in this world.
        The noble, king, and slave—all at the last must die.
        The small and humble hole that claims the orphan's
            body
        Will cover equally the conqueror of kingdoms.
        We leave a humble home departing from this world.
        The monarch too shall leave his high resplendent
            throne.
        There is an evenness in all the ways of nature.
        So is it that the kings of subjugated nations
        As well as humble slaves, born unexpectedly,
        In nature's struggles must all walk the common way.
        The tsar's enangered heart is made to feel emotions.
        My heart has feelings too, feelings of heavy sorrow,
        My God, turn not away, but listen to my prayer.
        Behold the tears that I today before You shed.
        Stretch forth the hand divine through the bright clouds
            of Heaven.
        Deliver me, O Lord, from this most anguished parting.
        In You, in You I hope to find deliverance.
        Let not my wretched heart fall deep into despair!
DIM.   You have been amply warned with words of admoni-
            tion.

> Go, wail against your God; suffer, and be tormented.
> It seems a pleasant thing for me to see your pain
> While in my power I hold all that is beautiful.

SCENE 7

Georgii (*alone*).

GEO. Rejecting God Immortal, hating mortals also,
Witness my suffering and be content, O tyrant!
You torment all my mind; you strike into my breast.
Boast, ruin, and destroy for your allotted time!
Ah, should I be deprived of that beloved beauty!
The mere imagining fills me with utter weakness.
My senses fail, grow numb; I see the sun grow dark.
The sky seems covered up by veils of gloomy clouds.
Above Moscow the air is filled with murky poison.
When shall I see you, sun, shining upon this city,
Shining on high again upon a happy land,
Sending out rays of light as in the days gone by?
Shall we behold again the playful splash of waters?
When shall we see return the days of longed-for
    freedom?
The hours of former joy, ah, when will they come
    back,
When I beheld the charms of Ksenia without tears?
From shamelessness and evil will Moscow be delivered?
Will golden spires once more shine on the tops of
    churches?
Alas, will malice close its ever greedy mouth?
Will prince and peasant laugh? Will they rejoice again?
Will Moscow hear again the sound of young girls'
    laughter,
And will their faces shine, their faces soft and lovely?
Will churches, palaces, no more be stained with blood?
Come back, sweet time of peace! Rejoice, O love,
    rejoice!
With happiness reborn let all our hearts be swelling!
Moscow, be you to us a new celestial dwelling!

CURTAIN

ACT FOUR
SCENE 1

Dimitrii and Ksenia.

DIM. When comes the hour to us, the time of tender joy,
O sight so lovely to my eyes, surpass yourself.
Make soft this heart of mine that rages never ceasing,
This heart wrought to be wrathful on the throne of
Russia.
The time is soon to come when you will be my wife
And to your kindly grace the citizens will run.
Well many are the souls because of me thought dying;
Show pity for their orphans, dry the tears of widows,
And my severities restrain, this as my friend.
To such a ruthless husband play the ruthful wife.
But if you cannot temper all your husband's harshness,
Yet can you soothe his subjects with your gentle
kindness
By showing them there's one whom they can turn to
still
In suffering, though you lack the means to offer aid.
Then let the people suffer as before they suffered,
Living in hopefulness that falsely fools the hopeless.
Just like a base man born to bear his master's yoke,
So will they live and suffer in an endless hope
That never comes, nor will come ever. Still they mutter,
"I know that I'll be happy when it is tomorrow!"
They find content in this, not knowing that the day
That follows will but add new troubles to the old.
What if my nation all in sickness lies forever,
Dimitrii feels no pity for a single subject.
The world and all within it live for gain alone
And all is baneful, all that's worldly is corrupt.
I'll be a tyrant, though the others talk of virtue,
For virtue on this earth has never found a witness.
However it may loom, I'm not afraid of hell,
And thus Dimitrii's right so many men to fell.

KSE. Death might be fitting punishment for malefactors
But, Sovereign, ought the innocent to perish with
them?
Is there no lawful way to punish lawlessness?

DIM. They punishment deserve as many as they are.

KSE.   If all men are thus marked for suffering by Dimitrii,
        How is it that he stands alone, excluded from them?

DIM.   If it had been that vanity were less my own,
        Dimitrii would have killed Dimitrii long ago.
        Could I have wrested half myself from all the other,
        I would have found amusement in my own self's
            torment,
        I would have sympathized most deeply with myself,
        Despairing as I gazed upon my own despair.

KSE.   It is a wondrous marriage to your wife you promise
        And wondrous peacefulness that now you augur to me!
        What pity will a wife in such a husband find,
        A man who without rhyme or reason harms himself?

DIM.   If you fear cruelty, and hope not to be punished,
        Then seek with all your soul the favor of your husband.
        Above the world of nature must you place your
            spouse,
        Respect in him the image of a deity!

KSE.   Majestic is the tsar, and glorious and respected,
        But even he must be an equal to his mistress.
        What if a bondwoman were wedded to the tsar?
        Would the tsaritsa to the tsar be just a slave?
        In matrimony seek a maid of equal station.

DIM.   In matrimony I am seeking only beauty,
        For high degree of birth can make no face more fair:
        In village and in town the flower grows the same.
        And when you are my wife, by destiny determined,
        To all creation's king be the obedient daughter.
        And also seek my love, submitting then to me. . . .
        If this you do not choose, then choose to live in fear!

KSE.   No words like these of women ever spoke Georgii.

DIM.   Georgii is a slave; Dimitrii is a ruler.

SCENE 2
    Dimitrii, Ksenia, and the Captain of the Guard.

CAP.   Throughout the city now there is no happy word:
        For with the sunset all your peace will disappear.
        This is an eve of horror; shudder with the nightfall.
        Your eyes will never from the throne again see sun-
            light.

The Patriarch Ignatii, steeped in heresies,
Afraid, has left the city walls and taken flight.
The boyars will this eve be guilty of betrayal,
The clergy will elect another as their father,
And all the nobles and the masses are enraged.
Beware foul weather, Sovereign, and the cruel times!
In you alone remains whatever your protection.
Already from your head the royal crown is falling.

DIM.   And with it all the boyars, too, will tumble down.

CAP.   The guard waits what Dimitrii will command to do.

DIM.   Send Parmen in at once and give the guards their
        orders.
        This night of many horrors sleep must be abandoned!

SCENE 3
    Dimitrii and Ksenia

DIM.   Behold the fruits of Russian princes' faithfulness!

KSE.   O heaven, turn away these princes from all woe!
        O Tsar, if all the people stand before you guilty,
        Are Prince Georgii and my father guilty with them?

DIM.   I've known them long. . . . But leave me, go away
        from here!

                (*Parmen arrives.*)

SCENE 4
    Dimitrii and Parmen.

DIM.   I want you to fulfill whatever I command!
        The night is ill, and ill for me the night's forebodings,
        While in my breast this day I feel full well all horrors.
        I shudder . . . falls the throne, and ended is my life. . . .
        Where in my hopelessness, in whom is there recourse?!
        Against me rises God, against me rise the people,
        Abysses open wide, hell's rivers high are flaming.
        I am transformed almost into a prisoner:
        And earth, and hell, and heaven have put on their
          arms.
        Relentless are the fiends that tear my murky spirit,
        The nation that I rule as one unites to loathe me,
        Bemoaning my barbarity the city quakes,

	And God Himself removes me from His sacred sight. I'm nature's enemy, betrayer of my homeland, And even my Creator now is hostile to me.
PAR.	Be not so constant in your cruelheartedness: As sinful as you are, so God is full of love.
DIM.	As great as is the amplitude of God's forgiveness, So is my impotence to keep His laws and statutes.
PAR.	His laws and statutes are in virtue to be found.
DIM.	But virtue is in contradiction to my way, And for my heart the path is difficult to goodness. Just God, where shall I find a place of hiding from you?! There is no place of refuge for me in my woe. The earth, and hell, and heaven all are in Your sway, And I have only endless torment waiting for me. Transform life into nothingness for me forever, Take thunder, fire, hurl lightning down, annihilate, Wipe out eternally the spirit of this man! Today and only this can give me any pleasure.
PAR.	Is truth the victor and the master of your reason?
DIM	(*handing him a document*). Whatever here is written you must carry out!
PAR	(*after reading the contents*). What fresh atrocity becomes your next intent!
DIM.	The boyars, pastors, all, I want to have them murdered!
PAR.	If this will be, then it is time to show my efforts.
DIM.	Have Shuiskii, Ksenia, and Georgii, under guard, Brought here to stand before my royal personage!

SCENE 5

Dimitrii (*alone*).

DIM.	To the embrace of God the blessed soul will journey, But I am pointed out the way from throne to hellfire. This my last night to me is everlasting night; Awake now I shall see the horrors seen asleep. The gloom that clouds the nation's skies will end its sorrows, Will take away from me my life and ruling power. The crimson of the sunset hastens to the skies, And far beyond the forests sinks the weary sun, So that it might return to nature ever fresher. . . .

Oh, linger, flaming star, a little while in heaven!
At the appointed hour you will go down again,
Forevermore, and I shall see you nevermore.

SCENE 6
Dimitrii, Shuiskii, Georgii, and guards.

DIM.   I know who kindled the rebellions, and I sentence
You both to die in public view before the windows.
SHU.   Great sovereign! . . .
DIM.   Do not waste more of your words in vain!
GEO.   If I have lost my love, I am prepared to die.
There's nothing left on earth to give me any pleasure.
SHU.   I ask your leave to bid a last farewell to Ksenia.
Because of her alone I fear the hour of death.
DIM.   To add to your misfortune this I wish myself.

SCENE 7
Shuiskii, Georgii, and guards.

GEO.   Without faintheartedness, and of ourselves the masters,
So let us die and show the city strength of spirit!
Then let us die!
SHU.   Let's die if our appointed fate,
So cruel, is the will of the Almighty One.

SCENE 8
Shuiskii, Georgii, Ksenia, and guards.

KSE.   The hours of untold suffering have come already.
Behold the day of my eternal parting with you!
These moments are beyond the limits of my strength.
O heaven, help me conquer my infirmity!
SHU.   The monarch crowns you on the throne in such a
manner!
GEO   (to Ksenia). And so he brings my love for you to its
conclusion.
KSE.   Then suffer, Ksenia, if you must, then suffer now!
GEO.   O my beloved princess!
SHU.   My beloved child!
I lose you now.

GEO.   And you are lost to me forever.

KSE.   My outcry cannot help, and all my tears are hopeless.

SHU.   My joy you've ever been since early childhood years,
       You blossomed into beauty, into virtue fair,
       Your conversations were adorned with this same
           beauty,
       And you exalted womankind with this same virtue.
       For me you ever were a source of sweet delight,
       And in Georgii you inspired the sweetest hope—

GEO.   Which on this very day forever is to vanish.

KSE.   My breast is numbed, oppressed, and it is heavy,
           weary. . . .
       Above a dread abyss I stand, afraid, alone.
       Take back my sorry life, O Heaven, take it back!
       Those things that used to be the pleasures of my life-
           time,
       That in this world became the objects of my seeking,
       Are lost to me forever, I forever lose
       That which to me was dearer than my life itself.
       My father and my prince! . . . The one I owe my
           being,
       The other with his love has won unhappy Ksenia.
       You gave your daughter life, now strike her with your
           sword
       And take away the wretchedness of that same life!
       Or you, my love, Georgii, be the one to strike me,
       And of my endless faithfulness to you be witness.

GEO.   O my beloved princess, try now to be strong!

SHU.   My death to me is needful.

GEO.   As is mine to me.

SCENE 9
       Shuiskii, Georgii, Ksenia with guards, Parmen and
guards.

PAR.   The tsar has ordered me to take you to the prison.

SHU.   And so I go there.

GEO.   And to cruel death most certain.

KSE.   Parmen!

SHU.   We go because we must; the limit's reached!

PAR.   If you upset the order of society,
       Accept the punishment.

SHU.   A citizen most worthy!

GEO.   To execute us you are fit, but not to judge us.

KSE.   You have exchanged compassion for barbarity,
        Which you yourself before well many times decried.

PAR.   Take them away.

SHU.   Restrain your grief, unhappy princess!

GEO.   Stay, Ksenia, know that more than yours my heart is
        breaking!

SCENE 10
        Ksenia with guards, and Parmen.

KSE.   Unmoved by such a sorry spectacle of shame,
        Content yourself, base tyrant, with my suffering!
        Respecting but the laws and codes of evildoing,
        Strike, draw the spirit from a torn and mangled body,
        And pour the blood of innocence into a pool
        To bathe your hands in it with no remorsefulness.
        And then raise up those bloodstained hands unto the
            heavens,
        Asking to be delivered from the pain of hellfire!
        As is God's mercy great, so is His judgment just.
        He will not heed the prayers that come from Tartarus.
        Wreak vengeance, Heavens, on this evildoer's spirit!
        Wreak vengeance! . . . Ah, but how will this relieve
            my suffering?!
        Dimitrii's soul will never break the bonds of hell,
        But neither will my father and my lover dead
        Rise from their coffins to return my heart's affection.
        To you, O God, a captive's thought I am entrusting.

PAR.   With tears like these that flow in currents endlessly,
        Stand in the tyrant's sight in grief as you do now.
        There's nothing more that I can say to you in answer.
        May God fulfill all that which I now wish and hope
            for!

KSE.   Vile tyrant, there awaits you fitting punishment!
        In hell you'll gather up the fruits of all you've sown.

SCENE 11
Ksenia and guards.

KSE. Now all has been fulfilled, my honor is accomplished.
Be patient, weary soul, by so much sorrow shattered.
In death they'll take into the grave their love for
   me. . . .
But now my breathing stops and with it stops my
   blood. . . .
Oh, no! Already has the time come for their murder,
The princes learn the taste of death; they fall and
   perish,
And as their souls move on, submitting to their fate,
They call unhappy Ksenia, bid her come with them,
They call a soul abandoned, desperate and or-
   phaned. . . .
I'll follow you into the world unknown by mortals. . . .
This city that was once a flower in full bloom,
Has now become a murky hell with no way out. . . .
Then open wider still your flaming mouth, Gehenna,
And let me by! But for what fault am I your captive?!
Is this not hell! Then where? . . . Am I alive? . . .
   Or not? . . .
And does the earth not crumble? . . . Does the sky
   not fall? . . .
Indeed the sky and earth continue their existence,
But I shall be forgot forever by my princes. . . .
Where, guards, am I to go? It does not matter now.
Nowhere is there for me contentment to be found.

CURTAIN

ACT FIVE
SCENE 1
    Dimitrii (*alone*).

> *The curtain rises. Dimitrii sits sleeping on a chair. On a table near him are the tsar's appurtenances. Awaking, Dimitrii speaks.*

DIM. I have endured enough, a shattered soul in torment!
    Whence come these evil dreams that magnify my anguish?
    The city's terror looms, and dream comes after dream;
    And all the hosts of hell rise up before my eyes.
        (*A bell is heard.*)
    They sound upon the bell! Why has it started ringing?
        (*He rises.*)
    In this, the dreaded hour, I feel my death approaching.
    O night, O starless night! And the accursed bell!
    Go tell the world my grief, my woe, my bitter cry!
    My spirit trembles now—for the first time it trembles,
    Despairing, without hope; all roads are closed before me.
    The royal palace quakes, the room about me reels.
    O God! . . . But God is gone. He has forsaken me.
    Shunned by all the realm who find my visage loathsome,
    Of refuge find I none. . . . Go now into Gehenna!
    Down now, my soul, descend down to the underworld.
    Ruler of all mankind! There too you'll seek me out!
    From the deep bowels of hell You'll hurl me for the judgment,
    Condemn me for my sins, my grievous sins, my evil.
    I am the enemy of man and God as well;
    Going against Your ways, so nature's laws I broke. . . .
    The air is stirred with noise, the enemy well armored;
    And at my very walls my guard is moved to fury.
    Deluged with their abuse, I'm rendered powerless.
    All have opposed me—all—in heaven and on earth.
    O city that was mine and that I rule no longer,
    On you the judgment falls for sins by me committed!

SCENE 2
   Dimitrii, guards, and the Captain of the Guard.

CAP.   The Kremlin has been lost. The mob runs everywhere.
        Against you every heart burns with an untold wrath.
        The guard's cut off. Alone we have survived to guard
           you.
DIM.   This is the cruelest fate; this, of all lots, most bitter!
        We'll conquer still! Go now! No, here! No, there!
           Run, run!
        With courage we can still put down the enemy.
        Hurry, do not relent! Make haste to save Dimitrii!
        Where are you running to? You would not dare to
           leave me?
        Oh, do not go away! Stay, stay, defend the door!
        Then let us flee! . . . Too late, too late; it's all in vain.
        Bring Ksenia to me!

SCENE 3
   Dimitrii (*alone*).

DIM.   The losing of my kingdom
        Is not my deepest loss, my deepest suffering,
        But this one thought: I burn with fierce and outraged
           fury
        And do not see the means to wreak a bloody ven-
           geance.
        In traitors' blood, in blood of slaves, of all the guilty,
        In laymen's blood, and in the clergy's would I bathe.
        I would show to them all what is a tsar enraged.
        With blood I'd drench the throne and holy altars, too.
        I'd make the whole wide world tremble with fear, and
           shudder.
        Proud Moscow I'd transform into a dusty relic.
        The city I would burn and watch its blazing towers
        Reach high into the clouds and streak the vaults of
           heaven.
        Ah, but these thoughts of blood in vain do bring me
           solace
        If I'm deprived by fate of any means for vengeance.

SCENE 4

    Dimitrii, Ksenia, and guards.

DIM.   You hear the rebels' noise; but think not joyfully
    Your days of tenderness are not now at an end.
    When you shall see me sit upon the throne no longer,
    Know that within the hour you too from earth will vanish.
    The traitor's deadly hand, when it has cut me down,
    Will lay you low as well—and that, by my own hand.
    A prisoner still you'll die, and not as a tsaritsa.

KSE.   Tell me, what is the crime of which you find me guilty?

DIM.   Daughter and friend of those by whom I am betrayed,
    You perish in their stead—if they in safety live!
    You also share the guilt of all those scheming nations
    Who now my boundless wrath, a tsar's wrath, are deserving.

KSE.   Death holds no fear for me, knowing that he I love,
    And that my father too, are safe from injury.
    That only was my fear, that only caused me anguish.
    Wash now your hands in blood, my blood, blameless and guiltless,
    Since mercy is a word you cannot understand.
    End a sad life in days just reaching their first bloom.
    Will not the universe, as will all Russia, wonder
    To hear how you have slain, murdered, a blameless maiden,
    One who supposedly was closest to your heart,
    Who never in her life did seek to work you harm?
    My father cannot know of this strange execution,
    Nor does the city feel the hate you pour upon me.
    No one can realize that I must pay their debt
    And that my blood shall flow like water on these floors.

DIM.   Your charms have worked on me; your beauty still entices.
    But still I have one dream: to see you dead before me.
    I truly pity you in these, our final hours.
    But you alone are left for this, my last revenge.
    Guilty or not, you make atonement for the city.
    When I fall from the throne, then death must claim you also.
    There in the outer room—what is that crashing sound?

An evil hour has come! My lustrous crown grows dark.
Prepare to feel the pain of evil being punished!
(*He seizes her by the hand, pulls out a dagger, and raises it above her.*)
Death comes, prepare to die—and light me to my coffin!

SCENE 5

Dimitrii, Ksenia, Shuiskii, Georgii, and soldiers.

GEO.   What gruesome sight is this!

SHU.   O wild demented soul!

DIM.   Bereft of throne, I'll still see you bereft of her!

GEO.   (*comes a little closer to him*).
If you desire someone on whom to deal destruction,
Then let it be on me; let me endure your hatred.
I am the guilty one.

SHU.   Not he, not Ksenia,
Shares guilt in front of you. I started the revolt.

DIM.   If you would seek to find compassion for your daughter,
Then leave us here at once; and go, say to the city
I shall be merciful and still will be their friend,
Or for the city's crimes this princess will be dead.

SHU.   Die for the native land! Die a cruel death, O princess!

GEO.   The horror of this hour falls heavily upon me.
Fate, could I have foreseen such a disastrous time? . . .
Princes and people, hear! . . . Dimitrii . . . holy Heaven!
Release the innocent; and let my blood outpouring
End of all loves on earth the one most truly tragic!

DIM.   That little sacrifice will not sate my revenge.

GEO.   (*stepping away and addressing the people*).
Deprived of all my hope, I fly to him for death.
(*Throwing himself on Dimitrii.*)
Farewell, beloved!

KSE.   Farewell!

DIM.   (*attempting to stab Ksenia*).
                O lovely rose, now wither!

PAR.   (*with drawn sword, wresting Ksenia from Dimitrii's arms*).

Your stormy cruelties and rages now are ended!
Our people are released from death, oppression,
  wounds.
The tyrant—powerless—shall frighten us no more.

DIM. Go then, my soul, to hell and be forever captive!
(*Strikes himself in the chest with a dagger and falls
  dying into the arms of the guards.*)
If only with me now the whole world too would perish!

CURTAIN

4. The End of an Age

24. *The Eighteenth Century*

ALEKSANDR N. RADISHCHEV

On March 11, 1801, Tsar Paul was assassinated in the course of a palace revolution that brought his son Alexander I to the throne. Shortly thereafter, the new ruler granted a pardon to Radishchev, and permitted him to return to St. Petersburg. Later that year the writer was again in the capital.

Radishchev's hopes for the future were high. The amnesty granted him raised his spirits, and the opportunity to serve as a member of a commission created to revise the Russian legal code once again held forth the promise of civic responsibility. Radishchev plunged enthusiastically into the work of the commission, producing a series of legal treatises. Their strong republican character and their author's call for the equality of all citizens before the law, the abolition of corporal punishment, and the right to trial by jury soon alienated the chairman of the commission, Count P. Zavadovskii, and brought a reprimand that carried with it the threat of a new exile to Siberia. Despondent over the shattering of his illusions and the frustration of his most cherished hopes, Radishchev ended his life a suicide on September 11, 1802.

Not long after he returned to St. Petersburg in late 1801, when his mood was one of enthusiasm over the happy reversal of his fortunes, Radishchev wrote a lengthy poem in classical elegaic couplets to which he gave the simple title *The Eighteenth Century* (Osmnadtsatoe stoletie). It was first printed in Volume One of his collected works in 1807. The poem, which Pushkin considered Radishchev's finest work, is a summation of the defeats and victories of the age that had just drawn to an end. Inspired by the apparent liberalism of the new ruler, the poet's gaze encompasses the entire eighteenth century, and takes the measure of its losses and its gains; it then turns hopefully to the future.

The poem is a monument to a great, turbulent age in the history of Russia—and an appropriate conclusion to this book as well.

The translation follows the text in A. N. Radishchev, *Izbrannye sochineniia*, ed. G. P. Makogonenko, Moscow, 1952.

❧

The urn of time pours out the hours like drops of water;
The drops have gathered into streams, the streams to rivers grown,
And on the distant shores they pour forth foaming waves
Of eternity into the ocean, where neither boundaries nor shores exist;
No island there does rise, no bottom finds the plummet;
The centuries have flowed into it, wherein all trace of them is lost.
But now, illustrious forever by its bloody current,
Our century with sounds of thunder flows therein.
And finally the ship that bore our hopes meets its destruction,
Consumed into the whirlpool already near its haven;
Happiness, virtue, and freedom are devoured by the raging pool.
See, fearsome wreckage still floats in the torrent.
No, you shall not be forgotten, O age of ours both mad and wise,
Accursed will you be forever, ever the wonderment of all,
In blood steeped in your cradle, your lullaby the thunder of battles;
Ah, soaked in blood shall you descend into the grave.
But see, in midst of bloody torrents two crags have risen up,
Catherine and Peter, children of Eternity and Russia.
Behind them dark shadows, in front of them the sun,
Its radiant brightness reflected by the solid rock.
O century unforgettable! You endow joyful mortals
With truth, liberty, and light, a constellation forever bright.
Tearing down the pillars of mortal wisdom, you created them again;
Kingdoms were destroyed by you, like a ship broken into pieces;
Kingdoms you create; they shall flourish and once again fall into ruin;
Whatever mortal man shapes, all that shall be destroyed, all that to dust shall return.

But you were a creator of ideas; they are the works of God;
And they shall not perish, though the earth itself perish.
Boldly, with skilled hand, you drew aside the curtain of
    creation,
And gazed on nature's secrets in the remote sanctuary of
    things.
From the Ocean arose new nations and new lands;
From the depths of black night, new metals at your call.
You count the luminaries, like a shepherd his gamboling
    lambs;
With guiding thread, you lead the comets back to earth;
The rays of light you have divided, and new suns into being
    called;
New moons from distant murk you summoned up before us;
You have impelled nature to the birth of new offsprings.
Even the flying steam you harnessed to your yoke;
Heaven's lightning you enticed into iron fetters on earth,
And bore up mortal men to heaven on wings of air.
Manfully have you destroyed the iron gates of phantoms,
And flung down to the ground the idols that men on earth
    revered.
You burst the bonds that oppressed our minds, that toward
    new truths
It might soar like winged lightning, rushing deeper ever deeper
    into space.
Mighty and great you were, O century! The soul of ages past
Fell prostrate and silent before your altar, marveling,
But your strengths did not suffice to expel all the spirits of hell,
Which gushed flaming venom throughout eternal ages;
Your strengths were not enough against the fury and bitterness
    that with iron heel
Crush the flowers of happiness and wisdom in us.
Mortals are still steeped in blood on the sacrificial altar of
    depredation,
And still is man transformed into a ferocious tiger.
The torch of battles, see, whirls along there on hills and plains,
In peaceful valleys, through meadows, it roars on its tem-
    pestuous course.
Behold their black companions! Terrible they are! . . . They
    come, behold, they come:
Like nightmare phantoms—savagery, turbulence, famine,
    plague!

Is peace, which brings bliss to nations, never to return again?
Is humanity to sink yet deeper?
From the depths of the tomb of the century the voice of
consolation resounds:
Away with despair! Mortal man, have hope, God lives!
He who commanded the spirit of storms to stir the mutinous
waves
Still holds in His mighty hand the chain of time:
The spirit of storms shall not sweep mortals away, though they
be merely creatures of one day
That blossom forth at sunrise, and with the setting of the sun
fade away. . . .
Wisdom alone is eternal. Victory crowns it;
After life's storms it will summon, now man's to grasp . . .
The dawn of the new century has appeared to us still drenched
in blood,
But already the light of day drives off night's grim darkness;
Higher and higher fly up to the sun, thou Russian eagle,
Bring down its radiance to earth, but leave behind its deadly
lightning.
Peace, justice, truth, and liberty shall flow from the throne,
Which Catherine and Peter raised up, that all Russia might
prosper.
Peter and thou, Catherine! Your spirit still abides with us.
Gaze upon this new age, behold your Russia.
O Alexander, remain forever our guardian angel. . . .

SELECTIVE BIBLIOGRAPHY

Although limited in scope, this bibliography particularly emphasizes English-language writings in the field of eighteenth-century Russian literature and more recent Russian research. No systematic effort has been made to cover historical studies, with the exception of a few books and papers that may be of interest to the general reader. In the case of several Russian collections, the entries have been made by book titles rather than by authors in view of the fact that editorship is not always clearly indicated, and the works are more easily located in libraries by titles. The reader should note that the entries under each author are arranged chronologically rather than alphabetically.

Babkin, D. S. *A. N. Radishchev*, Moscow-Leningrad, 1966.

Berkov, P. N. *Lomonosov i literaturnaia polemika ego vremeni 1750–1765*, Moscow-Leningrad, 1936.

———. "English Plays in St. Petersburg in the 1760's and 1770's," *Oxford Slavonic Papers*, Vol. VIII, 1958, pp. 90–97.

———. *A. P. Sumarokov*, Russkie Dramaturgi, Moscow-Leningrad, 1947.

Bittner, Konrad. "J. G. Herder und A. N. Radishchev," *Zeitschrift für slavische Philologie*, Band XXV, Heft 1, 1956, pp. 8–53.

Bogdanovich, I. F. *Stikhotvoreniia i poèmy*, Biblioteka Poèta, ed. I. Z. Serman, Leningrad, 1957.

Bucsela, John. "The Birth of Russian Syllabo-Tonic Versification," *The Slavic and East European Journal*, Vol. IX, No. 3, Fall 1965, pp. 281–94.

Burgess, Malcolm. "Russian Public Theatre Audiences of the Eighteenth and Early Nineteenth Centuries," *The Slavonic and East European Review*, Vol. XXXVII, No. 88, December 1958, pp. 160–83.

———. "Fairs and Entertainers in Eighteenth-Century Russia," *The Slavonic and East European Review*, Vol. XXXVIII, No. 90, December 1959, pp. 95–113.

441

Cherniavsky, Michael. "The Old Believers and the New Religion," *The Slavic Review*, Vol. XXV, No. 1, March 1966,
pp. 1–39.

Chizhevskii (Čiževskij), Dmitrii. *History of Russian Literature from the Eleventh Century to the End of the Baroque*,
's-Gravenhage, 1960.

Clardy, Jesse. "Radishchev's Notes on the Geography of
Siberia," *The Russian Review*, Vol. XXI, No. 4, October
1962, pp. 362–69.

———. *The Philosophical Ideas of Alexander Radishchev*, New
York, 1964.

Cross, A. G. "Karamzin and England," *The Slavonic and East
European Review*, Vol. XLIII, No. 100, December 1964,
pp. 91–114.

Derzhavin, G. R. *Stikhotvoreniia*, Biblioteka Poèta, ed. D.
Blagoi, Leningrad, 1957.

Dmytryshyn, Basil. "The Economic Content of the 1767
Nakaz of Catherine II," *The American Slavic and East
European Review*, Vol. XIX, No. 1, February 1960,
pp. 1–9.

Drage, C. L. "Trochaic Metres in Early Russian Syllabo-Tonic
Poetry," *The Slavonic and East European Review*, Vol.
XXXVIII, No. 91, June 1960, pp. 361–79.

———. "The *Anacreaonta* and Eighteenth-Century Russian
Poetry," *The Slavonic and East European Review*, Vol.
XLI, No. 96, December 1962, pp. 110–34.

Efimov, A. I. *Istoriia russkogo literaturnogo iazyka*, 3rd ed.,
Moscow, 1957.

Evans, R. J. Morda. "Antiokh Kantemir and His First Biog-
rapher and Translator," *The Slavonic and East European
Review*, Vol. XXXVII, No. 88, December 1958, pp.
184–95.

Fitzlyon, Kyril (trans., ed.). *The Memoirs of the Princess
Dashkov*, London, 1958.

Fonvizin, D. I. *Sobranie sochinenii*, ed. G. P. Makogonenko,
2 vols., Moscow-Leningrad, 1959.

Gorshkov, A. I. *Istoriia russkogo literaturnogo iazyka*, 3rd
ed., Moscow, 1965.

Grasshoff, Helmut. *Antioch Dmitrievic Kantemir und West-
europa*, Berlin, 1965.

Grey, Ian. *Peter the Great*, Philadelphia and New York, 1960.

———. *Catherine the Great*, Philadelphia and New York, 1962.

Grot, Ia. (ed.). *Sochineniia Derzhavina*, 2nd Acad. ed., 7 vols., St. Petersburg, 1868.

Gudzy, N. K. *History of Early Russian Literature*, New York, 1949.

Gukovskii, G. A. *Khrestomatiia po russkoi literature XVIII veka*, 3rd ed., Moscow, 1938.

——. *Ocherki po istorii russkoi literatury i obshchestvennoi mysli XVIII veka*, Leningrad, 1938.

——. *Russkaia literatura XVIII veka*, Moscow, 1939.

Hans, Nicholas. "Russian Students at Leyden in the Eighteenth Century," *The Slavonic and East European Review*, Vol. XXXV, No. 85, June 1957, pp. 551–62.

Harkins, William E. *The Russian Folk Epos in Czech Literature 1800–1900*, New York, 1951.

Huntington, W. Chapin. "Michael Lomonosov and Benjamin Franklin: Two Self-Made Men of the Eighteenth Century," *The Russian Review*, Vol. 18, No. 4, October 1959, pp. 294–306.

Iroi-komicheskaia poema, Biblioteka Poèta, ed. B. Tomashevskii, intro. V. A. Desnitskii, Leningrad, 1933.

Johnson, C. A. "Lomonosov's Dedication to His *Russian Grammar*," *The Slavic Review*, Vol. XXIII, No. 2, June 1964, pp. 328–32.

Kahan, Arcadius. "The Costs of 'Westernization' in Russia: The Gentry and the Economy in the Eighteenth Century," *The Slavic Review*, Vol. XXV, No. 1, March 1966, pp. 40–66.

Karamzin, N. M. *Letters of a Russian Traveler 1789–1790*, tr. Florence Jonas, intro. Leon Stilman, New York, 1957.

——. *Izbrannye sochineniia*, ed. P. Berkov, G. Makogonenko, 2 vols., Moscow-Leningrad, 1964.

Katenin, P. A. *Izbrannye proizvedeniia*, Biblioteka Poèta, ed. G. V. Ermakova, Leningrad, 1965.

Kheraskov, M. M. *Izbrannye proizvedeniia*, Biblioteka Poèta, ed. A. V. Zapadov, Leningrad, 1961.

Kniazhnin, Ia. B. *Izbrannye proizvedeniia*, Biblioteka Poèta, ed. L. I. Kulakova, Leningrad, 1961.

Kokorev, A. V. (ed.). *Khrestomatiia po russkoi literature XVIII veka,* 3rd ed., Moscow, 1961; 4th ed., 1965.

Krejčí, Karel, *Heroikomika v básnictví Slovanů*, Prague, 1964.

Kuznetsov, B. G. *Tvorcheskii put' Lomonosova*, Moscow, 1956.

444   Selective Bibliography

Lang, David M. "Sterne and Radishchev. An Episode in Rus-
    sian Sentimentalism," *Revue de Littérature Comparée*, 21e
    Année, April-June 1947, pp. 254–60.
——. "Radishchev and the Legislative Commission of Alex-
    ander I," *The American Slavic and East European Review*,
    Vol. VI, Nos. 18–19, December 1947, pp. 11–24.
——. "Sumarokov's 'Hamlet.' A Misjudged Russian Tragedy
    of the Eighteenth Century," *The Modern Language Review*,
    Vol. XLIII, No. 1, January 1948, pp. 67–72.
——. "Boileau and Sumarokov; The Manifesto of Russian
    Classicism," *The Modern Language Review*, Vol. XLIII,
    No. 4, October 1948, pp. 500–506.
——. "Some Western Sources of Radishchev's Political
    Thought," *Revue des Études Slaves*, t. 25, fasc. 1, 1949,
    pp. 73–86.
——. *The First Russian Radical. Alexander Radishchev 1749–
    1802*, London, 1959.
Lipski, Alexander. "A Re-examination of the 'Dark Era' of
    Anna Ioannovna," *The American Slavic and East European
    Review*, Vol. XV, No. 4, 1956, pp. 477–88.
——. "Some Aspects of Russia's Westernization During the
    Reign of Anna Ioannovna," *The American Slavic and East
    European Review*, Vol. XVIII, No. 1, February 1959,
    pp. 1–11.
Lomonosov, M. V. *Sochineniia*, ed. A. A. Morozov, Moscow-
    Leningrad, 1961.
——. *Izbrannye proizvedeniia*, Biblioteka Poèta, ed. A. A.
    Morozov, Moscow-Leningrad, 1965.
Maikov, Vasilii. *Izbrannye proizvedeniia*, Biblioteka Poèta,
    ed. A. V. Zapadov, Moscow-Leningrad, 1966.
Makogonenko, G. P. *D. I. Fonvizin*, Russkie Dramaturgi,
    Moscow-Leningrad, 1950.
——. *Nikolai Novikov i russkoe prosveshchenie XVIII veka*,
    Moscow-Leningrad, 1951.
——. *Radishchev i ego vremia*, Moscow, 1956.
——. *Denis Fonvizin, Tvorcheskii put'*, Moscow-Leningrad,
    1961.
Martel, A. *Michel Lomonosov et la langue littéraire russe*,
    Paris, 1933.
McConnell, Allen. "Radishchev's Political Thought," *The
    American Slavic and East European Review*, Vol. XVII,
    No. 4, December 1958, pp. 439–53.

——. "Pushkin's Literary Gamble," *The American Slavic and East European Review*, Vol. XIX, No. 4, December 1960, pp. 577–93.

——. "Soviet Images of Radishchev's *Journey*," *The Slavic and East European Journal*, Vol. VII, No. 1, Spring 1963, pp. 9–17.

——. "Helvetius' Russian Pupils," *The Journal of the History of Ideas*, Vol. XXIV, No. 3, July-September 1963, pp. 373–86.

——. "The Empress and Her Protegé: Catherine II and Radishchev," *The Journal of Modern History*, Vol. XXXVI, No. 1, March 1964, pp. 14–27.

——. "Rousseau and Radishchev," *The Slavic and East European Journal*, Vol. VIII, No. 3, Fall 1964, pp. 253–72.

——. *A Russian Philosophe Alexander Radishchev 1749–1802*, The Hague, 1964.

McNally, Raymond T. "Chaadaev's Evaluation of Peter the Great," *The Slavic Review*, Vol. XXIII, No. 1, March 1964, pp. 31–44.

Menshutkin, Boris N. *Lomonosov*, Princeton, N. J., 1952.

Morozov, A. A. *Iunost' Lomonosova*, 2nd ed., Arkhangel'sk, 1958.

——. *M. V. Lomonosov. Put' k zrelosti 1711–1741*, Moscow-Leningrad, 1962.

Muratov, M. *Zhizn' Radishcheva*, Moscow-Leningrad, 1949.

——. *Denis Ivanovich Fonvizin*, Moscow-Leningrad, 1953.

Novikov, N. I. *Izbrannye sochineniia*, ed. G. P. Makogonenko, Moscow-Leningrad, 1951.

N. I. Novikov i ego sovremenniki, ed. I. V. Malyshev, Moscow, 1961.

Oldenbourg, Zoé. *Catherine the Great*, New York, 1965.

Orlov, Vl. *Radishchev i russkaia literatura*, Leningrad, 1962.

Pigarev, K. V. *Tvorchestvo Fonvizina*, Moscow, 1954.

Pipes, Richard. "Karamzin's Conception of the Monarchy," *Harvard Slavic Studies*, Vol. IV, 1957, pp. 35–58.

——. *Karamzin's Memoir on Ancient and Modern Russia*, Cambridge, Mass., 1959.

Poèty nachala XIX veka, Biblioteka Poèta (Malaia seriia), 3rd ed., ed. Iu. M. Lotman, Leningrad, 1961.

Poèty-Radishchevy, Biblioteka Poèta (Malaia seriia), 3rd ed., ed. Vl. Orlov, Leningrad, 1961.

Poèty XVIII veka, Biblioteka Poèta (Malaia seriia), 3rd ed.,

446 _Selective Bibliography_

ed. I. Z. Serman, intro. G. P. Makogonenko, 2 vols., Leningrad, 1958.

Pozdneev, A. V. "Rannie masonskie pesni," _Scando-Slavica,_ Tomus VIII, Copenhagen, 1962, pp. 26–64.

Prokopovich, Feofan. _Sochineniia,_ ed. I. P. Eremin, Moscow-Leningrad, 1961.

Radishchev, A. N. _Izbrannye sochineniia,_ ed. G. P. Makogonenko, Moscow, 1952.

——. _A Journey From St. Petersburg to Moscow,_ tr. Leo Wiener, ed. Roderick Page Thaler, Cambridge, Mass., 1958.

Radiszczew, Aleksander. _Podróż z Petersburga do Moskwy,_ Biblioteka Narodowa, Ser. II, No. 87, tr. Seweryn Pollak, ed. Wiktor Jakubowski, Wroclaw, 1954.

Raeff, Marc. "Home, School, and Service in the Life of the Eighteenth-Century Russian Nobleman," _The Slavonic and East European Review,_ Vol. XL, No. 95, June 1962, pp. 295–307.

——. _Origins of the Russian Intelligentsia. The Eighteenth-Century Nobility,_ New York, 1966.

Reve, Karel van Het. "The Silence of Krylov," _Dutch Contributions to the Fourth International Congress of Slavists,_ 's-Gravenhage, 1958.

Rogger, Hans. "The Russian National Character: Some Eighteenth-Century Views," _Harvard Slavic Studies,_ Vol. IV, 1957, pp. 17–34.

——. _National Consciousness in Eighteenth-Century Russia,_ Cambridge, Mass., 1960.

Rosyjskie czasopiśmiennictwo satyryczne XVIII w., Biblioteka Narodowa, Ser. II, No. 120, trans., ed. Ryszard Łużny, Wrocław-Kraków, 1960.

Rother, Hans. "Karamzinstudien," _Zeitschrift für slavische Philologie,_ Band XXIX, Heft I, 1960, pp. 102–25.

——. "Karamzinstudien II," _Zeitschrift für slavische Philologie,_ Band XXX, Heft 2, 1962, pp. 272–306.

Russkaia basnia XVIII i nachala XIX veka, Biblioteka Poèta (Malaia seriia), 2nd ed., ed. N. L. Stepanov, Leningrad, 1951.

Russkaia komediia i komicheskaia opera XVIII veka, ed. P. N. Berkov, Moscow-Leningrad, 1950.

Russkaia literatura XVIII veka. Epokha klassitsizma, ed. P. N. Berkov, I. Z. Serman, Moscow-Leningrad, 1964.

Russkie povesti pervoi treti XVIII veka, ed. G. N. Moiseeva, Moscow-Leningrad, 1965.

Satiricheskie zhurnaly N. I. Novikova, ed. P. N. Berkov, Moscow-Leningrad, 1951.

Schroeder, Hildegarde. *Russische Verssatire im 18. Jahrhundert*, Cologne-Graz, 1962.

Sherech (Šerech), Jurij. "Stefan Yavorsky and the Conflict of Ideologies in the Age of Peter I," *The Slavonic and East European Review*, Vol. XXX, No. 74, December 1951, pp. 40–62.

———. "On Teofan Prokopovich as Writer and Preacher in His Kiev Period," *Harvard Slavic Studies*, Vol. II, 1954, pp. 211–23.

Shishkov, Aleksandr Semënovich. *Razsuzhdenie o starom i novom sloge rossiiskogo iazyka*, St. Petersburg, 1803.

Simmons, Ernest J. *English Literature and Culture in Russia (1533–1840)*, Cambridge, Mass., 1935.

Startsev, A. *Radishchev v gody "Puteshestviia,"* Moscow, 1960.

Stikhotvornaia komediia kontsa XVIII-nachala XIX v., Biblioteka Poèta, ed. M. O. Iankovskii, Moscow-Leningrad, 1964.

Striedter, Jury. *Der Schelmenroman in Russland*, Wiesbaden, 1960.

———. "Zur unterschiedlichen Kompositionstechnik syllabischer und syllabontonischer Versionen eines Gedichtes von Trediakovskij," *Orbis Scriptus Dmitrij Tschiżewskij zum 70. Geburtstag*, Munich, 1966, p. 827–34.

Sumarokov, A. P. *Izbrannye proizvedeniia*, Biblioteka Poèta, ed. P. N. Berkov, Leningrad, 1957.

Sumner, Benedict Humphrey. *Peter the Great and the Emergence of Russia*, London, 1950.

Svetlov, A. B. *A. N. Radishchev*, Moscow, 1958.

Thaler, Roderick Page. "Radishchev, Britain and America," *Harvard Slavic Studies*, Vol. IV, pp. 59–75.

———. "Catherine II's Reaction to Radishchev," *Études Slaves et Est-Européennes*, Vol. II, Part 3, Autumn 1957, pp. 154–60.

Thomson, Gladys Scott. *Catherine the Great and the Expansion of Russia*, London, 1947.

Trediakovskii, V. K. *Izbrannye proizvedeniia*, Biblioteka Poèta, ed. L. Timofeev, Moscow-Leningrad, 1963.

Trubetzkoy, N. S. *Die russischen Dichter des 18. und 19. Jahrhunderts*, Cologne-Graz, 1956.

Unbegaun, B. O. *Russian Versification*, New York, 1956.

——. "Russian Grammars before Lomonosov," *Oxford Slavonic Papers*, Vol. VIII, No. 58, 1958, p. 98–116.

Varneke, B. V. *History of the Russian Theatre*, New York, 1951.

Vetter, Eveline. *Studien zu Sumarokov*, Berlin, 1961.

Wedel, Erich. "A. N. Radiščev's 'Reise von Petersburg nach Moskau' und N. M. Karamzin's 'Reisebriefe eines Russen'," *Die Welt der Slaven*, Jahrgang IV, Heft 3, 1959, pp. 302–28, and *ibid.*, Jahrgang IV, Heft 4, 1959, pp. 435–43.

Welsh, David J. " 'Philosophers' and 'Alchemists' in Some Eighteenth-Century Russian Comedies," *The Slavic and East European Journal*, Vol. VIII, No. 2, Summer 1964, pp. 149–58.

——. "Satirical Themes in Eighteenth-Century Russian Comedies," *The Slavonic and East European Review*, Vol. XLII, No. 99, June 1964, pp. 403–14.

Whaples, Miriam Karpilow. "Eighteenth-Century Russian Opera in the Light of Soviet Scholarship," *Indiana Slavic Studies*, Vol. II, 1958, pp. 113–34.

Worth, Gerta H. *Die Bereicherung des russischen Wortschatzes im XVIII. Jahrhundert*, Vienna, 1956.

——. "Trediakovskij's *Feoptija*," *Orbis Scriptus Dmitrij Tschižewskij zum 70. Geburtstag*, Munich, 1966, pp. 963–72.

XVIII vek, Vol. I, ed. A. S. Orlov, Moscow-Leningrad, 1935; Vol. II, ed. G. A. Gukovskii, 1940; Vol. III, ed. P. N. Berkov, 1958; Vol. IV, ed. P. N. Berkov, 1959; Vol. V, ed. P. N. Berkov, 1962.

Zapadov, A. *Masterstvo Derzhavina*, Moscow, 1958.

——. *Otets russkoi poezii. O tvorchestva Lomonosova*, Moscow, 1961.

——. *Russkaia zhurnalistika XVIII veka*, Moscow, 1964.

——. *Gavrila Romanovich Derzhavin*, Moscow-Leningrad, 1965.

Zenkovsky, Serge A. (ed.). *Medieval Russia's Epics, Chronicles, and Tales*, New York, 1963.